Guide
INVERTEBRAT

J. E. WEBB
Professor of Zoology, Westfield College,
University of London

J. A. WALLWORK
Reader in Zoology, Westfield College,
University of London

J. H. ELGOOD
Formerly Associate Professor of Zoology,
University of Ibadan, Nigeria

Second Edition

First edition 1975
Second edition 1978
Reprinted (with corrections) 1979, 1980, 1981

Published by
THE MACMILLAN PRESS LTD
London and Basingstoke
Companies and
representatives
throughout the
world

Printed in Hong Kong

British Library Cataloguing in Publication Data

Webb, Joseph Ernest
Guide to invertebrate animals. - New ed.
1. Invertebrates - Classification
I. Title II. Wallwork, John Anthony
III. Elgood, John Hamel
592'.001'2 QL362.5

ISBN 0-333-24745-0 Pbk

Preface

This Guide to Invertebrate Animals has evolved over the past 35 years from lecture notes and cyclostyled information sheets given to university students in the United Kingdom and Africa. The original version, which was produced by two of us (JEW and JHE), was published in 1955 under the title Animal Classification by the University of Ibadan Press, primarily for the use of students of that University. In the present volume, this Classification has been brought up to date and illustrated with numerous blackboard-style drawings to show the more important anatomical and morphological features of most of the animals concerned.

This book is intended for the use of sixth-formers and university undergraduates taking introductory courses in invertebrate biology, although its use may extend into fields of terrestrial, freshwater and marine ecology. By reducing to a pocket size format, the volume can be handled with equal ease in the field and the laboratory. The picture it attempts to present is one of an overall, yet detailed, view of the diversity of invertebrate life, coupled with a scheme of classification which brings order to this diversity. Hopefully, the presentation of a considerable amount of basic information in this compact form will allow the reader to explore other aspects of zoology.

The success of the invertebrate guide has encouraged us to undertake the production of further volumes covering the living vertebrate animals. A *Guide to Living Mammals* has already appeared and volumes on the remaining vertebrate classes are in preparation. The need for a second edition of the *Guide to Invertebrate Animals* has given us the opportunity to make improvements in style and presentation which have already been brought into effect in the mammal guide. The page size has been increased to improve the readability of the text. Each chapter now begins with a vignette on the groups it contains, dealing with aspects of their classification and evolutionary relationships of particular significance. When read sequentially these vignettes give a succinct statement of the major current opinions on invertebrate evolution. Use of the guide in the laboratory and on field courses by student classes has shown the value of indicating for each group of animals the 'spot' characters that are of special importance in forming a diagnosis. This has now been done throughout the guide by marking such characters with a black spot. Some additional illustrations have been included and the classification of some of the groups has been taken further, notably in the arthropods and molluscs, where this seemed to be desirable. A few distribution maps have been added, not nearly so many as in the mammal guide since most of the invertebrate groups are extremely widespread and the limits of their distribution of little significance.

Some modification of the placing, classification and character lists of some of the groups has been made in accordance with changing current opinion. In this we are grateful to Professor Norman Millott for help with the echinoderms, to Dr. P. F. Newell and Professor J. A. Allen for a revised classification of the bivalve molluscs, to Dr. R. C. Tinsley for corrections to the sections on parasitic worms, to Dr. S. M. Manton for information on the distribution of the Onychophora and to Dr. J. P. Harding for advice on the Crustacea. Finally we owe a very special debt of gratitude to Mrs. Margaret Clarke who prepared the typescript with accuracy, patience and willingness.

JEW
JAW
JHE

London, August 1977

Contents

1 Introduction

When zoology involved little more than a knowledge of the different kinds of animals, students were content to spend much of their time studying the anatomy, relationships and classification of the various groups. But in the last few decades things have changed. We now know much more of the biochemistry and physiology of the cell and the genetics of populations. Ecology has come very much to the fore with overtones of conservation and environment, and animal behaviour has become the new science of ethology. Now that there are so many new and exciting things to learn, students are no longer prepared to devote long hours acquiring the detailed knowledge of animal form and classification which was once their delight. But this is the language of the subject and is perhaps of greater importance today than it ever was in the past. In ecology, for example, surveys and projects abound from sixth form work at school to postgraduate theses. These depend on the identification of the different animals that are found together in a pond, or forest litter or whatever habitat is being studied. A first step in this process is the recognition of the major groups - phylum, class, order - to which the animals belong. This guide is intended to help with the placing of animals into groups and to provide the information on which their classification is based. The book is therefore a summary of an immense amount of knowledge about invertebrate animals.

INTRODUCTION

The Purpose of Classification

Classification is a man-made system for the orderly storage and retrieval of things or bits of information about them. In biology the different kinds of organism run into millions. Before we can refer to them each has to have a name and preferably an allotted place in a classificatory system which shows its relationship with other organisms. Naming and classification provide a terminology essential in the exchange of knowledge and ideas in research and teaching. Terms represent information by implication. The name *Echinus*, for example, means to zoologists not only a particular genus of sea urchin but also a particular body structure, mode of life and so forth. When we speak of the Echinodermata we imply a range of animals with various characters in common but with a particular diversity in form, behaviour and distribution. The terminology of classification is part of the language of the science of biology. Its importance increases as the subject expands into new fields of knowledge, such as ecology, where the recognition of different kinds of organism and the interactions between them forms a significant part.

Naming Animals

Biological classification as we use it today dates from the 18th century and is based on the binomial system, a standard method for naming plants and animals. In this, every different kind of plant or animal (the species) is given two names. The first is the generic name written with a capital letter as a Latin singular (whatever its derivation) thus - *Arenicola*. The second is the trivial name often called the specific name. It is not capitalised and is treated as a Latin noun in apposition with the generic name thus - *marina*. The name of the species therefore is the binomial, in this case *Arenicola marina*. A second closely related species, belonging to the same genus, shares the generic name but has a different trivial name and can be written *A. ecaudata*.

INTRODUCTION

Although lists of names in binary form appeared more than once in 15th century manuscripts and were more extensively used by Gaspard Bauhin at the end of the 16th century and then by Joachim Jung a little later, it was Karl Linnaeus (1707-78) who established the system. Linnaeus was a Swedish biologist who set himself the task of recording the animals and plants as God had created them. He produced classified lists of names, many of which were binary, gave a brief description of the plants and animals and arranged them according to a variety of characters which seemed to him to be important. The first work in which he adhered rigidly to the binomial system was *Species Plantarum* published in 1753 and containing binary names for over 7000 plants. For the animals Linnaeus achieved similar uniformity in the 10th edition of his *Systema Naturae* in 1758. These works now constitute the origins of modern botanical and zoological nomenclature and names given before these dates are considered invalid. Although the same name cannot be used for two different animals, it can be used for a plant and an animal, that is the name for a plant cannot preoccupy that for an animal. For example *Bougainvillea* applies both to a tropical shrub and to a colonial hydrozoan.

The Type System

It was Linnaeus' practice to select a 'typical' specimen of a plant or animal for description and to keep this specimen in his museum as the *type* or reference specimen. It is therefore to this type that the description refers and not to the species as a whole. In this way there can be no ambiguity arising from variation within the species. This procedure is still followed and type specimens are carefully preserved for the most part in the great museums of the world. But ambiguities arise in other ways. Doubt may exist about who first described a species, or when the same name is used for two different organisms, or the procedure for combining two species, or splitting a third. Such problems call for a set of regulations. International Rules for Zoölogical Nomenclature were prepared in 1931 to clarify the position with an International Commission to interpret the 'Rules' and to suspend them where a change in nomenclature would result in undue confusion. The Commission publishes its findings as 'Opinions' and these together with the 'Rules' constitute the most widely accepted authority on zoological nomenclature.

The Linnaean Hierarchy

In addition to introducing the binomial system, Linnaeus subdivided the plant and animal kingdoms into groups or taxa. In the 1st edition of the *Systema Naturae* the natural world of stones, plants and animals, the *Imperium Naturae*, is divided into a descending sequence of categories.

Empire
Kingdom
Class
Order
Genus
Species
Variety

The animals known to Linnaeus were thus arranged in a single scheme from Man to worms. The names given to the groups were all Latinised, those in the categories above the genus, unlike generic and subgeneric names, being treated as plurals. Empire and Variety are no longer recognised as legitimate terms in formal classification although varietal names are sometimes used informally. Later workers increased the number of categories by adding the Phylum and the Family. The Linnaean hierarchy has thus been modified to give the following seven obligatory categories into which in modern taxonomic practice all animals must be classified.

Kingdom
Phylum
Class
Order
Family
Genus
Species

These are sufficient for a relatively small group of animals, but some, such as the arthropods, are so numerous and diverse that five categories below phylum level results in groups that are still too large and heterogeneous for convenient systematic handling. In this case the number of categories can be increased by using the prefixes _super_-, _sub_- and _infra_- while other categories, not obligatory, for example, '_division_', '_cohort_', '_tribe_', may also be employed.

Phylogenetic Classification

Linnaeus' purpose was to catalogue the species as they had been created. In doing so he believed he had revealed the pattern of the Creation which, for the plants and animals, implied that their species had existed distinct and unchanging from the beginning without genetic connections between them. His divisions into hierarchical categories, therefore, represented structural differences and no more. With the acceptance of evolution by biologists in the latter part of the 19th century it became clear that classification had phylogenetic significance and that morphological (and other) characteristics could be used to group organisms rather than to separate them. The emphasis, therefore, moved away from structural differences toward similarities. But, as characters that separate some organisms are usually those that link others, surprisingly little change in classification followed this fundamental change in outlook. Today biological classifications are phylogenetic in construction, that is they represent as nearly as possible within the limited hierarchy available current views on the genetic interrelations between the groups consonant always, of course, with the utility of a storage and retrieval system. Every classification is a compromise attempting to coordinate the different views of systematists on phylogeny and is thus subject to change as new information causes opinions to alter.

Basic and Trivial Characters

Many of the structures used in classifications are basic features of a level of body organisation, such as the coelom or the presence of metameric segmentation, but others are apparently trivial, such as the presence or absence of a velum in coelenterate medusae. Basic features evidently remain part of an animal's organisation because at their time of origin they allowed the development of organisms with a greater bodily efficiency which has continued to confer evolutionary advantage through to the present. On the other hand, the widespread retention of trivial characters may well be because they are of little adaptive significance and tend to remain relatively unaltered and thus common to the members of a group over very long periods of time. Such characters may serve as indicators of phylogenetic relationship and are often particularly valuable in classification at the lower subordinal levels.

The Value of Comparison

Isolated facts are not in themselves of much interest, it is only when relevant comparisons are made between them and they 'talk to each other', that an absorbing dialogue emerges revealing significant patterns of organisation. This is particularly so in animal form and function. It is not, for example, of much interest to know that the annelid worms have one preoral segment. However, it is quite another matter to realise that this is part of an evolutionary sequence ranging from animals, such as the nemertines that have no segmentation to the higher arthropods with as many as three preoral segments incorporated in a complex head.

To aid comparisons of this kind, we have adopted in this book the approach whereby the general characters of each group are given as a list. For all parallel groups, that is all phyla, all classes within a phylum and all orders within a class, the characters are in the same numerical sequence. Thus character 5, for example, for the classes in a particular phylum refers to the same structure or event throughout the phylum. To do this it has been necessary to include negative as well as positive characters, for it is as important to know that a structure is absent in one group as that it is present in another of the same taxonomic level.

Diagnosis

When an animal is examined it presents a host of features. Some are characteristic of its phylum, class, order or family, while the majority are only of generic or specific importance. A student needs to recognise the important characters and to apply them for diagnostic purposes to the category to which they refer. This classification, therefore, should help in deciding the relevant points to note, both in demonstration specimens in the laboratory and in animals collected in the field, and in this way to identify the groups to which they belong. From this point onward further information will be found in the various specialised works dealing with the particular group in question. We recognise that students cannot be expected to know the meaning of the terms referring to these significant structures without further illustration. To give this and show in outline what some of the animals look like a large number of blackboard-style drawings and diagrams is included at appropriate places in the text. There is also a short glossary to some of the terms.

I N T R O D U C T I O N

Some groups are likely to be of more importance to the student than others. The breakdown of the various phyla, therefore, has not been carried to the same level of class, order or suborder and some of the more obscure groups have been omitted.

The student will find this guide helpful in a number of ways of which a few are listed below.

- It provides a conspectus of the invertebrates from which the range of diversity can be appreciated.
- Schematic diagrams show the basic classification in terms of the relationships thought to exist between the groups.
- The reasons for the classification are evident from the lists of matching characters. Here negative as well as positive characters are given and irrelevant features omitted.
- The diagrams and drawings are simplified giving only essential detail and for this reason are easy to remember.
- In the laboratory the guide serves as a reference book indicating the points for special note in demonstration specimens.
- The treatment lends itself to the construction of dichotomous keys.
- The guide forms a compact summary for revision purposes.

The preparation of lists of matching characters for the groups does not appear to have been attempted on this scale before and has involved a considerable search in the literature with, in some cases, reference back to specimens. The classification used, while cognisant of modern views, has also to be one that works in these terms. Consequently some compromises have been made, not for the specialist, but for students for whom the guide is intended.

2 Protista

There is a wide range of organisms in which the body is not divided into cells and may therefore be regarded as acellular. Biologists in the past referred to them as unicellular organisms or free-living cells, but controversy arising partly from the enormous complexities revealed by the electron microscope and partly from the different views about the possible origins of many-celled organisms has led to speculation as to what precisely a cell is. It is therefore probably better to use the term acellular. Some protistans are plant-like in that they have chlorophyll, or some other pigment for photosynthesis, and may have a cellulose wall. These can be called Protophyta. Others are animal-like, having no chlorophyll or cellulose wall, and feed on organic matter either in solution or in particulate form. These can be called Protozoa. But there is no clear distinction between the two types for closely related forms sometimes behave like an animal and at others like a plant. It is convenient, therefore, to group all these forms together as the subkingdom and phylum Protista.

Much of the classification of the Protista is based on their locomotory organelles. The most primitive group, the Mastigophora, have one, a few, or many long whip-like processes known as flagella. The most advanced, the Ciliata, use large numbers of shorter whip-like processes, the cilia, for swimming and creating feeding currents. An intermediate group in evolutionary terms is the Sarcodina which move by means of the pseudopodium, a projection of the body that can be protruded and withdrawn as required. In some the pseudopodia are blunt and lobose while in others they are long thin structures which are more or less permanent. But these distinctions are not absolute for some of the flagellate protistans also have an amoeboid stage with pseudopodia.

A fourth class, the Sporozoa, is characterised by reproductive processes and not by locomotion. They are all parasites and include important causal organisms of human disease such as malaria. In common with other parasites they face the problem of transference from one host to another for survival. Like many parasites, they have solved this problem by rapid and extensive multiplication thereby increasing the chance of transmission.

In the Sporozoa multiplication is achieved by the formation of spores, or sporozoites or resistant cysts, usually after the sexual process of syngamy, and this has given rise to their name. But also in common with other parasites there has been a loss of the structures and processes associated with free-living organisms, such as those involved in locomotion. It is therefore difficult or impossible to trace the origins of the various sporozoans from one or other free-living ancestor.

It is reasonably certain that the sporozoan life-form has arisen more than once, perhaps many times, from other, free-living, protistan groups. It is doubtful, therefore, if the Sporozoa are a phylogenetic entity, but we have little option in classification but to treat them as such.

The Protista, like many other groups, demonstrates the basic requirement of classification that it must provide a workable system. Biological classification enables information about organisms to be arranged in an order that is internationally understood and therefore is retrievable by workers throughout the world. It is not always possible to achieve this and at the same time fully reflect current opinion on phylogenetic relationships. Some compromise then becomes necessary.

Kingdom Animalia

Living organisms in which:-

- 1. The cell or cells usually do not possess plastids and are unable to synthesise organic compounds from inorganic constituents.
- 2. Feeding is heterotrophic, holozoic, parasitic, or saprozoic.
  3. The metabolism of the body results in the production of toxic nitrogenous waste which requires to be excreted.
- 4. There is no cellulose cell wall.

Subkingdom & Phylum Protista

Living organisms in which:-

- 1. The body is non-cellular.
  2. If sexual reproduction occurs the entire body is fragmented to form gametes or the body itself acts as a gamete.

P R O T I S T A

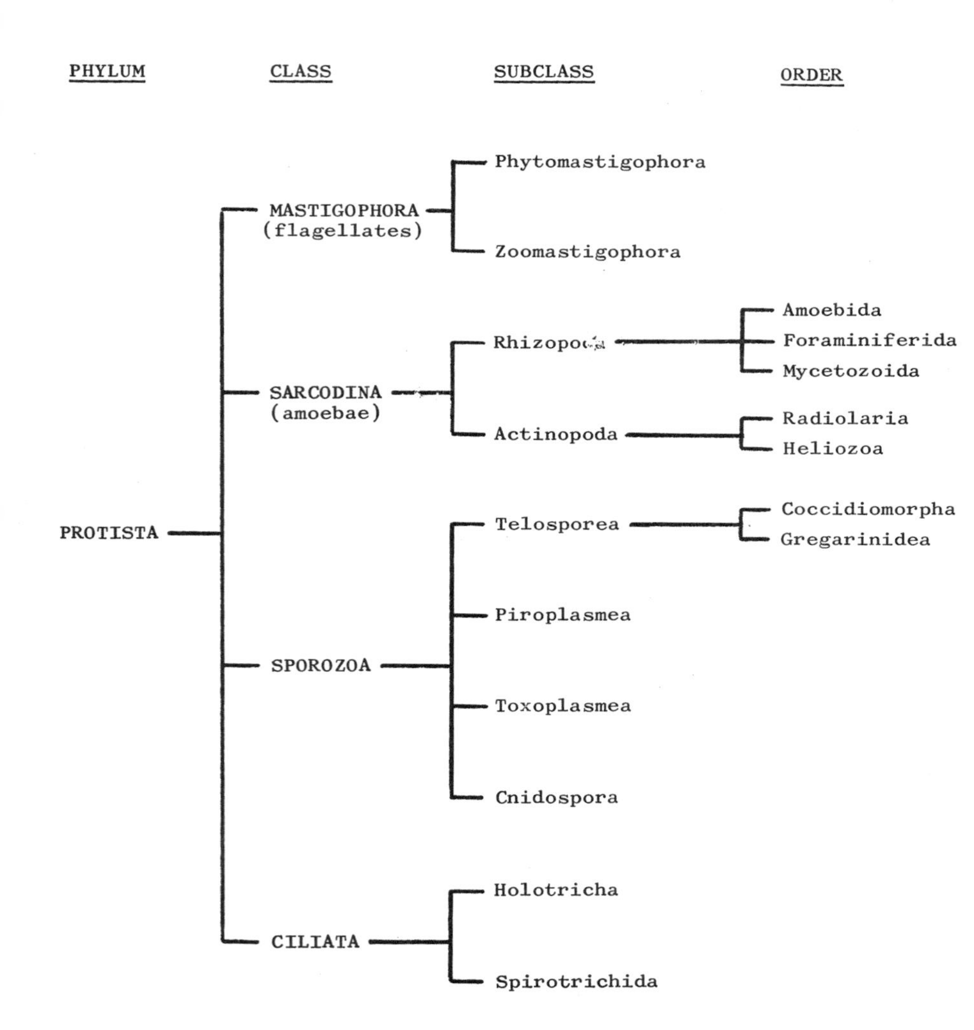
PHYLUM
CLASS
SUBCLASS
ORDER
PROTISTA
MASTIGOPHORA
(flagellates)
Phytomastigophora
Zoomastigophora
SARCODINA
(amoebae)
Rhizopoda
Amoebida
Foraminiferida
Mycetozoida
Actinopoda
Radiolaria
Heliozoa
SPOROZOA
Telosporea
Coccidiomorpha
Gregarinidea
Piroplasmea
Toxoplasmea
Cnidospora
CILIATA
Holotricha
Spirotrichida

P R O T I S T A

Class Mastigophora (Flagellata)

Protozoa in which:-

- ● 1. The body possesses one or more flagella.
- 2. Amoeboid action is rare.
- 3. Syngamy occurs in only a few groups and is then not followed by abundant spore formation.
- 4. Most members are free-living but some are parasitic.

Subclass Phytomastigophora

Mastigophora in which:-

- ● 1. There are usually chromoplasts (coloured plastids) or the members resemble forms in which such plastids are present.
- ● 2. There are usually not more than two flagella.
- 3. Carbodydrate or oil reserves are present.

Examples:- Euglena, Chlamydomonas, Volvox, dinoflagellates.

(see page 18)

Subclass Zoomastigophora

Mastigophora in which:-

- ● 1. There are no plastids and the members do not resemble forms in which plastids are present.
- ● 2. There are frequently more than two flagella.
- 3. Carbohydrate (other than glycogen) and oil reserves are absent.

Examples:- Trypanosoma (sleeping sickness parasite), choanoflagellates, Trichomonas, Opalina, Giardia, Trichonympha.

(see page 18)

Class Sarcodina

Protozoa in which:-

- ● 1. Flagella are rarely present in the adult.
- ● 2. Pseudopodia of some type are developed.
- 3. In those few cases where spores are formed after syngamy, they are few in number.
- 4. Most members are free living but there are some parasitic forms.

P R O T I S T A

Subclass Rhizopoda

Sarcodina in which:-

- ● 1. Pseudopodia are blunt, finger-like extensions of the ectoplasm containing endoplasm (lobopodium), or filamentous extensions of the ectoplasm only, which may be branched and anastomosing (rhizopodium) or unbranched (filopodium).

Order Amoebida - Amoebae and testate amoebae

Rhizopoda in which:-

- ● 1. The skeleton, where present, is single-chambered and non-calcareous.
- ● 2. The pseudopodia are lobose and mobile.
- ● 3. The ectoplasm is non-vacuolated.
- 4. The members are chiefly fresh-water forms.

Examples:- *Amoeba*, *Difflugia*. (see page 19)

Order Foraminiferida

Rhizopoda in which:-

- ● 1. The skeleton is usually a many-chambered calcareous shell.
- ● 2. The pseudopodia form a reticulum of filamentous threads.
- ● 3. The ectoplasm extends over the shell and is vacuolated in pelagic forms.
- 4. The members are (or were) nearly all marine.

Examples:- *Globigerina*, *Polystomella*, *Nummulites*.

(see page 19)

Order Mycetozoida - Slime moulds

Rhizopoda in which:-

- ● 1. There is no skeletal structure.
- ● 2. The pseudopodia are numerous and blunt.
- ● 3. The ectoplasm is non-vacuolated.
- 4. Most forms occur on rotting wood or are parasitic in plants.

Example:- *Plasmodiophora*

Subclass Actinopoda

Sarcodina in which:-

● 1. Pseudopodia are semi-permanent and consist of an axial rod covered with cytoplasm (axopodium).

Order Radiolaria

Actinopoda in which:-

● 1. The skeleton comprises a pseudochitinous central-capsule, and usually an internal siliceous framework.
2. There are fine, radial pseudopodia.
3. The ectoplasm is highly vacuolated.
4. The members are marine.

Examples:- Thalassicola, Acanthometra, Lithocircus, Aulactinium.

(see page 19)

Order Heliozoa

Actinopoda in which:-

● 1. There is usually no skeleton but in some forms a siliceous or a pseudochitinous skeleton is present.
2. The pseudopodia are fine, stiff and radial.
3. The ectoplasm is highly vacuolated.
4. They are generally fresh-water forms.

Examples:- Actinosphaerium, Actinophrys, Clathrulina.

(see page 19)

Class Sporozoa

Protozoa in which:-

● 1. There are no flagella.
2. The body may be amoeboid.
● 3. Multiplication is typically by the formation of large numbers of spores following syngamy.
4. They are exclusively parasitic.

Subclass Telosporea

Sporozoa in which:-

● 1. The trophozoite is uninucleate.
● 2. The spore cases are simple and contain several sporozoites.

P R O T I S T A

Order Coccidiomorpha

Telosporea in which:-

- 1. The trophozoite remains intracellular.
- 2. The female gamete is a hologamete.
- 3. The members are either blood or gut parasites.

Examples:- Plasmodium (malarial parasite), Eimeria.

Order Gregarinidea

Telosporea in which:-

- 1. The trophozoite becomes extracellular.
- 2. The female gametes are merogametes.
- 3. The members are intestinal and coelomic parasites usually of arthropods and Annelida.

Examples:- Monocystis, Gregarina. (see page 20)

Subclass Piroplasmea

Sporozoa in which:-

- 1. The trophozoite is uninucleate but is capable of budding
- 2. The spore cases are simple and contain several sporozoites.
- 3. The members are blood parasites and are transmitted by ticks.

Example:- Piroplasma.

Subclass Toxoplasmea

Sporozoa in which:-

- 1. The trophozoite is uninucleate and produces cysts asexuall containing many trophozoites.
- 2. There are no spores.
- 3. They are intracellular parasites of birds and mammals chiefly attacking connective tissues and muscle.

Example:- Toxoplasma.

Subclass Cnidospora

Sporozoa in which:-

- 1. The trophozoite is multinucleate.
- 2. The spore case usually contains a single sporozoite and one or more pole-capsules.
- 3. The members are parasites of annelids, arthropods and fish.

Examples:- Myxobolus, Triactinomyxon, Nosema.

Class Ciliata

Protozoa in which:-

- 1. Cilia are present in the adult.
- 2. Amoeboid action is rare.
- 3. Exchange of genetic material takes place by conjugation.
- 4. Free living and parasitic forms are well represented.
- 5. The members usually possess more than one nucleus and the nuclei are typically of two kinds, meganuclei and micronuclei. Other protistans are typically uninucleate, but where there is more than one, have nuclei of the same kind.

Subclass Holotricha

Ciliata in which:-

- 1. There is no adoral zone of membranelles (AZM) forming a wreath of long cilia or ciliated spiral peristome.

Examples:- Paramecium, Prorodon. (see page 21)

Subclass Spirotricha

Ciliata in which:-

- 1. An adoral zone of membranelles (AZM) forming a wreath of long cilia is present, or it is replaced by a spiral peristome wound clockwise and ciliated on the inner surface.

Examples:- Balantidium, Stylonichia, Spirochona.

(see page 21)

PHYLUM PROTISTA

CLASS MASTIGOPHORA

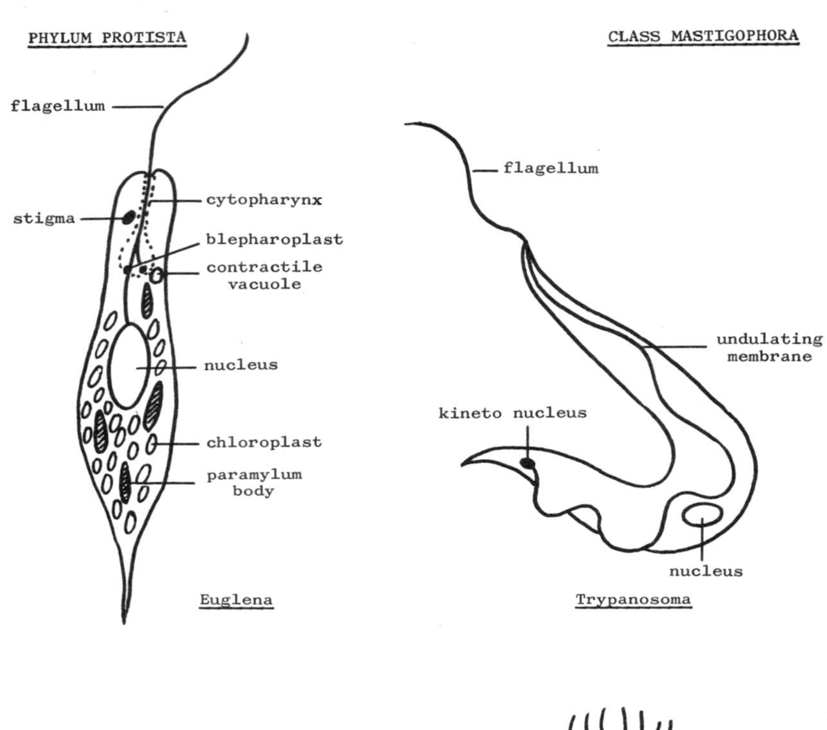

Euglena

Trypanosoma

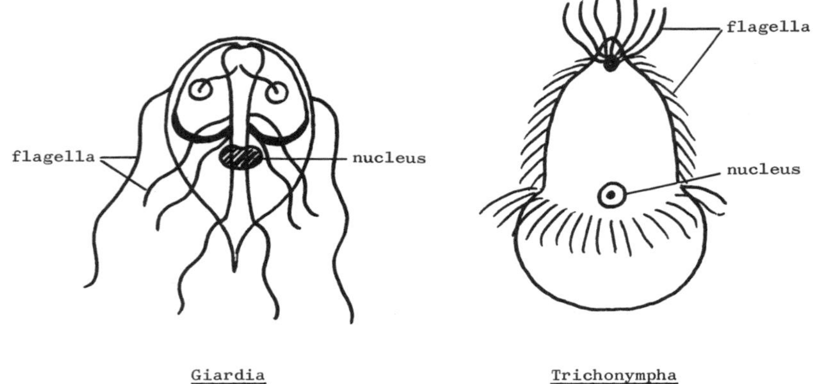

Giardia

Trichonympha

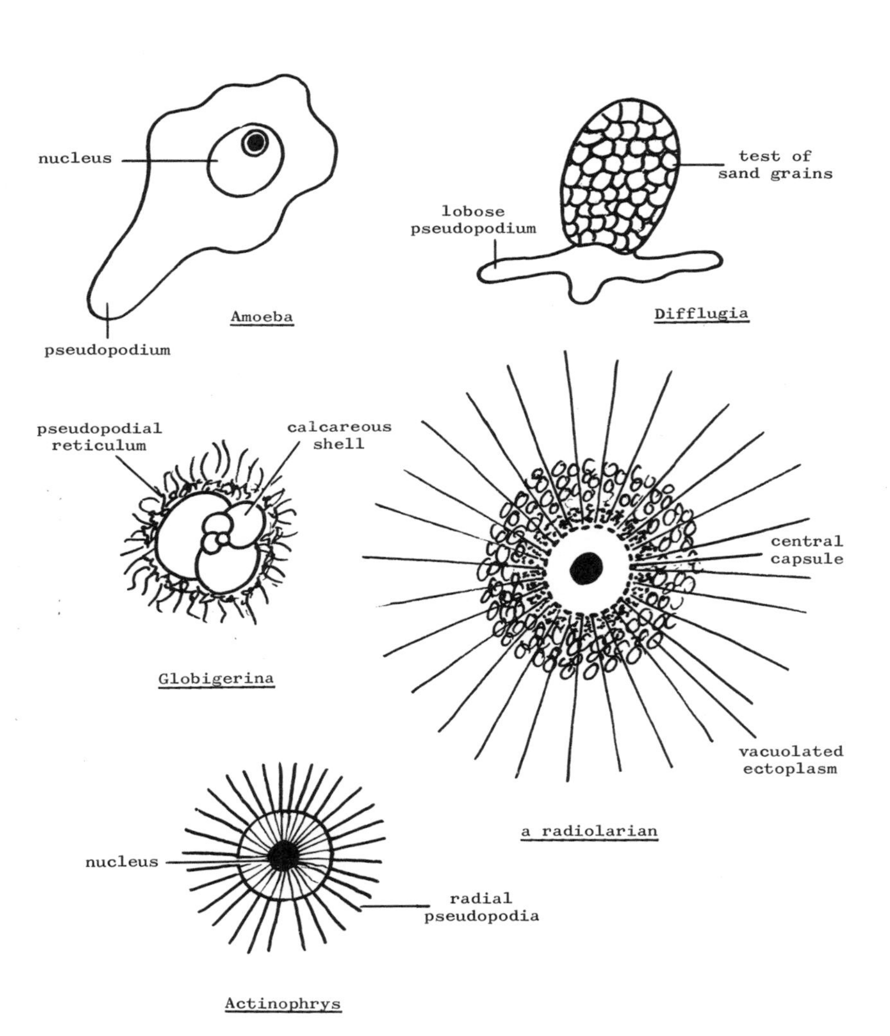
nucleus
pseudopodium
Amoeba
test of sand grains
lobose pseudopodium
Difflugia
pseudopodial reticulum
calcareous shell
Globigerina
central capsule
vacuolated ectoplasm
a radiolarian
nucleus
radial pseudopodia
Actinophrys

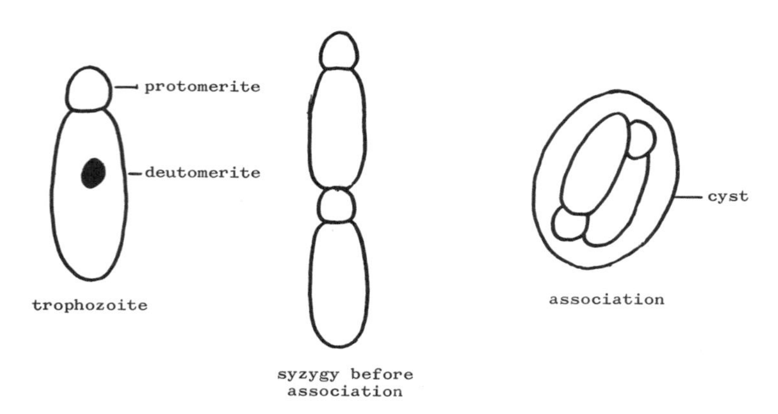

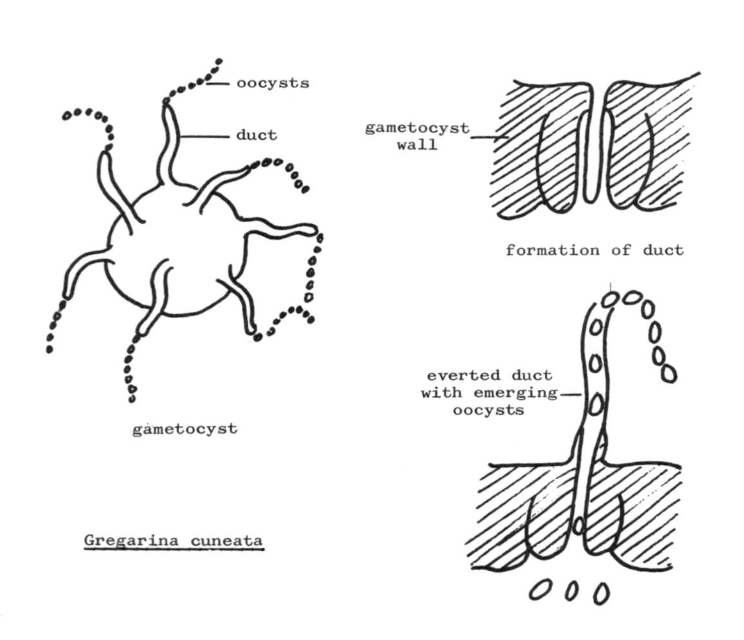

Gregarina cuneata

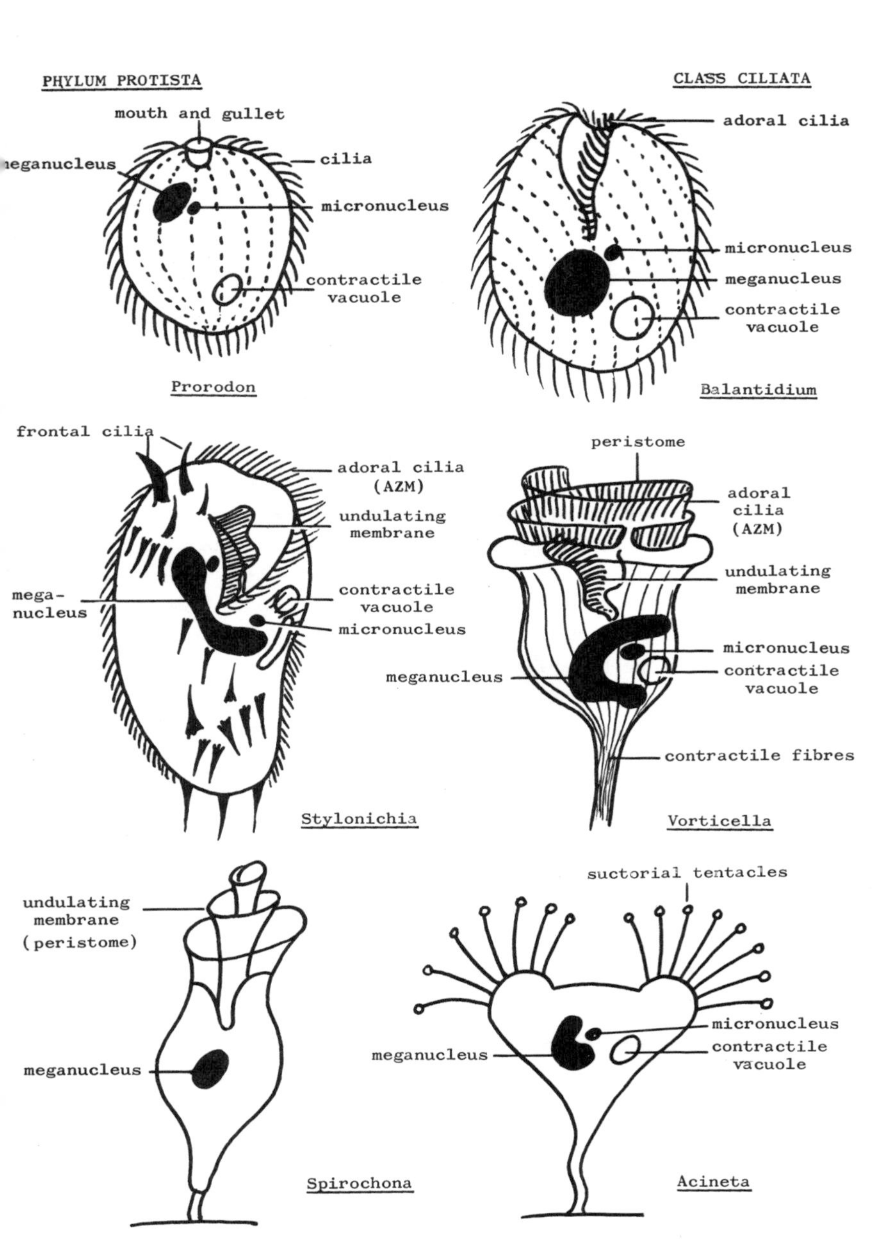
PHYLUM PROTISTA
CLASS CILIATA
mouth and gullet
meganucleus
cilia
micronucleus
contractile
vacuole
Prorodon
adoral cilia
micronucleus
meganucleus
contractile
vacuole
Balantidium
frontal cilia
adoral cilia
(AZM)
undulating
membrane
mega-
nucleus
contractile
vacuole
micronucleus
Stylonichia
peristome
adoral
cilia
(AZM)
undulating
membrane
micronucleus
meganucleus
contractile
vacuole
contractile fibres
Vorticella
undulating
membrane
(peristome)
meganucleus
Spirochona
suctorial tentacles
micronucleus
meganucleus
contractile
vacuole
Acineta

3 Mesozoa and Sponges

The initial advantage of becoming multicellular is the opportunity for increase in size. Larger organisms are less subject to attack, they have greater reserves within the body to withstand temporary unfavourable conditions and they are better able to determine their direction of movement against the flow of the medium in which they live. Multicellularity has been achieved independently perhaps four or five times, in the plants (and probably separately in the fungi), in the Mesozoa, the sponges and in the Metazoa. There appear to have been two main methods: either a number of acellular individuals clumped together and became organised as one, which is probably what happened in the origin of the plants and sponges and perhaps the Mesozoa, or a multinuclear acellular organism became internally subdivided into cells, which many authorities believe was the origin of the Metazoa. The ancestors of the plants and sponges were probably among the flagellate protistans, the Mastigophora, while those of the Metazoa were almost certainly ciliates.

In protistan reproduction either the entire body acts as a gamete or it fragments to form gametes, so that protistans are in a sense immortal. Multicellular organisms, on the other hand, reserve special cells for reproduction which in the same sense are immortal. The multicellular body or soma, then, is mortal and dies at some point after reproduction. This is a prerequisite for evolution since, if the soma did not die (except by accident) or was excessively long-lived, the material on which natural selection could act would be limited and evolutionary advancement correspondingly slow. Death, therefore is an essential evolutionary consequence of multicellularity. A second consequence, not particularly evident in protistans, is the development from the fertilised egg or zygote of an ontogenetic sequence, that is, an embryo leading through juvenile forms to the adult.

We are not here concerned with the plants nor, in this chapter, with the Metazoa, but with two groups the Mesozoa and the sponges, neither of which has achieved much eminence in evolutionary terms. The Mesozoa are an obscure, though not uncommon, group of parasites of various invertebrate animals, notably cephalopods, and are included for the sake of completeness. The sponges, on the other hand, are well known, even to the layman, with a wide range of different forms in aquatic environments and particularly in the sea.

Sponges are sessile organisms with a low degree of individuality and organisation. They can be broken up and will grow into new sponges, or two individuals will grow together and apparently become one. Each is a hollow structure in which water is taken in through numerous minute pores scattered over the surface and passed out through one or several large apertures. Food particles and possibly dissolved organic matter are taken from the water. This type of feeding in which the major aperture is exhalent demands that the body of the sponge should be more or less rigid since collapse would preclude the intake of water. All sponges therefore have skeletons which may be either composed of spicules, calcareous or siliceous, or of an anastomosis of elastic fibres, as in the familiar bath sponge. The form of the skeleton is the major basis for sponge classification.

Some groups of animals may be recognised by a single feature which is unique to them. The sponges are one of these. They all have choanocytes, flagellate cells with a collar encircling the base of a single flagellum. Similar flagellate protistans occur singly or in colonies, when they are known as Proterospongia, but in no other multicellular organism are they present.

Subkingdom & Phylum Mesozoa

Animals in which:-

- 1. The body is cellular.
- 2. The gametes and agametes are formed from specialised cells composing the central mass of the body.
- 3. The life cycle involves an alternation of asexual and sexual generations.
- 4. The members are parasitic in various invertebrates.

Example:- Dicyema.

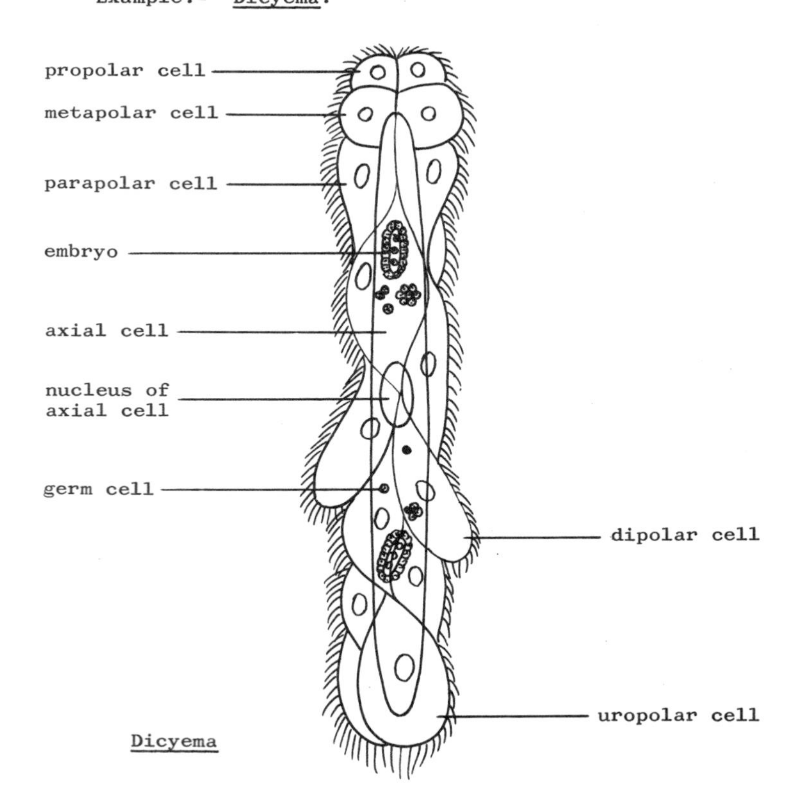

Dicyema

Subkingdom Parazoa
Phylum Porifera

Animals in which:-

1. The body is cellular.
2. The gametes are formed from specialised cells.
3. ● Choanocytes are always present.
4. ● The principal aperture of the body is exhalent.
5. ● During development (amphiblastula) the outer flagellate cells migrate inwards to form choanocytes and thus give rise to a reversal of cell layers not found elsewhere in the animal kingdom.
6. The cells are comparatively independent of one another.
7. ● There are no sense organs or nervous system.
8. There is no enteron lined by endodermal cells.

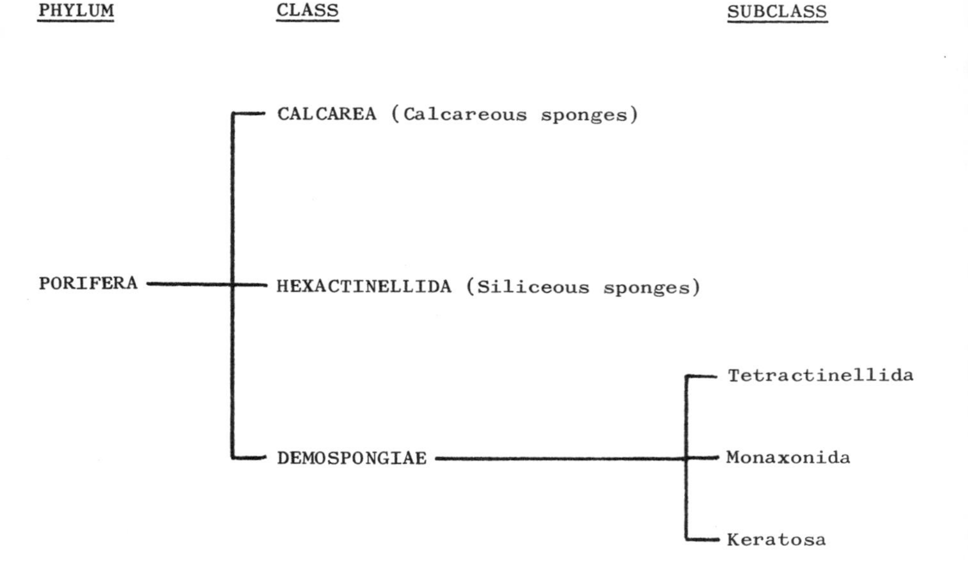

PORIFERA

Class Calcarea

Porifera in which:-

● 1. The spicules are calcareous.
2. The choanocytes are comparatively large.
3. The flagellate chambers, where present, are usually elongated

Examples:- Sycon, Grantia, Leucosolenia.

Class Hexactinellida

Porifera in which:-

● 1. The spicules are siliceous and fundamentally of triaxon (i.e. six-rayed) origin.
2. The choanocytes are small and restricted to flagellate chambe
3. The flagellate chambers are ovoid.

Examples:- Euplectella, Hyalonema (deep sea forms).

Class Demospongiae

Porifera in which:-

1. The skeleton, when present, may consist of siliceous spicules other than six-rayed forms, and/or spongin.
2. The choanocytes are small and restricted to flagellate chambe
3. The flagellate chambers are spherical.

Subclass Tetractinellida

Demospongiae in which:-

● 1. The spicules are siliceous and tetraxon, i.e. four-rayed

Example:- Pachymatisma

Subclass Monaxonida

Demospongiae in which:-

● 1. The spicules are siliceous and monaxon, i.e. one-rayed.

Examples:- Halichondria, Spongilla, Cliona.

Subclass Keratosa

Demospongiae in which:-

● 1. Spicules are absent but there is a skeleton of spongin fibres.

Example:- Euspongia.

PHYLUM PORIFERA

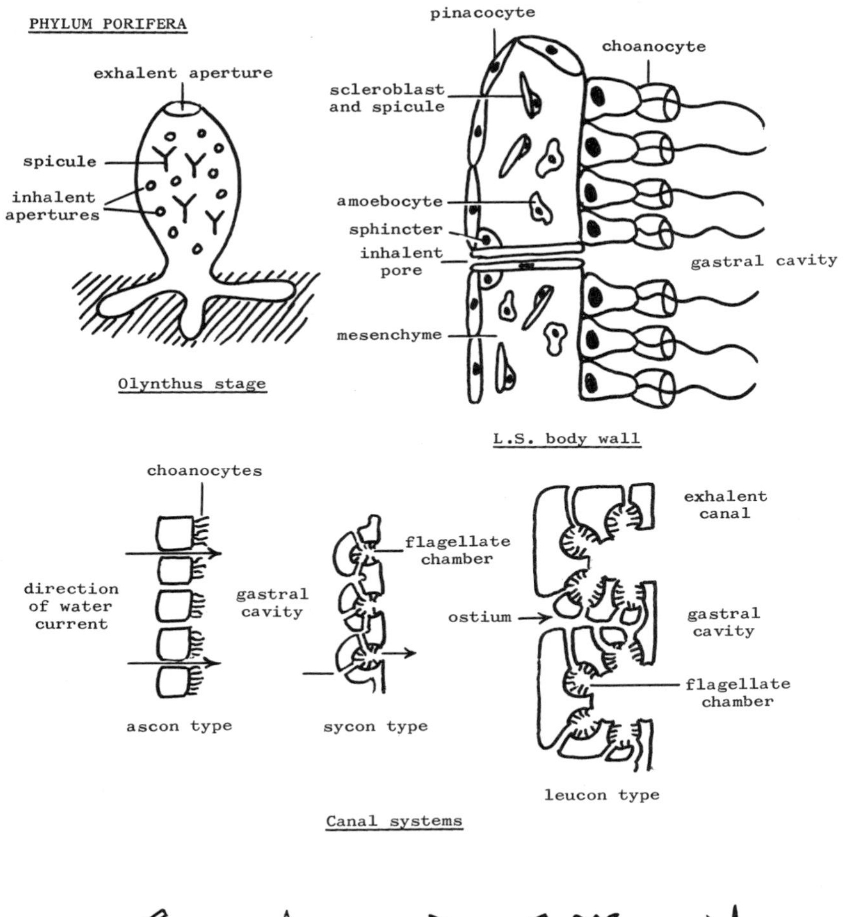

Canal systems

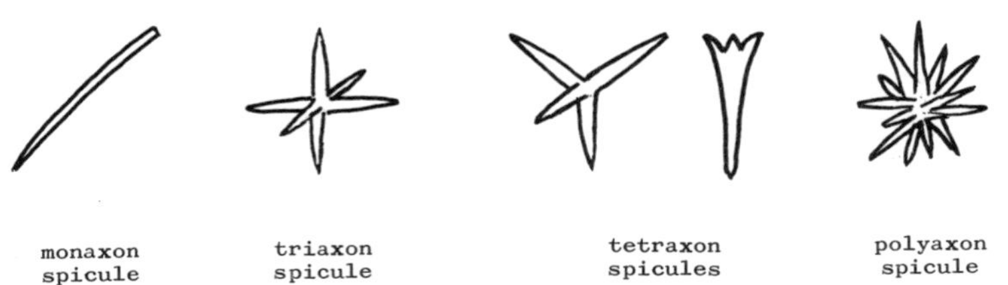

4 Coelenterates and Ctenophores

Zoologists in the latter half of the 19th century were absorbed with the interpretation of their subject in terms of the new theory of evolution by natural selection propounded by Darwin and Wallace. In this, the development of echinoderms and amphioxus from a single-celled egg, through the hollow blastula and two-layered gastrula to the three-layered adult appeared to exemplify the course of evolution from a protozoan to the higher forms of animal life. Many, but chief among them Ernst Haeckel, sought to relate the embryological stages with a corresponding sequence of adult forms of organisms representing an apparently similar increase in complexity and organisation. Consequently the coelenterates, and in particular _Hydra_, with a two-layered or diploblastic body wall and a single aperture leading in to a capacious gut or enteron, were readily compared with the gastrula. Moreover both _Hydra_ and the gastrula have radial symmetry. Radial symmetry has only one axis of symmetry and may be considered more primitive than bilateral symmetry which requires in addition the determination of a plane and is characteristic of most Metazoa. It is not surprising, therefore, that the coelenterates, and allied with them the ctenophores which are also diploblastic, should be considered the most primitive of the Metazoa.

This view of the origin and evolution of the Metazoa has been challenged by Jovan Hadži in a series of publications in Slovene, Serbian or German, but summarized by Gavin de Beer in _Evolution as a Process_ (ed. by Julian Huxley, A.C. Hardy and E.B. Ford), 1954, Allen and Unwin,

London. Briefly the argument proposed by Hadži has the following main stages.

The three classes of the Coelenterata are the Hydrozoa, the Scyphozoa and the Anthozoa. The Hydrozoa, because of their simplicity of structure and typical radial symmetry, are usually regarded as the most primitive, while the Anthozoa, the sea anemones and corals, with the most highly developed structure, are thought to be the most advanced. But whereas the Anthozoa are radially symmetrical on the outside, their internal structure is bilaterally symmetrical. Bilateral symmetry is associated with an active free-moving life and is first evident in the external structures which are in contact with the medium in which the animal lives. It would be expected, therefore, in an active animal that has become sessile, that external bilateral symmetry would be replaced by radial symmetry and that this process would proceed in a degenerating line until the entire animal was radially symmetrical throughout. Thus it could be concluded that the Anthozoa are descended from a bilaterally symmetrical metazoan ancestor and are the most primitive of the coelenterates, while the Hydrozoa, secondarily achieving complete and simple radial symmetry, are the most advanced. This view of Hadži at once removes the coelenterates from the position of most primitive living metazoans and at the same time turns them upside down, that is the Anthozoa, could be considered to have arisen before the Hydrozoa.

If this is the case, what then is the most primitive living metazoan? As has been pointed out in the previous chapter, the aggregation of protistan individuals into a single organism, such as Volvox, is not thought to be probable for the Metazoa, although this may have happened in the sponges. The reason for the doubt is the high level of integration and axiation, that is the development of head-tail polarity, characteristic of Metazoa which is most likely to have been attained by internal subdivision of a protistan body in which integration and axiation were already in existence. The transition of a multinucleate ciliate into the most primitive of the Turbellaria, the Acoela, on these grounds, is a most attractive theory. The Acoela have no gut cavity, they are imperfectly cellularized and they are of the same order of size as the larger ciliates. This is Hadži's view.

Among the Turbellaria, the Rhabdocoela have a lobed hollow gut cavity, a pair of tentacles containing hollow gut diverticula and epithelio-muscular cells in the epidermis. It would not be difficult to convert a rhabdocoel into a hollow-tentacled, macrophagous anthozoan polyp. For other cogent reasons a case can be made for the origin of the ctenophores from a different group of turbellarians, the Polycladida.

These proposals of Hadži have much to commend them, and although the major groups in this book have not been arranged in accordance with his views, they serve to remind us of the potentially fluid situation that exists throughout classification even at the level of the highest taxa.

Subkingdom Metazoa

Animals in which:-

● 1. The body is cellular.
2. The gametes are formed from specialised cells.
3. Choanocytes are never present.
● 4. The principal aperture of the body is inhalent.
5. During development there is no reversal of cell layers.
6. The cells are highly inter-dependent upon one another.
● 7. Sense organs and a nervous system are present.
8. There is an enteron lined by endoderm.

OUTLINE CLASSIFICATION OF THE METAZOA

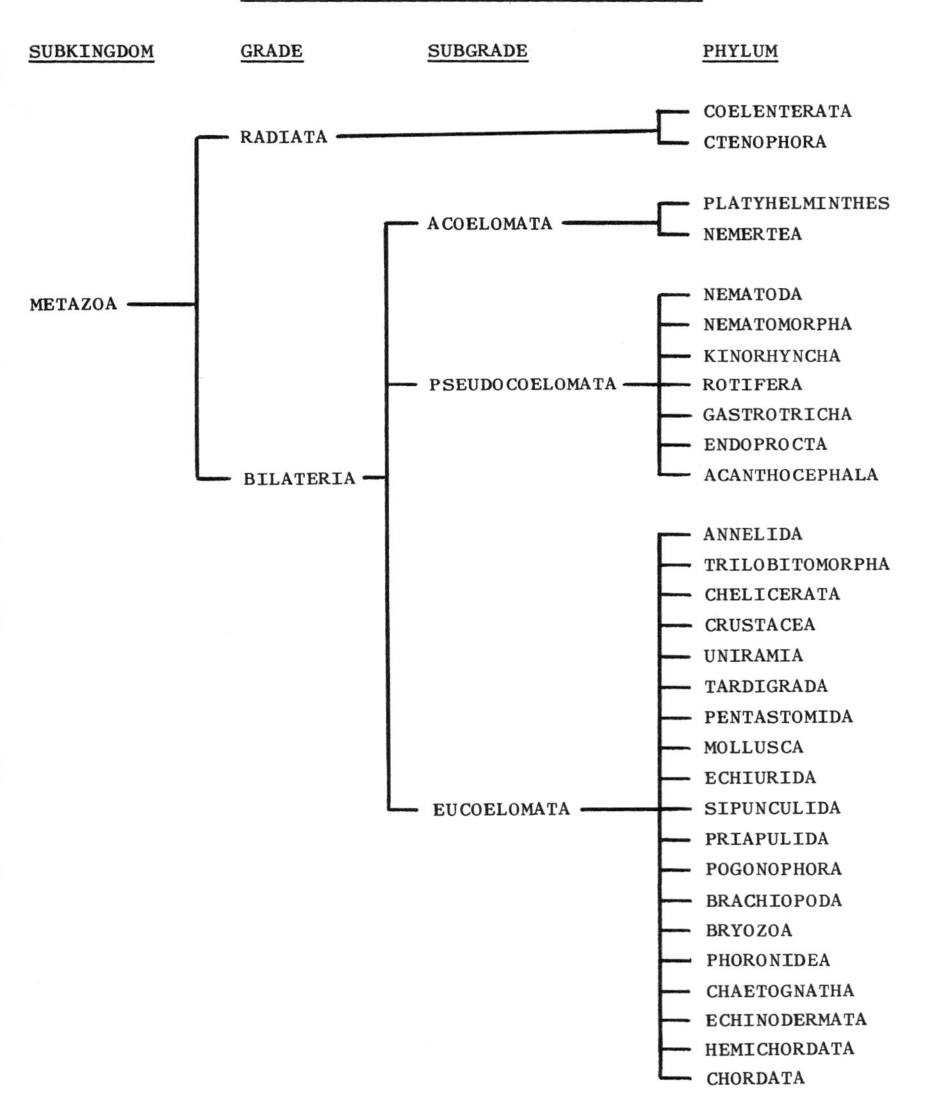

Grade Radiata (Diploblastica)

Metazoa in which:-

- ● 1. The body is primarily radially symmetrical (usually associated with pelagic or sessile life).
- ● 2. The body is diploblastic, i.e. ectoderm and endoderm alone are present.
- 3. The germ cells are necessarily ectodermal or endodermal in origin.
- 4. The nervous system is a network of cells showing little, if any, concentration.
- ● 5. Even in those forms which show some secondary bilateral symmetry, there are no signs of cephalisation.

Phylum Coelenterata (Cnidaria)

Radiata in which:-

- ● 1. Nematocysts are present.
- ● 2. Adult movement is by muscular activity.
- ● 3. The body is either a polyp or a medusa, and these alternate in the life cycle of many species.
- 4. A planula larva is developed.

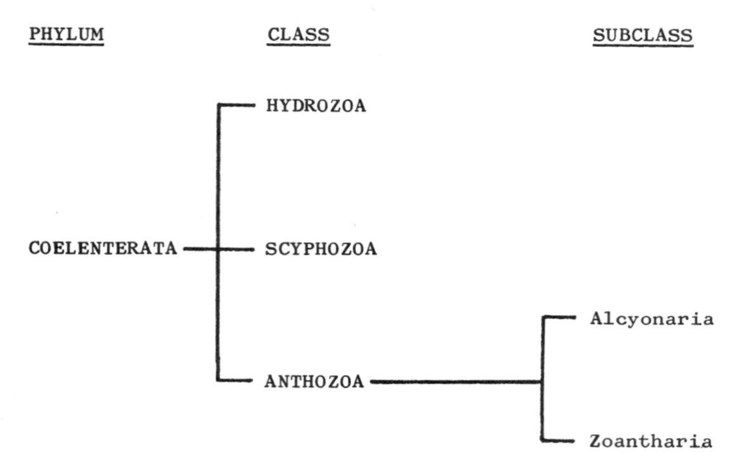

PHYLUM COELENTERATA

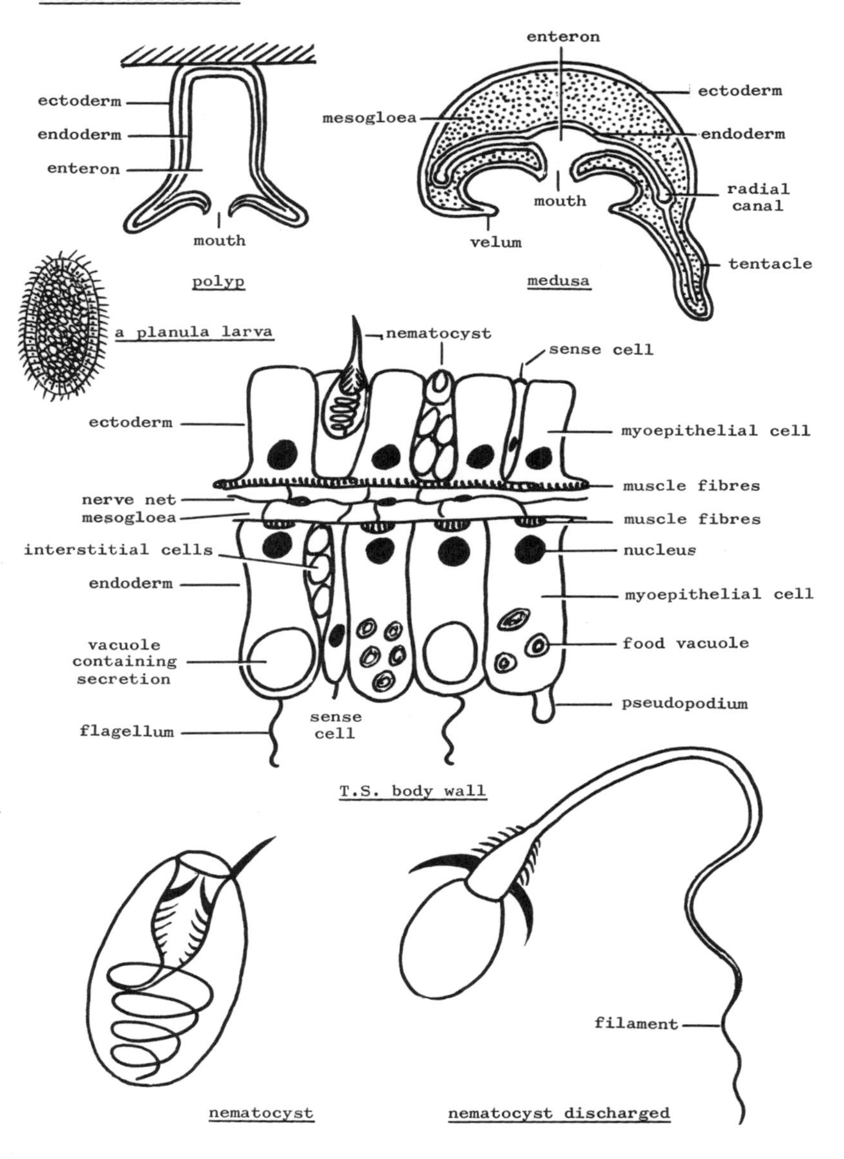

COELENTERATA

Class Hydrozoa

Coelenterata in which:-

1. The polyp typically alternates with the medusa.
2. The medusa possesses a velum and a nerve ring.
3. The enteron is not subdivided by vertical septa.
4. The gonads are ectodermal in origin.
5. There may or may not be a skeleton.
6. The tentacles of the polyp are generally solid.
7. The members almost always form colonies.

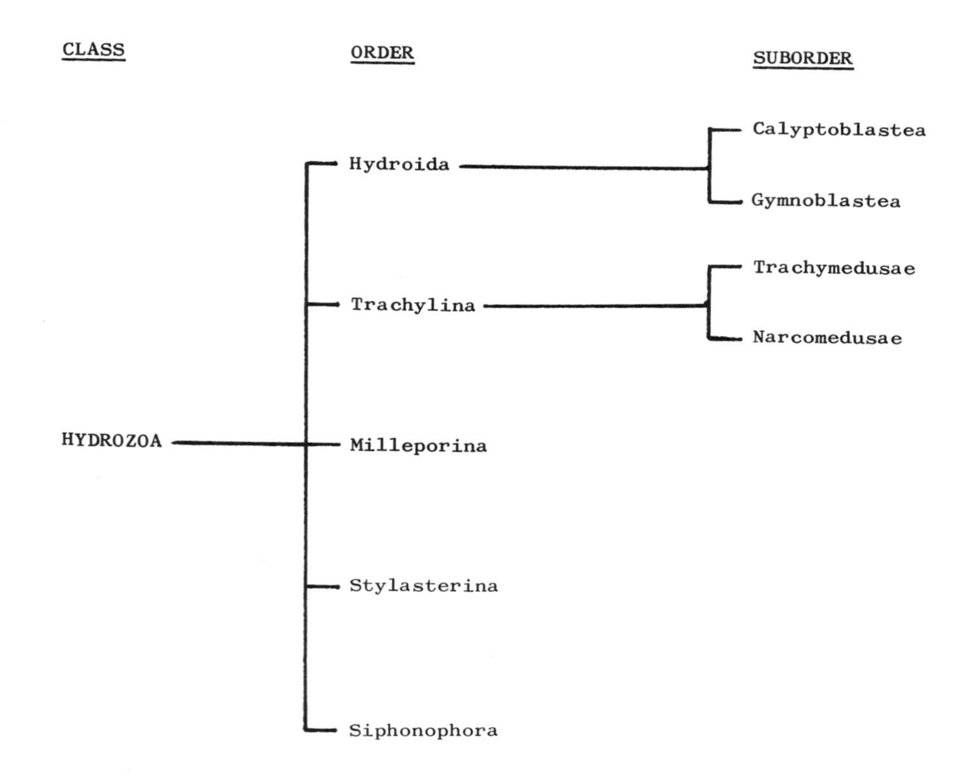

C O E L E N T E R A T A

Order Hydroida - Hydroids

Hydrozoa in which:-

- ● 1. There is typically a horny perisarc covering the coenosarc; polyps may or may not be covered.
- 2. Medusae (if present) are discoid or bell-shaped.
- 3. Gonads are borne either on radial canals or the manubrium of the medusa.
- 4. Sense organs are statocysts or eyes.
- ● 5. Polyps are usually colonial.

Suborder Calyptoblastea - Sea firs

Hydroida in which:-

- ● 1. There is a horny perisarc covering the coenosarc and the polyps.
- ● 2. The medusae are discoid.
- ● 3. The gonads are borne on the radial canals of the medusae.
- ● 4. The medusae usually possess statocysts.
- 5. The polyps are colonial.

Examples:- *Obelia*, *Plumularia*, *Sertularia*.

(see page 45)

Suborder Gymnoblastea

Hydroida in which:-

- ● 1. There is a horny perisarc covering the coenosarc but not the polyps.
- ● 2. The medusae are bell-shaped (or absent in *Hydra*).
- ● 3. The gonads are borne on the manubrium of the medusa.
- ● 4. The medusae do not possess statocysts but bear eyes.
- 5. The polyps are usually colonial, but some solitary forms occur.

Examples:- *Hydra*, *Bougainvillea*, *Tubularia*, *Sarsia*.

(see page 46)

C O E L E N T E R A T A

Order Trachylina

Hydrozoa in which:-

● 1. There is no perisarc.
2. The medusa is large and the polyp reduced or wanting.
3. The gonads are borne on the radial canals or on the floor of the gastric cavity.
4. The sense organs are modified tentacles (tentaculocysts).
● 5. The members are solitary, although in a few cases budding takes place.

Suborder Trachymedusae

Trachylina in which:-

● 1. The tentacles arise from the margin of the umbrella.
2. The tentaculocysts are enclosed in pits or vesicles.
● 3. The gonads are borne on the radial canals.

Examples:- Liriope, Carmarina, Limnocnida.

(see page 46)

Suborder Narcomedusae

Trachylina in which:-

● 1. The tentacles arise from the exumbrella and are not marginal.
2. The tentaculocysts are not enclosed.
● 3. The gonads are borne on the floor of the gastric cavity.

Examples:- Solmundella, Cunina.

Order Milleporina

Hydrozoa in which:-

● 1. There is a massive calcareous external skeleton.
2. The medusae are reduced, lacking velum.
3. The gonads are borne on the manubrium of the medusa.
4. There are no specialised sense organs.
● 5. The polyps are differentiated into gastrozoids and dactylozoids.

Example:- Millepora.

(see page 45)

C O E L E N T E R A T A

Order Stylasterina

Hydrozoa in which:-

● 1. There is a massive, calcareous external skeleton.
2. The medusae are reduced to sporosacs and are not detached.
3. Gonozoids are lacking.
4. There are no specialized sense organs.
● 5. The polyps are differentiated into gastrozoids and dactylozoids.
6. Dactylozoids are small, solid and without tentacles.

Example:- Stylaster.

Order Siphonophora - Portuguese-man-of-war etc.

Hydrozoa in which:-

● 1. There is no skeleton.
● 2. The medusae are bell-shaped and give rise to pelagic colonies by a process of budding.
3. The gonads are borne on special gonophores or gonozoids.
4. There are no specialised sense organs.
● 5. The polyps and medusae show a high degree of polymorphism.

Examples:- Velella, Diphyes, Physalia, Muggiaea.

(see pages 45, 47)

Class Scyphozoa (Scyphomedusae) - Jellyfishes

Coelenterata in which:-

1. The medusoid form is dominant and the polyp form greatly reduced or absent.
● 2. The medusa possesses neither a velum nor a nerve ring.
(Charybdeidae have a velum-like structure called a velarium and also a nerve ring. The velarium is merely an infolding of the subumbrella and, unlike the velum, lacks muscle fibres).
● 3. The enteron of either the adult or the larva is subdivided by vertical septa.
4. The gonads are endodermal in origin.
5. There is no skeleton.
6. The tentacles are solid (rarely hollow).
● 7. The members are solitary.

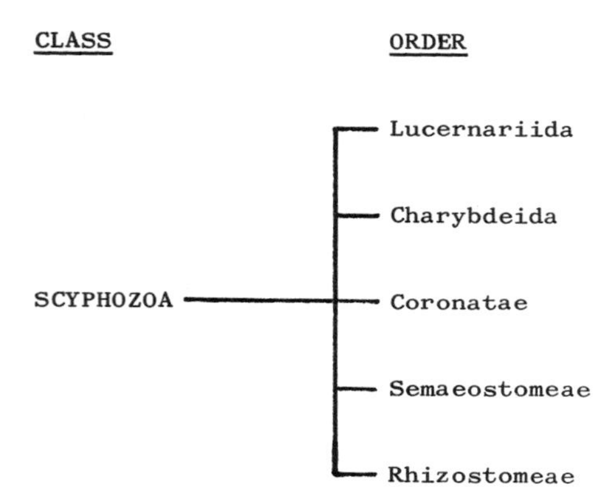

Order Lucernariida (Stauromedusae)

Scyphozoa in which:-

- 1. There are no tentaculocysts.
  2. The tentacles are per-radial and inter-radial.
  3. Inter-radial mesenteries divide the gastric cavity into four per-radial gastric pouches.
- 4. The body is conical in shape (scyphistomoid).
- 5. There is usually an exumbrella peduncle for attachment.
  6. There is no alternation of generations.

Examples:- Lucernaria, Haliclystus. (see page 48)

Order Charybdeida (Cubomedusae) - Sea wasps

Scyphozoa in which:-

1. There are four per-radial tentaculocysts.
2. The tentacles are inter-radial.
3. Four peripheral mesenteries divide the gastric cavity into four per-radial pouches.
4. The body is almost cubical.
5. There is no exumbrella peduncle.
6. There is no alternation of generations.

Example:- Charybdea. (see page 48)

Order Coronatae (Peromedusae)

Scyphozoa in which:-

1. There are four inter-radial tentaculocysts.
2. The tentacles are per-radial and adradial.
3. Four mesenteries inserted on the body wall at two points only divide the gastric cavity into two circular sinuses, one ventrally and one peripherally placed.
4. The body is conical and divided transversely by a groove.
5. There is no exumbrella peduncle.
6. There is no alternation of generations.

Examples:- Nausithoe, Periphylla, Pericolpa.

(see page 48)

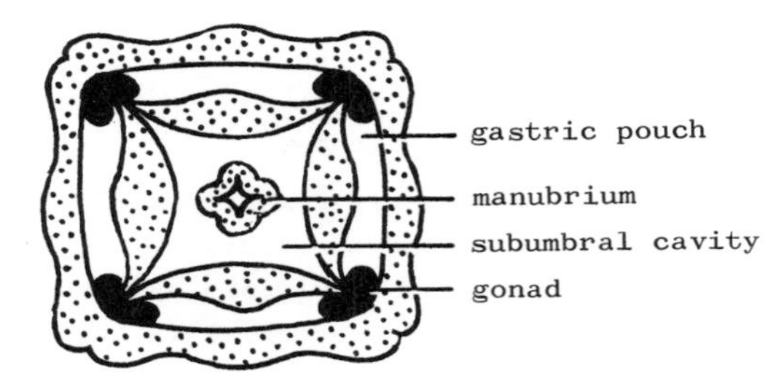

T.S. Charybdea

C O E L E N T E R A T A

Order Semaeostomeae

Scyphozoa in which:-

1. There are not less than eight (four per-radial and four inter-radial) tentaculocysts.
● 2. The tentacles are usually numerous.
3. There are no laminar mesenteries in the adult, but they are present in the scyphistoma.
4. The body is discoid.
5. There is no exumbrella peduncle.
6. The medusa alternates with a scyphistoma.
● 7. The mouth is extended to form four oral arms.

Examples:- Aurelia, Cyanea. (see page 49)

Order Rhizostomeae

Scyphozoa in which:-

1. There are not less than eight (four per-radial and four inter-radial) tentaculocysts.
● 2. Tentacles are absent.
3. There are no laminar mesenteries in the adult, but they are present in the scyphistoma.
4. The body is discoid to nearly hemispherical.
5. There is no exumbrella peduncle.
6. The medusa alternates with a scyphistoma.
● 7. The mouth is closed by the four bifurcated oral arms each of which bears numerous oral canals leading from the gastric cavity and ending in sucking mouths.

Examples:- Rhizostoma, Cassiopeia. (see page 49)

Class Anthozoa (Actinozoa)

Coelenterata in which:-

1. The polyp form is dominant and the medusoid form absent.
2. There is no medusa stage.
● 3. The enteron is subdivided by vertical septa.
4. The gonads are endodermal in origin.
5. A skeleton may or may not be present.
● 6. The tentacles are hollow.
7. The members are colonial or solitary.

C O E L E N T E R A T A

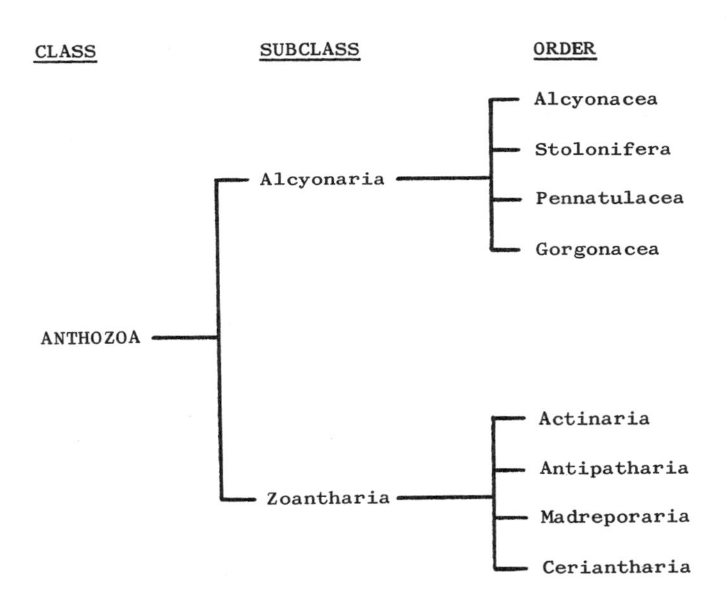

Subclass Alcyonaria

Anthozoa in which:-

- 1. The tentacles are pinnate and eight in number.
- 2. The mesenteries are eight in number and are not arranged in pairs.
- 3. The stomodaeum possesses typically a single siphonoglyph (ciliated groove).

4. The longitudinal muscles of the mesenteries are on the surfaces facing the siphonoglyph.
5. The members are exclusively colonial.

C O E L E N T E R A T A

Order Alcyonacea - Dead-mens'-fingers and precious coral

Alcyonaria in which:-

1. There is a calcareous skeleton of spicules which may or may not become aggregated to form a continuous mass.
2. The coenenchyma is typically canaliferous.
3. The colony is usually massive.

Examples:- Alcyonium, Corallium. (see pages 50, 51)

Order Stolonifera - Organ pipe coral

Alcyonaria in which:-

1. The skeleton consists of separate calcareous spicules only, or the spicules may fuse to form tubes and platforms.
2. The coenenchyma is canaliferous.
3. ● The polyps are connected by creeping stolons.

Example:- Tubipora

Order Pennatulacea - Sea pens and sea pansy

Alcyonaria in which:-

1. There is a calcareous or horny axial skeleton (possibly endodermal).
2. The coenenchyma is not canaliferous.
3. ● The colony comprises a single axial polyp from which secondary dimorphic polyps are budded off usually on lateral branches.

Examples:- Pennatula, Veretillum, Renilla.

(see page 51)

Order Gorgonacea - Horny corals

Alcyonaria in which:-

1. There is a calcareous or horny axial skeleton of ectodermal origin.
2. The coenenchyma is not canaliferous.
3. ● The colony is tree-like and the polyps are not dimorphic.

Examples:- Gorgonia, Eunicella. (see page 51)

Subclass Zoantharia

Anthozoa in which:-

- ● 1. The tentacles are simple and are usually arranged in multiples of six (except Metridium).
- ● 2. The mesenteries are usually arranged in multiples of six and are frequently in pairs.
- ● 3. The stomodaeum possesses typically two siphonoglyphs.
- 4. The longitudinal muscles of the mesenteries are arranged in many different ways.
- 5. Both solitary and colonial forms occur.

Order Actinaria - Sea anemones

Zoantharia in which:-

- ● 1. The skeleton is absent.
- ● 2. The tentacles are numerous.
- 3. There are two siphonoglyphs.
- ● 4. They are solitary.

Examples:- Peachia, Adamsia, Actinia, Anemonia, Metridium.

(see page 50)

Order Antipatharia - Black corals

Zoantharia in which:-

- ● 1. There is a branched, axial, chitinoid skeleton of ectodermal origin.
- ● 2. Tentacles are few (6-24) in number.
- 3. The siphonoglyphs are reduced.
- ● 4. They are colonial.

Example:- Antipathes. (see page 51)

Order Madreporaria - True or Stony corals.

Zoantharia in which:-

- ● 1. There is a massive calcareous exoskeleton.
- ● 2. The tentacles are numerous.
- 3. There are two siphonoglyphs.
- ● 4. They are usually colonial.

Examples:- Porites, Caryophyllia, Meandrina, Fungia.

(see page 51)

Order Ceriantharia

Zoantharia in which:-

1. There is no true skeleton.
2. The tentacles are of two kinds, marginal and oral.
3. ● There is a single dorsal siphonoglyph.
4. ● They are solitary, burrowing into sand, leaving only the oral disc exposed.

Example:- Cerianthus.

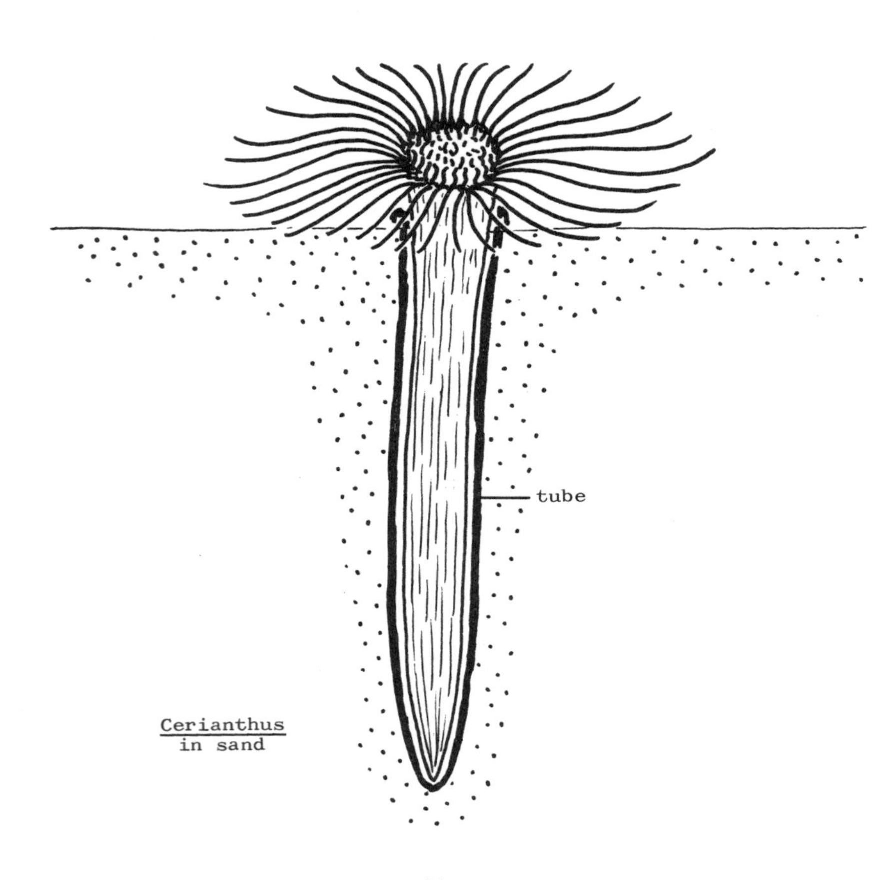

Cerianthus in sand

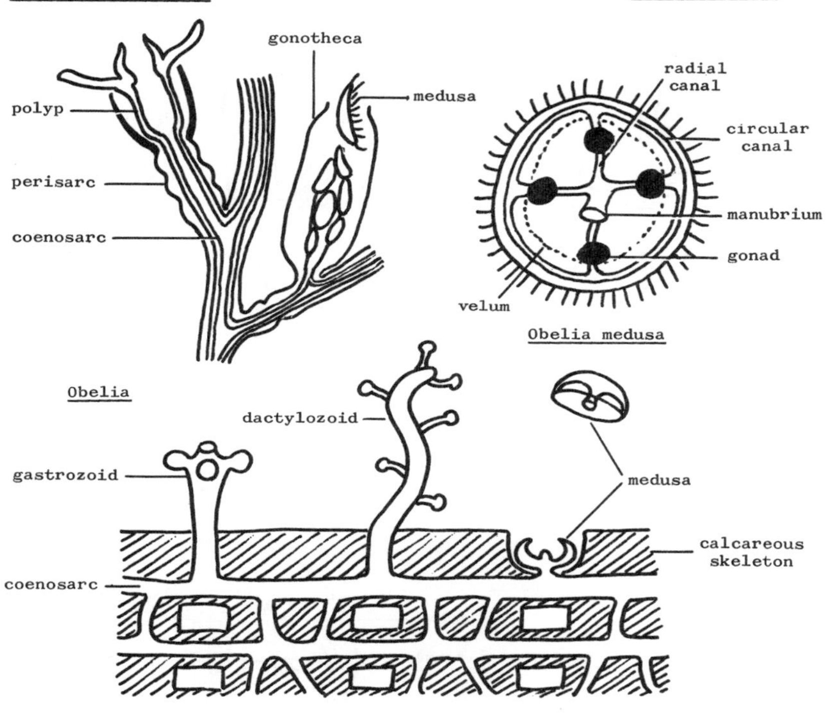
gonotheca
medusa
polyp
perisarc
coenosarc
radial canal
circular canal
manubrium
gonad
velum
Obelia medusa
Obelia
dactylozoid
gastrozoid
medusa
calcareous skeleton
coenosarc
Millepora

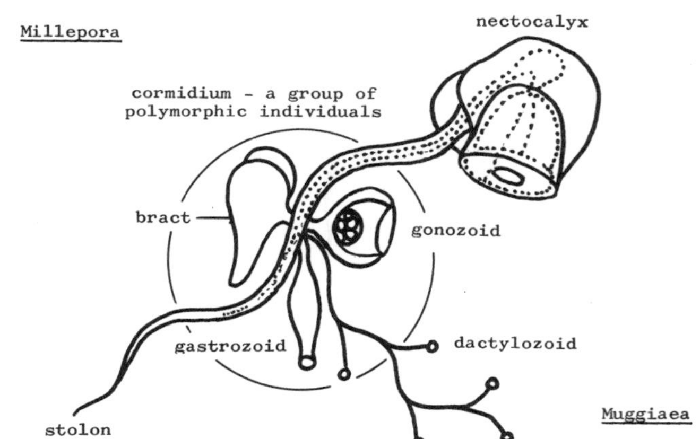
nectocalyx
cormidium - a group of polymorphic individuals
bract
gonozoid
gastrozoid
dactylozoid
stolon
Muggiaea

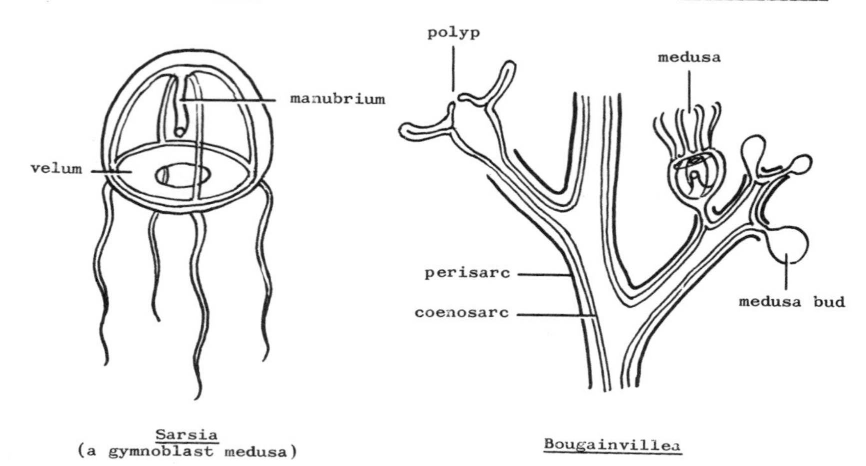

Sarsia
(a gymnoblast medusa)

Bougainvillea

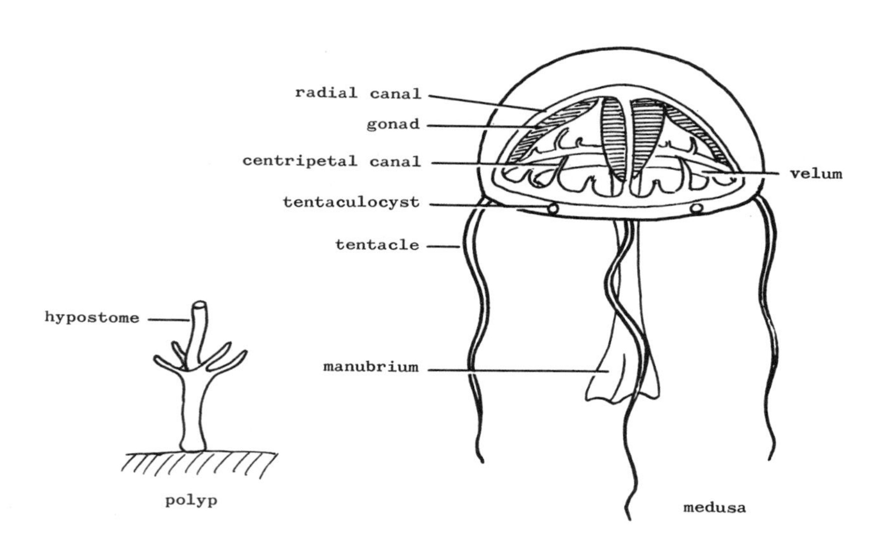

Liriope

PHYLUM COELENTERATA

CLASS HYDROZOA

ORDER SIPHONOPHORA

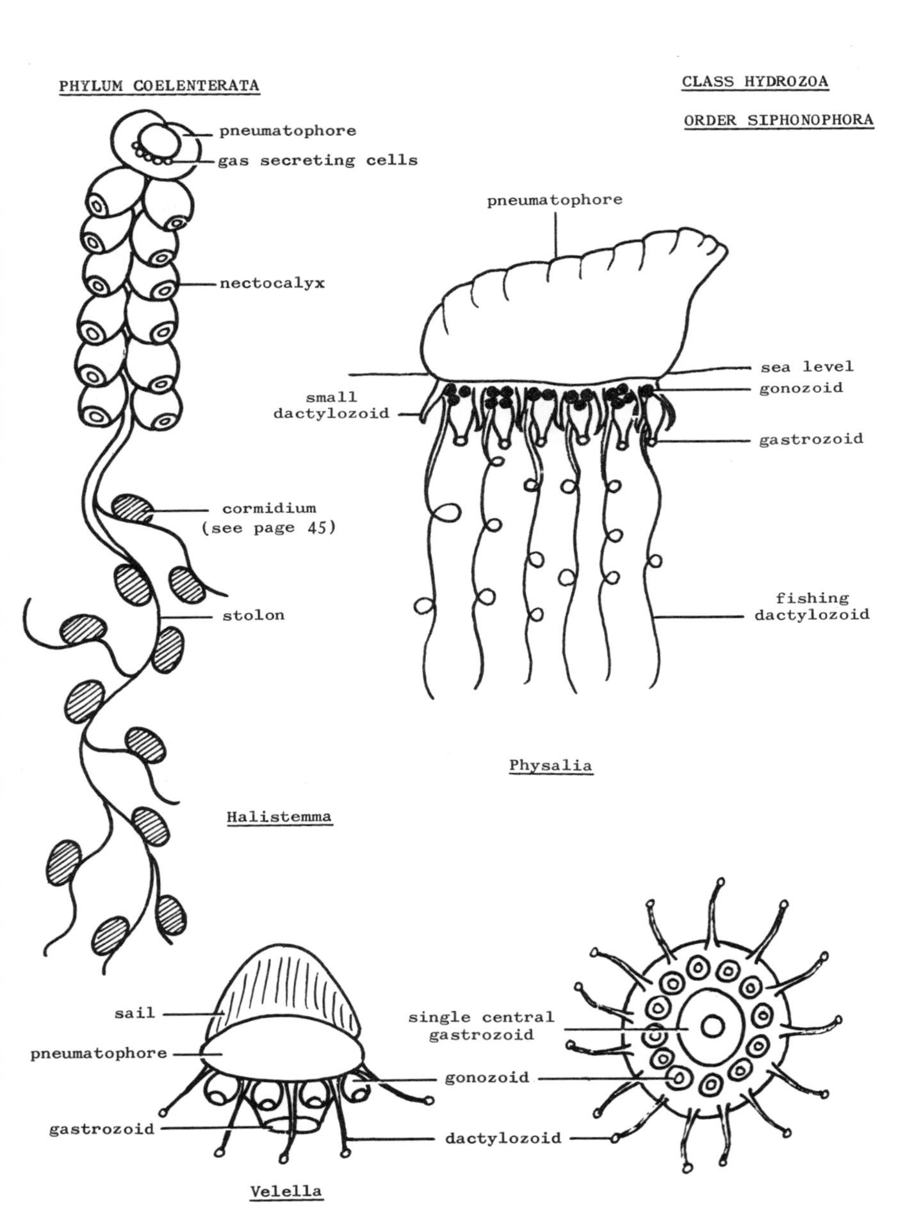

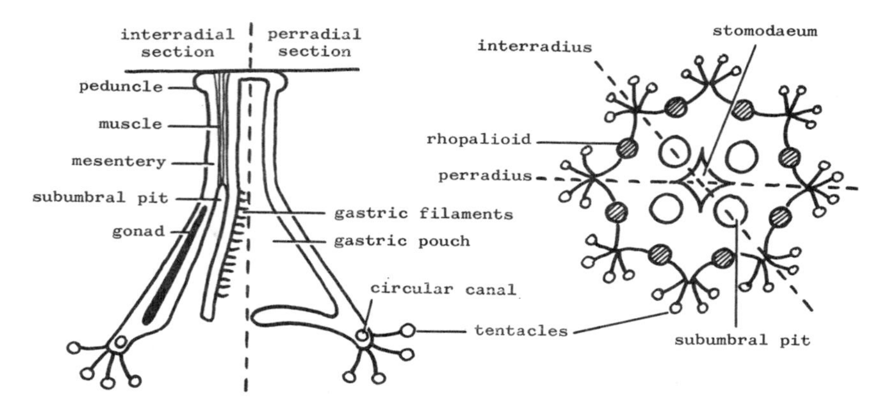

Haliclystus

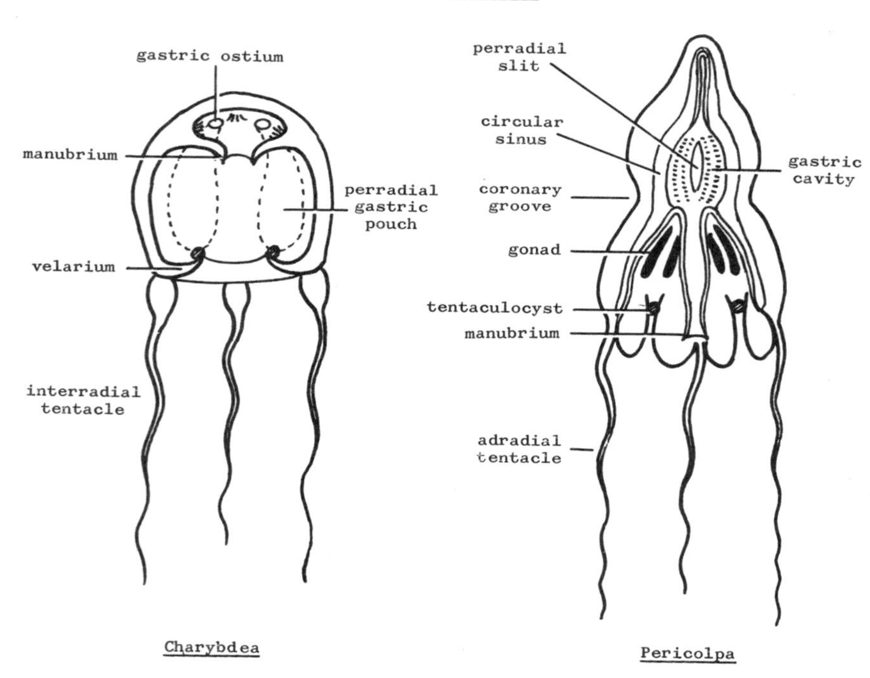

Charybdea

Pericolpa

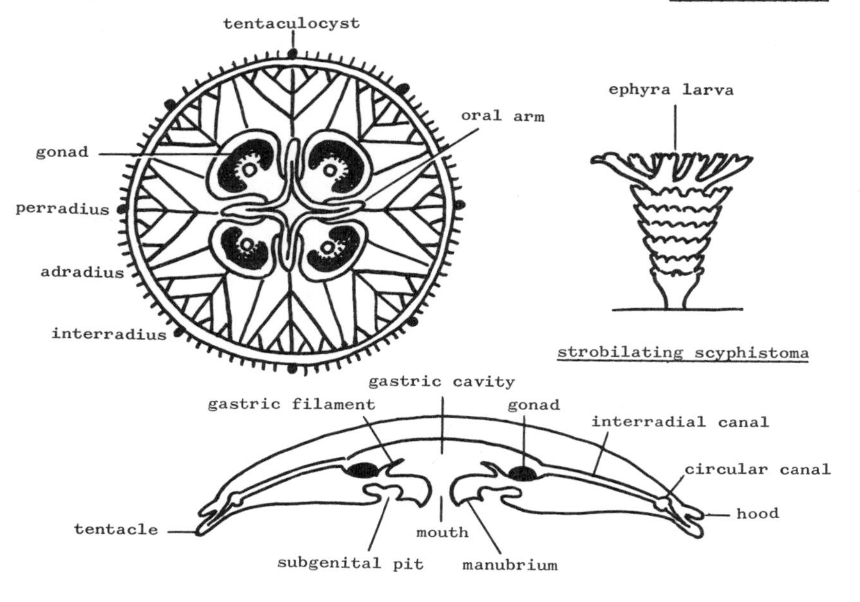

Aurelia

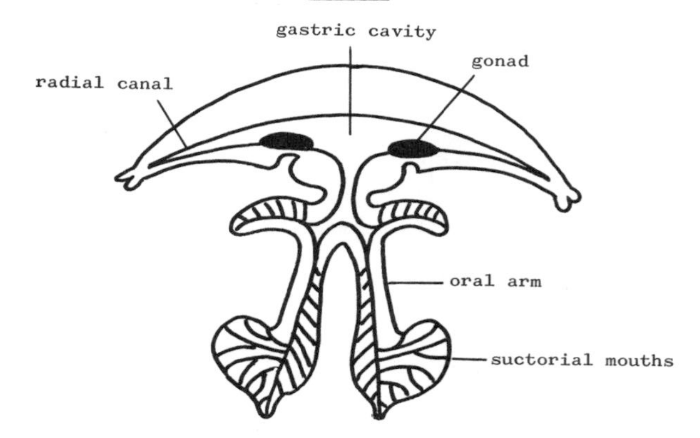

Rhizostoma

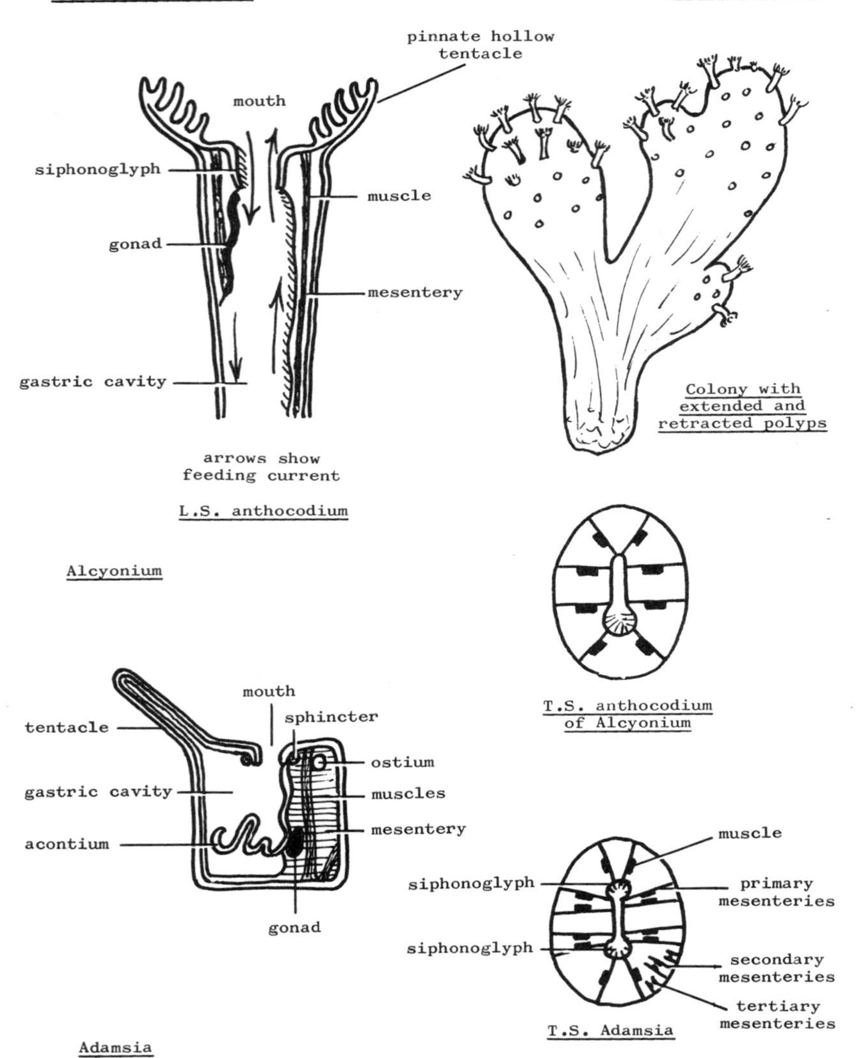
pinnate hollow tentacle
mouth
siphonoglyph
muscle
gonad
mesentery
gastric cavity
arrows show feeding current
L.S. anthocodium
Colony with extended and retracted polyps
T.S. anthocodium of Alcyonium
Alcyonium
mouth
sphincter
tentacle
ostium
gastric cavity
muscles
mesentery
acontium
gonad
muscle
siphonoglyph
primary mesenteries
siphonoglyph
secondary mesenteries
tertiary mesenteries
T.S. Adamsia

Adamsia

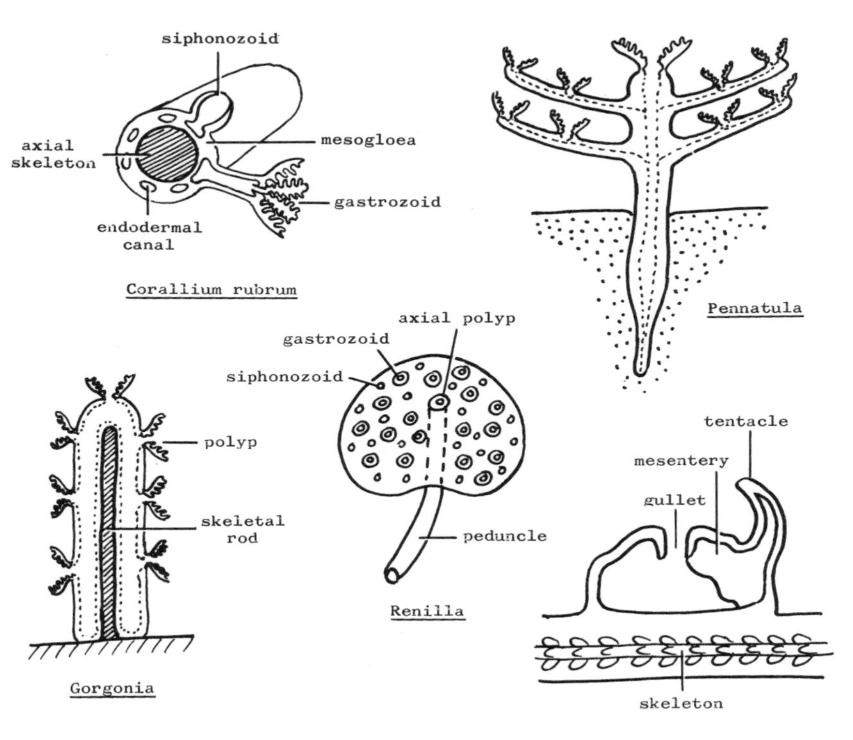
siphonozoid
axial skeleton
mesogloea
gastrozoid
endodermal canal
Corallium rubrum
Pennatula
axial polyp
gastrozoid
siphonozoid
polyp
skeletal rod
peduncle
Renilla
Gorgonia
tentacle
mesentery
gullet
skeleton
Antipathes

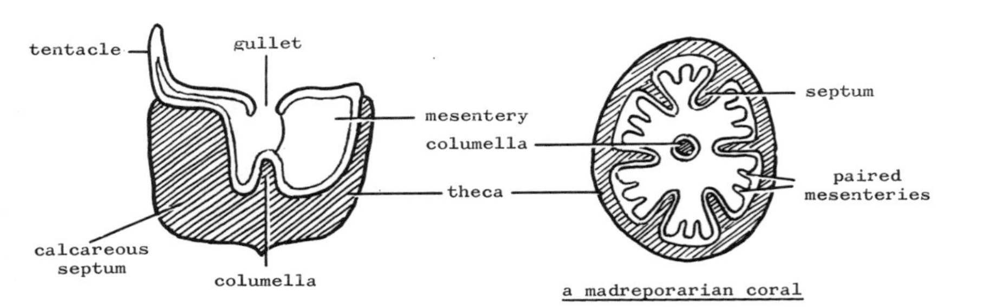
tentacle
gullet
mesentery
columella
theca
calcareous septum
columella
septum
paired mesenteries
a madreporarian coral

Phylum Ctenophora

Radiata in which:-

- 1. Nematocysts are absent but colloblasts ('lasso cells') are present.
- 2. Movement is by ciliary action.
- 3. There is no alternation of generations, the body being neither a polyp nor a medusa.
- 4. There is no planula larva, but development is through a cydippid-like stage.

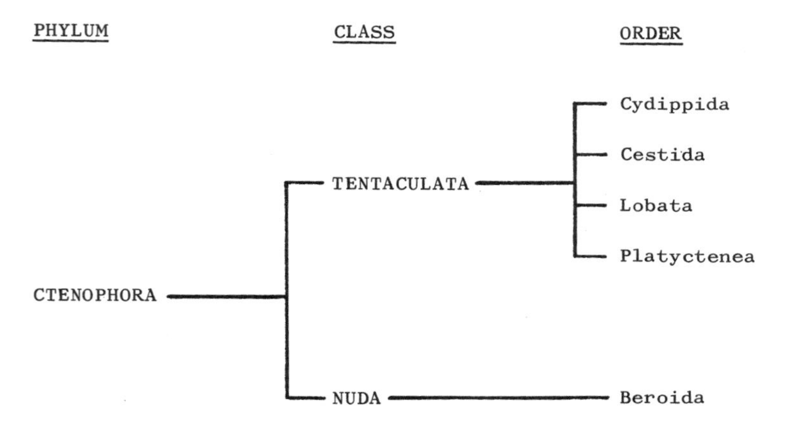

C T E N O P H O R A

Class Tentaculata

Ctenophora in which:-

● 1. Tentacles are present.

Order Cydippida - Sea gooseberries

Tentaculata in which:-

1. There are two branched tentacles, retractile into sheaths.
● 2. The body is spheroidal.

Examples:- Pleurobrachia, Hormiphora.

(see pages 54, 55)

Order Cestida - Venus' girdle

Tentaculata in which:-

1. The ensheathed bases of the two principal tentacles remain, and in addition there are numerous small tentacles along the oral edge.
● 2. The body is ribbon-shaped, being flattened in the tentacular plane.

Example:- Cestus. (see page 56)

Order Lobata

Tentaculata in which:-

1. The bases only of the two principal tentacles remain and are not ensheathed, and there are numerous lateral tentacles in a groove.
● 2. The body is laterally compressed and is formed into two large peristomial lobes and four lappets.

Example:- Deiopea. (see page 56)

Order Platyctenea

Tentaculata in which:-

1. There are two retractile lateral tentacles.
● 2. The body is dorso-ventrally flattened.

Examples:- Ctenoplana, Coeloplana. (see page 56)

C T E N O P H O R A

Class Nuda

Ctenophora in which:-

- 1. There are no tentacles.

Order Beroida

Nuda in which:-

- 1. The mouth is wide and the gullet very large.
- 2. The body is compressed ovoid.

Example:- Beroe. (see page 56)

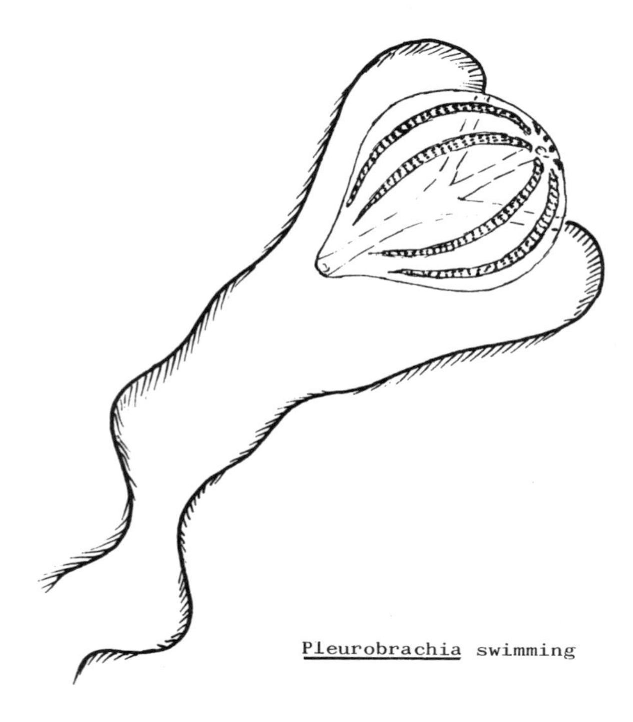

Pleurobrachia swimming

PHYLUM CTENOPHORA

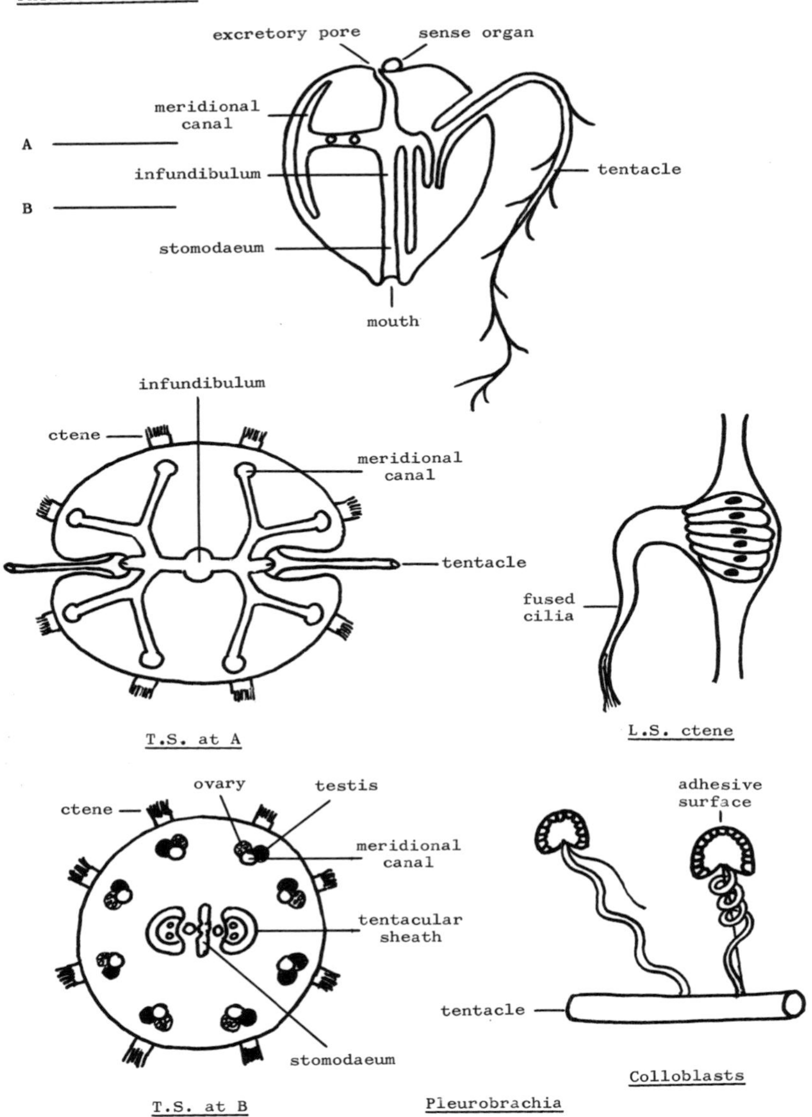

Pleurobrachia

PHYLUM CTENOPHORA

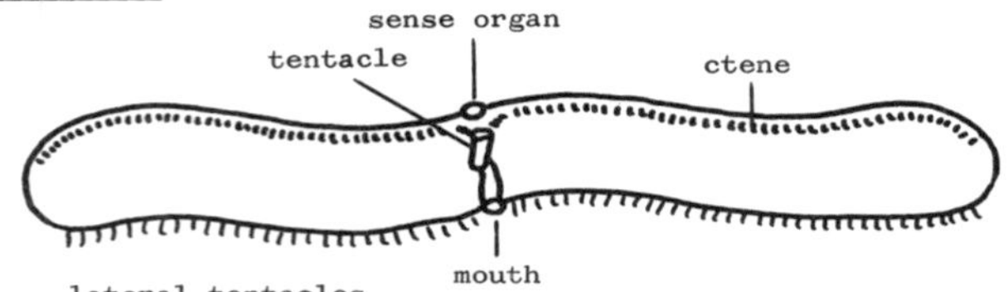

Cestus

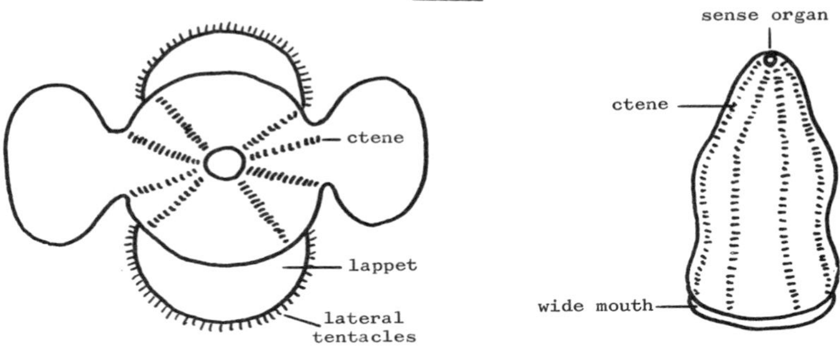

Deiopea

Beroe

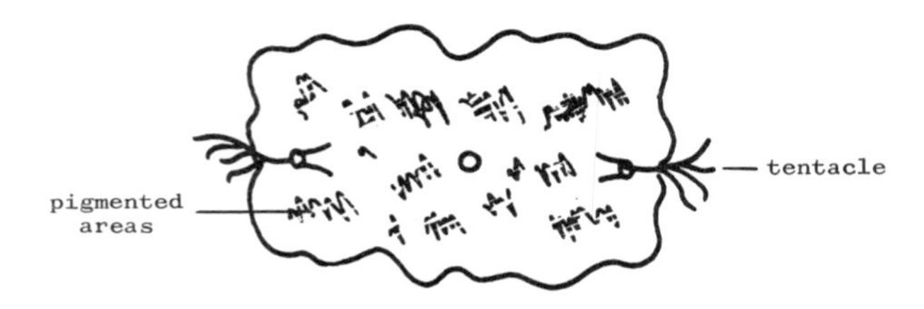

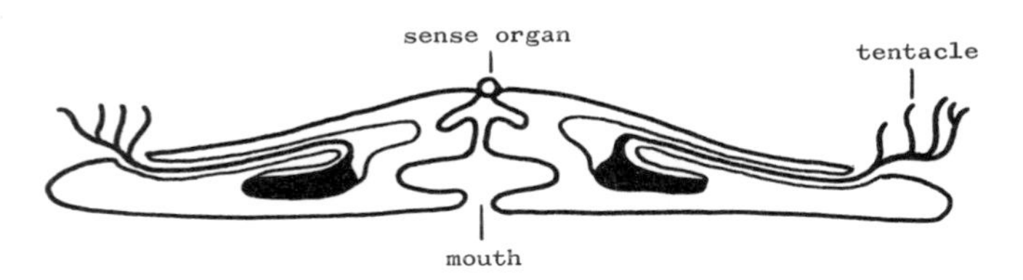

Coeloplana

5 Acoelomate Animals

The question posed in chapter four as to whether coelenterates or platyhelminthes are the more primitive involves the nature of the mesogloea in the coelenterates. If the coelenterates are derived from a turbellarian stock, then the mesogloea should be a reduced mesoderm and the coelenterates are triploblastic. But for practical purposes of classification the mesogloea does not now appear to be a third cell layer between ectoderm and endoderm, so that the coelenterates may be regarded as diploblastic. In the platyhelminthes, on the other hand, the mesoderm certainly is cellular and this group and all higher metazoa are therefore triploblastic.

The platyhelminthes are bilaterally symmetrical flatworms. Some are free living, the planarians, but most are parasitic, such as the flukes and tapeworms. Their leaf-shaped or ribbon-like body has a high surface area to volume ratio with all regions of the body close to the surface. This allows for the supply of oxygen and the escape of metabolites by diffusion. The platyhelminth gut is often highly branched for the transport of food to all parts of the body. Platyhelminthes are carnivores when free-living or feed on products of the host body when parasitic. In the planarians the pharynx is protruded into the body of the prey whose contents are sucked into the flatworm's gut. The food particles are taken in by cells lining the gut and digestion takes place within these phagocytes. There is evidently, therefore, no need for a second opening of the gut for voiding indigestible material, so that in this group, as in the coelenterates, there is no anus.

The body is filled with parenchymatous cells which form an anastomosis with fluid-filled interconnected spaces between the cells acting as a hydrostatic skeleton. But there is no distinct perivisceral space separating the gut from the body wall either in the Platyhelminthes or in their more advanced relatives the Nemertea, so that they are grouped together as the Acoelomata.

The nemertine worms resemble the planarians in their general body architecture, but most are much larger with a more or less cylindrical body, often of very great length. The change in body proportion has called for two adaptations of great significance. It is no longer feasible with such a length of gut to make do with a single opening, the mouth, and so there is a second aperture, the anus. This permits the food to pass in a stream in one direction along the gut. It provides the opportunity for progressive digestion in the different gut regions and for indigestible material to be voided away from the mouth. The second adaptation is the development of a vascular system for the transport of food and oxygen along the length of the body. It is a primitive system without a heart, though some of the vessels are contractile, and also without a capillary system. These improvements on the platyhelminth plan mean that the nemertine has the potential for greater activity which is realised through the development of a much more extensive muscular system than that of the flatworms. Nemertines catch their prey with a long protrusible proboscis which is everted from the head. In relation to their greater activity we see the further development of the head carrying sense organs beyond that of the rudimentary head of the freeliving flatworms.

Both planarians and nemertines have flame cells for osmoregulation and excretion. These cells are the internal terminations of a system of tubules discharging to the exterior. They have tufts of flagella extending into the tubule which beat with a flickering movement recalling a flame.

Grade Bilateria (Triploblastica)

Metazoa in which:-

- ● 1. The body is bilaterally symmetrical, having an antero-posterior axis (usually associated with free locomotion).
- ● 2. The body is triploblastic, i.e. a definite mesoderm is present as well as ectoderm and endoderm.
- 3. The germ cells are of mesodermal origin.
- 4. The nervous system shows concentration into longitudinal cords and an anterior cerebral ganglion.
- 5. The anterior end characteristically shows some signs of cephalisation.

Subgrade Acoelomata

Bilateria in which:-

- ● 1. There is no perivisceral (coelomic) cavity.
- ● 2. The organs are connected by a primitive tissue known as parenchyma.
- ● 3. Flame cells are found in the excretory system.
- 4. A blood vascular system may or may not be present.

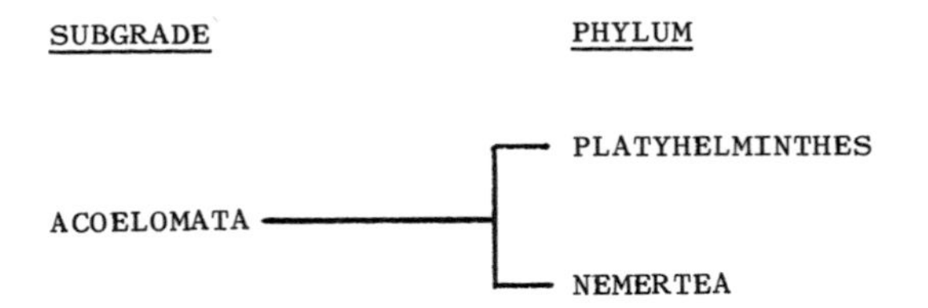

Phylum Platyhelminthes

Acoelomata in which:-

- 1. The body is usually dorso-ventrally compressed.
  2. There is no proboscis dorsal to the gut.
- 3. The gut, when present, has a single aperture (the mouth) and tends to be complex, ramifying throughout the body.
  4. There is no blood vascular system.
  5. The excretory system consists of a series of scattered flame cells which occur throughout the body.
  6. They are usually hermaphrodite.
- 7. The reproductive organs are very complex.
  8. The female gonad is usually divided into an ovarium and a vitellarium.
  9. The genital ducts are complex and permanent.
  10. They may be free-living, epizoic, or ecto- or endoparasites.

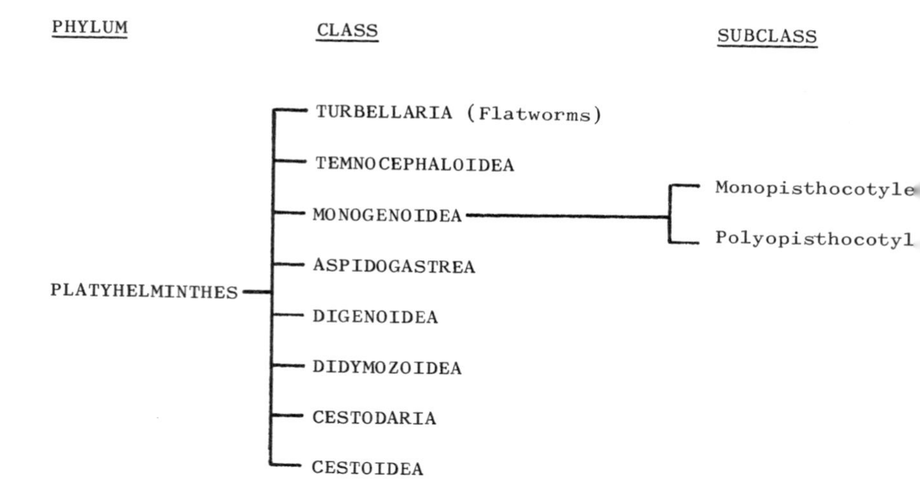

P L A T Y H E L M I N T H E S

Class Turbellaria - Planarians

Platyhelminthes in which:-

- 1. The surface of the body is ciliated.
- 2. The epidermis possesses special cells which either give rise to rhabdites or to mucus.
- 3. There is a gut.
- 4. Suckers are almost always absent.
- 5. Proglottides are never formed.
- 6. The members are almost always free living.

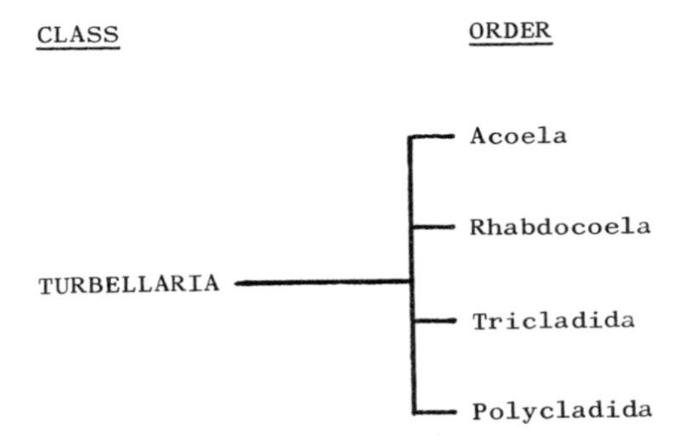

Order Acoela

Turbellaria in which:-

- 1. The gut is represented by a syncytium of endodermal cells.
- 2. A muscular pharynx is absent.
- 3. The mouth is towards the centre of the body.

Example:- Convoluta. (see page 63)

Order Rhabdocoela

Turbellaria in which:-

- 1. The gut is more or less simple and is hollow.
- 2. The pharynx is variable.
- 3. The mouth is near the anterior end of the body.

Example:- Vortex. (see page 63)

P L A T Y H E L M I N T H E S

<u>Order Tricladida</u>

Turbellaria in which:-

- ● 1. There are three main divisions of the gut, each of which bears lateral diverticula.
- 2. The pharynx is tubular.
- ● 3. The mouth is situated towards the centre of the body.

Examples:- <u>Procerodes</u>, <u>Planaria</u>, <u>Dugesia</u>, <u>Dendrocoelum</u>.

(see page 63)

<u>Order Polycladida</u>

Turbellaria in which:-

- ● 1. The gut comprises many diverticula arising from an inconspicuous stem.
- 2. There is a muscular pharynx.
- ● 3. The mouth is situated towards the posterior end of the body.
- ● 4. They are exclusively marine forms with a planktonic larva (Muller's larva).

Example: <u>Leptoplana</u>.

(see page 63)

<u>Class Temnocephaloidea</u>

Platyhelminthes in which:-

- ● 1. The body surface is ciliated in part and covered with a cuticle elsewhere.
- 2. Rhabdites occur in the ectodermal cells of the tentacles.
- 3. A gut is present.
- ● 4. There is a large posterior sucker.
- 5. Proglottides are never formed.
- ● 6. Members are epizoic on invertebrates, chiefly freshwater Crustacea.
- ● 7. Members can be recognized by the possession of tentacles anterior to the mouth.

Example:- <u>Temnocephala</u>.

(see page 66)

PHYLUM PLATYHELMINTHES

CLASS TURBELLARIA

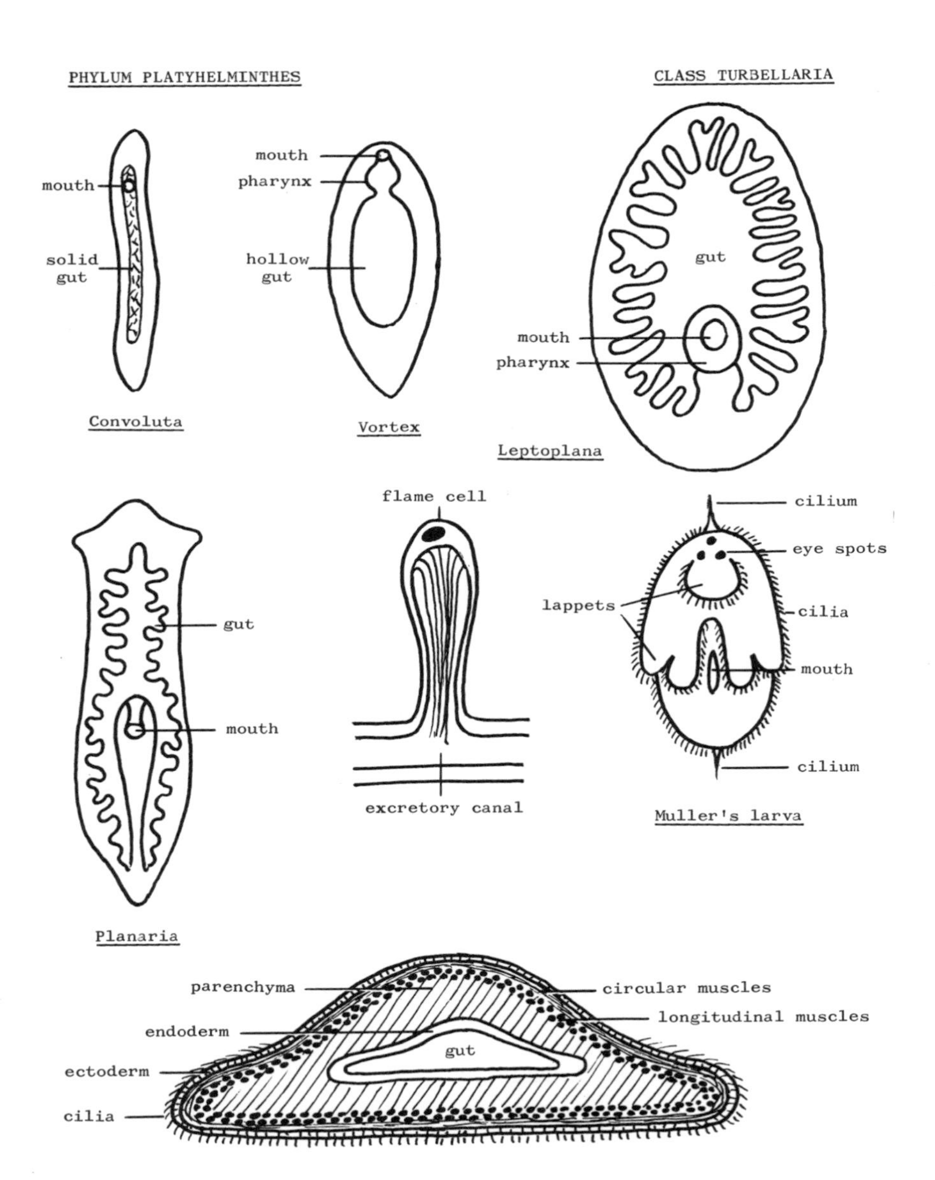

P L A T Y H E L M I N T H E S

Class Monogenoidea

Platyhelminthes in which:-

- ● 1. The body surface is not ciliated.
- 2. Rhabdites are lacking.
- 3. A gut is present.
- ● 4. The ventral (posterior) sucker is single and large, or subdivided, and possesses chitinous supports.
- 5. Proglottides are never formed.
- ● 6. The members are ectoparasites or inhabit body cavities of the host which are in direct communication with the exterior. They are confined to one host.

Subclass Monopisthocotylea

Monogenoidea in which:-

- ● 1. The posterior sucker is in the form of a single, well developed disc, which may or may not be subdivided by radial septa. It is armed with from one to three pairs of large hooks and from 12 to 16 marginal hooklets.
- 2. The genito-intestinal canal is lacking.
- ● 3. The diet is host epidermis and mucus and the gut normally appears whitish.

Examples:- Gyrodactylus, Acanthocotyle.

Subclass Polyopisthocotylea

Monogenoidea in which:-

- ● 1. The sucker comprises a number of suckerlets or clamps.
- 2. A genito-intestinal canal is present.
- ● 3. The diet is blood and the gut is brown or black.

Examples:- Polystoma, Diplozoon. (see page 66)

P L A T Y H E L M I N T H E S

Class Aspidogastrea

Platyhelminthes in which:-

● 1. The body surface is not ciliated.
2. Special marginal sense organs are present, but rhabdites lacking.
3. A gut is present.
● 4. The greater part of the ventral surface is covered by an elongate adhesive disc.
5. Proglottides are never formed.
● 6. The members are internal parasites in a range of hosts from molluscs to vertebrates.

Example:- Aspidogaster. (see page 67)

Class Digenoidea - Flukes

Platyhelminthes in which:-

● 1. The body surface is not ciliated.
2. Rhabdites are lacking.
3. A gut is present.
● 4. The ventral (not always posterior) sucker is single and never possesses chitinous supports.
5. Proglottides are never formed.
● 6. The members are internal parasites with a complicated life cycle involving one or two intermediate hosts of which one is a mollusc.

Examples:- Fasciola, Schistosoma, Dicrocoelium. (see page 67)

Class Didymozoidea

Platyhelminthes in which:-

● 1. Pairs of individuals are usually associated together in a cyst. Cilia are lacking.
2. Rhabdites are lacking.
3. A gut is present.
● 4. There is a small anterior sucker.
● 5. Proglottides are never formed. The body has a narrow thread-like anterior region arising from the end or the side of a much swollen posterior region.
● 6. Members are internal parasites, mainly of marine fishes.

Example:- Didymozoon.

PHYLUM PLATYHELMINTHES

CLASS TEMNOCEPHALOIDEA

CLASS MONOGENOIDEA

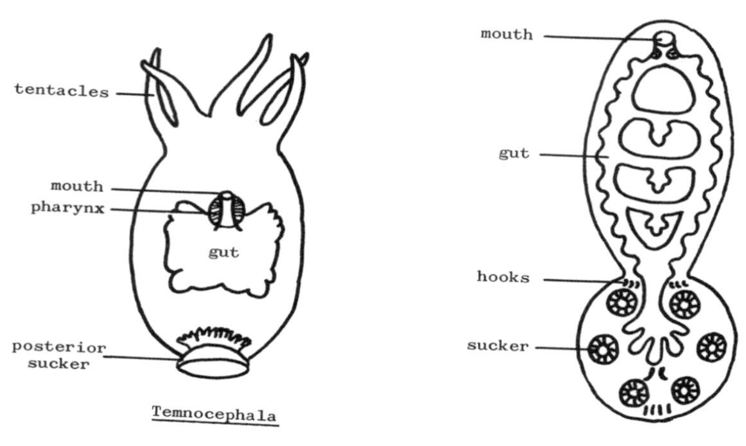

Temnocephala

Polystoma

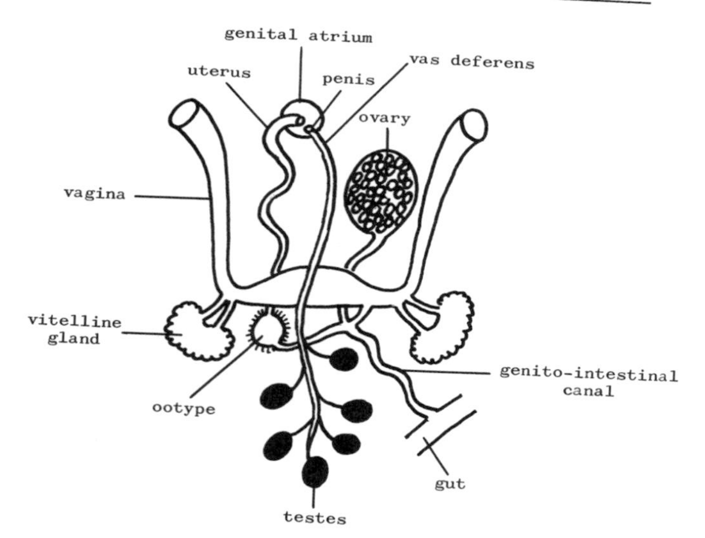

reproductive system of Polystoma

PHYLUM PLATYHELMINTHES

CLASS ASPIDOGASTREA

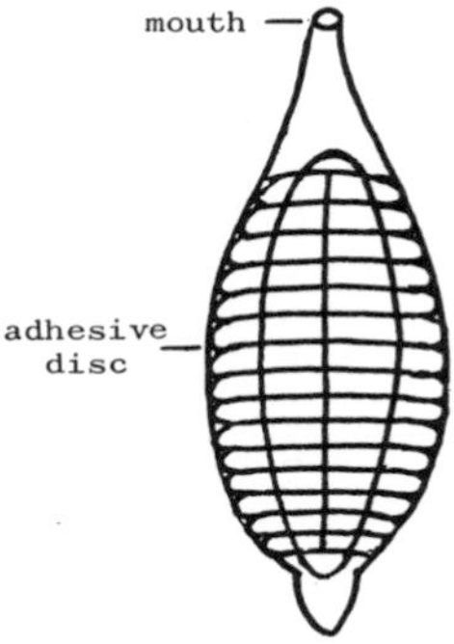

mouth
adhesive disc

Aspidogaster

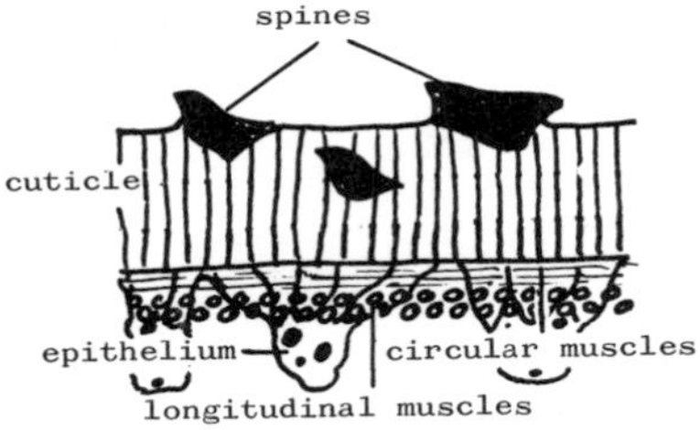

spines
cuticle
epithelium
circular muscles
longitudinal muscles

T.S. surface layers

CLASS DIGENOIDEA

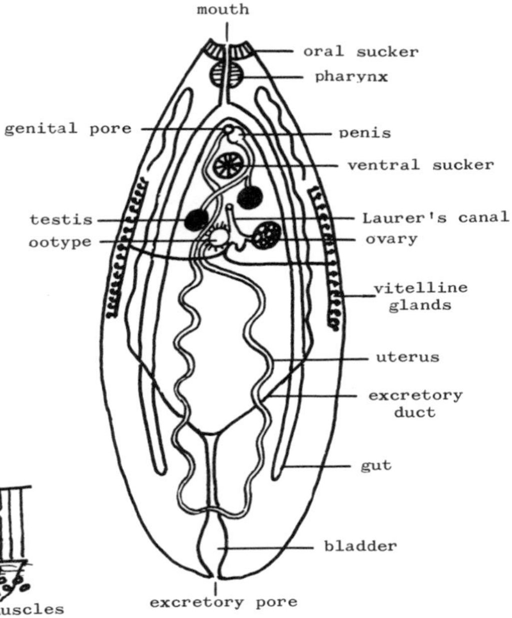

mouth
oral sucker
pharynx
genital pore
penis
ventral sucker
testis
Laurer's canal
ootype
ovary
vitelline glands
uterus
excretory duct
gut
bladder
excretory pore

Dicrocoelium

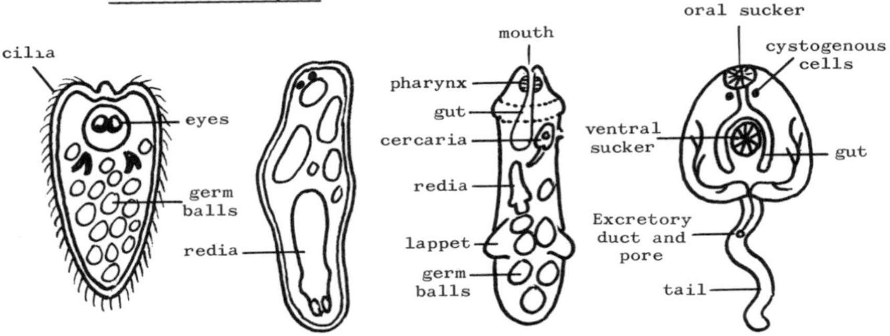

cilia
eyes
germ balls
redia

miracidium

sporocyst

mouth
pharynx
gut
cercaria
redia
lappet
germ balls

redia

oral sucker
cystogenous cells
ventral sucker
gut
Excretory duct and pore
tail

cercaria

larval stages of Fasciola hepatica

P L A T Y H E L M I N T H E S

Class Cestodaria

Platyhelminthes in which:-

- ● 1. The body is not ciliated, but is frequently wrinkled.
- 2. Rhabdites are lacking.
- 3. A gut is absent.
- ● 4. There is a 'frilled' organ at the posterior end of the body and a sucker or proboscis at the anterior end.
- 5. There are no proglottides.
- ● 6. The members are gut and coelomic parasites of fish, chiefly elasmobranchs.

Examples:- Amphilina, Gyrocotyle. (see page 70)

Class Cestoidea - Tape worms

Platyhelminthes in which:-

- ● 1. The body is not ciliated.
- 2. Rhabdites are lacking.
- 3. A gut is lacking.
- ● 4. Suckers and/or hooks are borne on the scolex.
- ● 5. Proglottides are formed.
- ● 6. The adults are gut parasites of vertebrates.

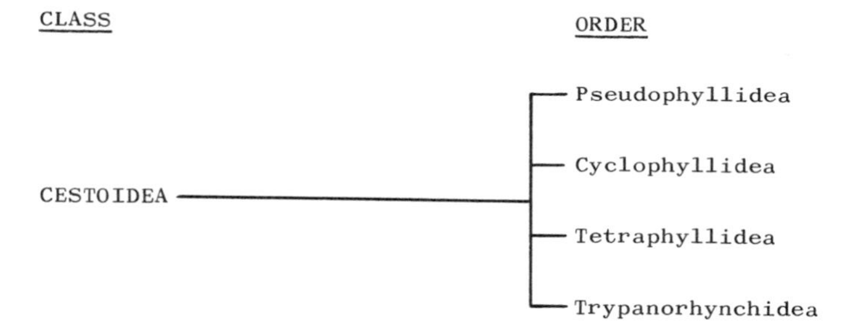

N.B. The following minor orders about which there is no general agreement are not treated here:- Protocephalida (in fishes, amphibians, reptiles), Caryophyllidea (in teleosts and aquatic annelids), Spathebothriidea (in teleosts), Aporidea (in birds), Diphyllidea (in elasmobranchs), Lecanicephalidea (in elasmobranchs), Nippotaeniidea (in teleosts), Litobothridea (in elasmobranchs).

Order Pseudophyllidea

Cestoidea in which:-

- 1. The scolex bears two shallow grooves (bothria).
- 2. The vitellaria are scattered.
  3. Adults occur in teleosts and fish-eating birds and mammals. Larvae are free-swimming and occur in Crustacea and fish.

Example:- *Diphyllobothrium*.

(see page 70)

Order Cyclophyllidea

Cestoidea in which:-

- 1. The scolex bears four cup-shaped suckers.
- 2. The vitellaria are compact and form two lobes.
- 3. Adults occur mainly in birds and mammals. Gravid segments containing resistant eggs are shed and occur in terrestrial arthropods and vertebrates.

Examples:- *Taenia*, *Echinococcus*, *Dipylidium*.

(see page 70)

Order Tetraphyllidea

Cestoidea in which:-

- 1. The scolex bears four trumpet-shaped suckers.
- 2. The vitellaria are lateral.
- 3. Adults are in elasmobranchs only. Larvae are free-swimming and occur in copepods and teleosts.

Example:- *Phyllobothrium*.

(see page 70)

Order Trypanorhynchidea (*Tetrarhynchidea*)

Cestoidea in which:-

- 1. The scolex has four spiny eversible proboscides and two or four suckers.
- 2. Vitellaria form a sleeve around the internal organs.
- 3. Adults are in elasmobranchs only. Larvae are free-swimming and occur in Crustacea and teleosts.

Example:- *Grillotia* (= *Tetrarhynchus*).

(see page 70)

PHYLUM PLATYHELMINTHES

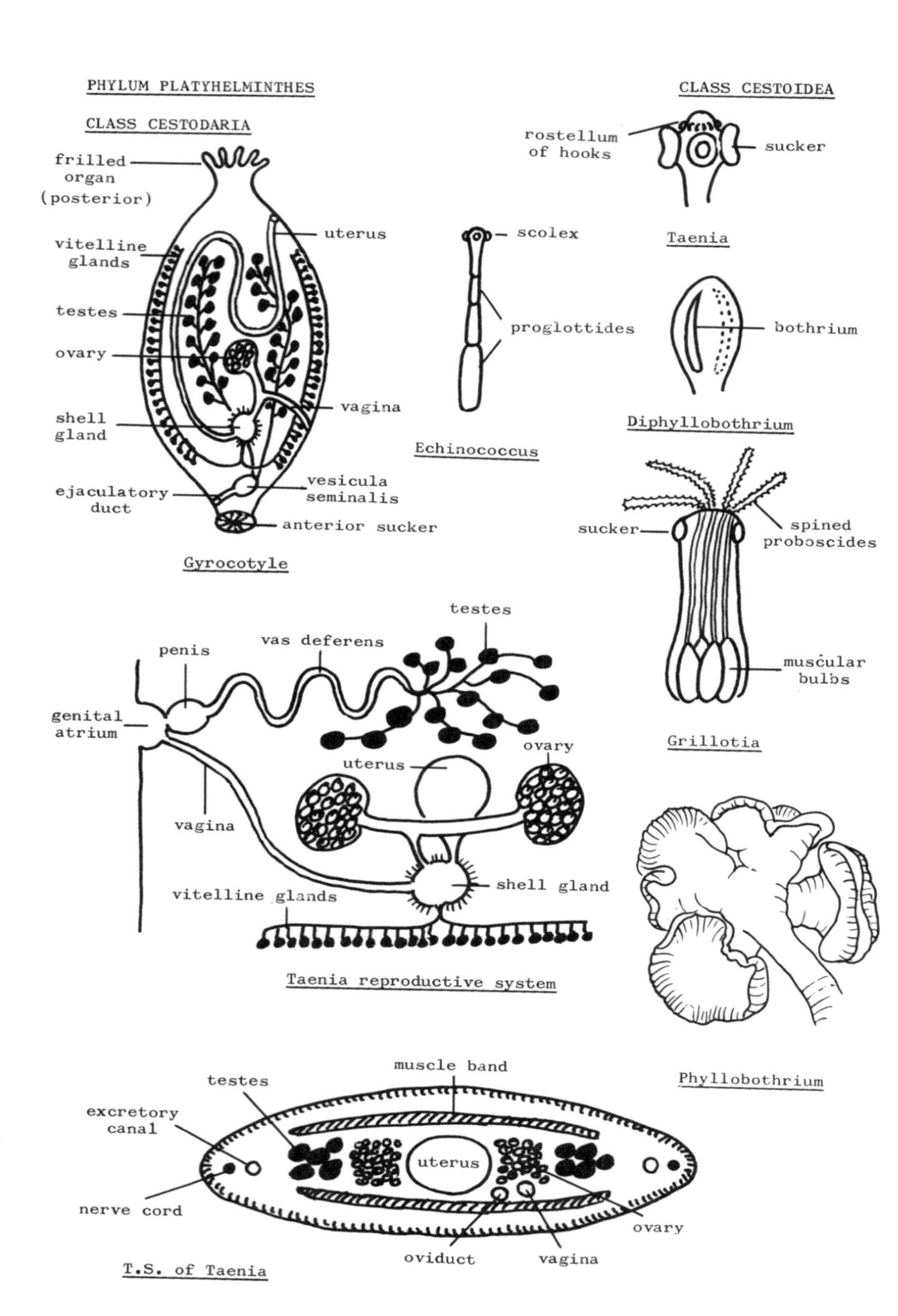

Phylum Nemertea

Acoelomata in which:-

1. The body is sub-cylindrical.
- ● 2. There is an eversible proboscis in a sheath lying dorsal to the gut.
- ● 3. The gut has both a mouth and an anus and has only simple lateral pouches along its length.
- ● 4. A primitive blood vascular system is present.

5. The excretory system consists of flame cells grouped into tufts and these are concentrated into a part of the body.
6. The sexes are usually separate.

- ● 7. The reproductive organs are extremely simple paired gonads.

8. The ovary is not divided into an ovarium and a vitellarium.
9. The genital ducts are simple and temporary.
10. Almost all forms are free living.

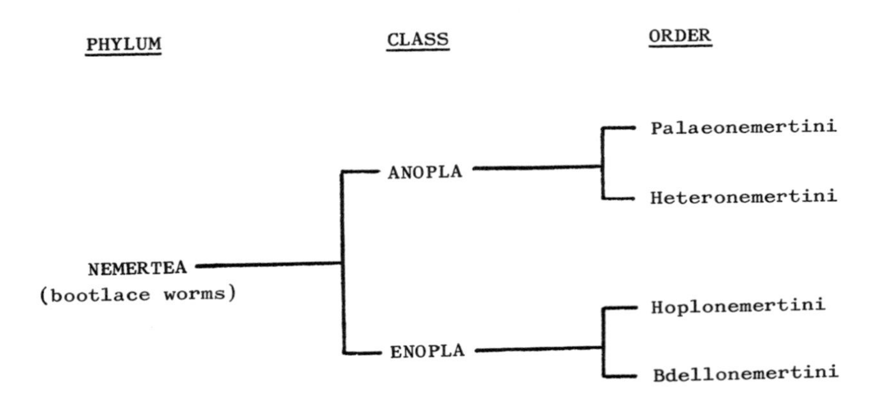

N E M E R T E A

Class Anopla

Nemertini in which:-

- 1. The mouth is situated behind the brain.
2. The proboscis lacks stylets.

Order Palaeonemertini

Anopla in which:-

1. Body wall musculature is of two or three layers.
2. Dermis poorly developed with the lateral nerve cords outside or within the muscular layers.

Example:- *Tubulanus*.

Order Heteronemertini

Anopla in which:-

1. Body wall musculature is of three layers.
2. Dermis is well developed and fibrous.

Examples:- *Lineus*, *Cerebratulus*.

Class Enopla

Nemertini in which:-

- 1. The mouth is in front of or under the brain.
2. The proboscis is generally armed with stylets (absent in the Bdellonemertini).

Order Hoplonemertini

Enopla in which:-

1. Proboscis with one or two stylets.
- 2. Intestine straight and with lateral paired diverticula.

Example:- *Prostoma*.

Order Bdellonemertini

Enopla in which:-

1. Proboscis without stylets.
- 2. Intestine sinuous and without diverticula.
- 3. Posterior adhesive organ present.

Example:- *Malacobdella*.

PHYLUM NEMERTEA

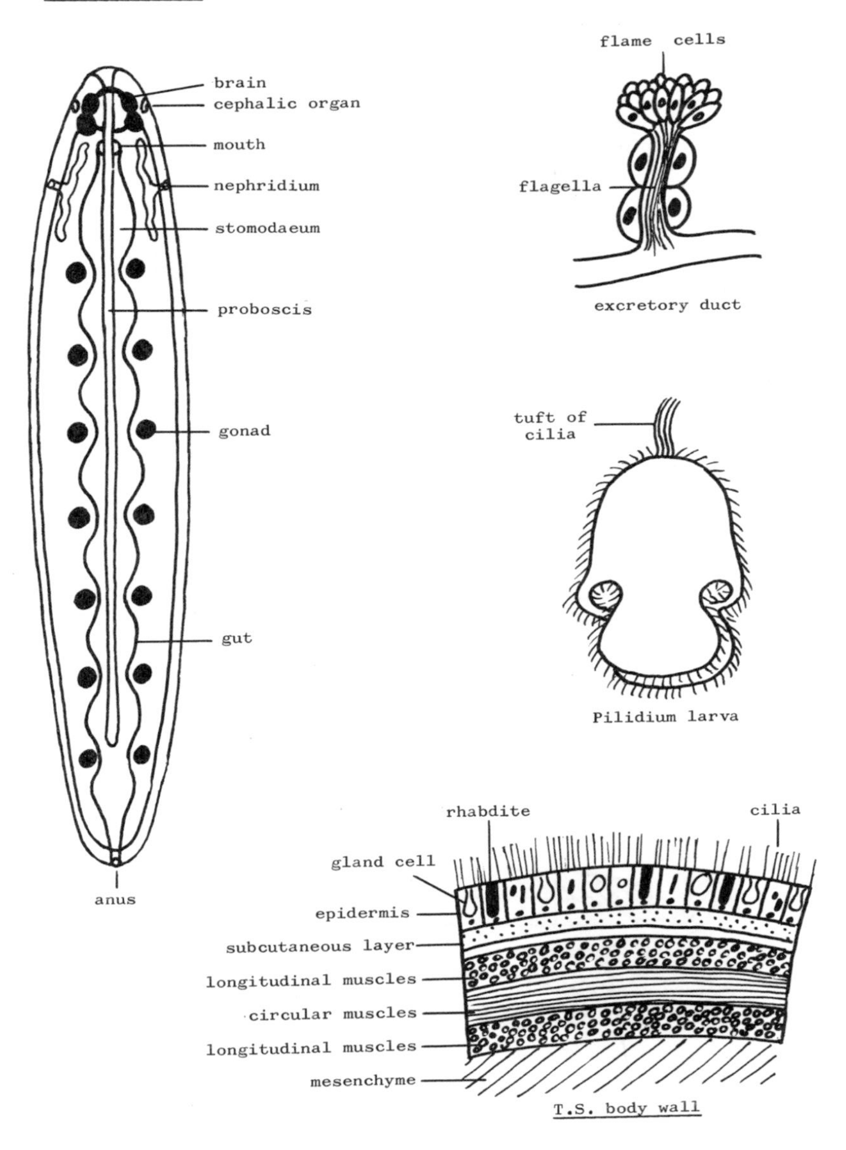

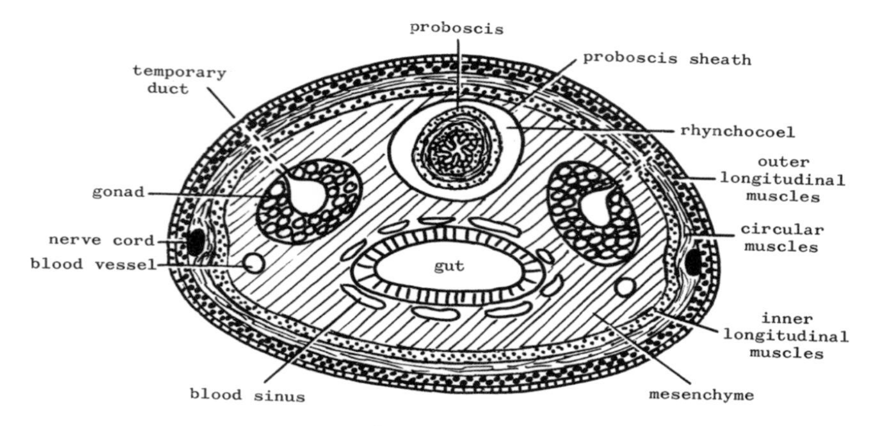

T.S. nemertine

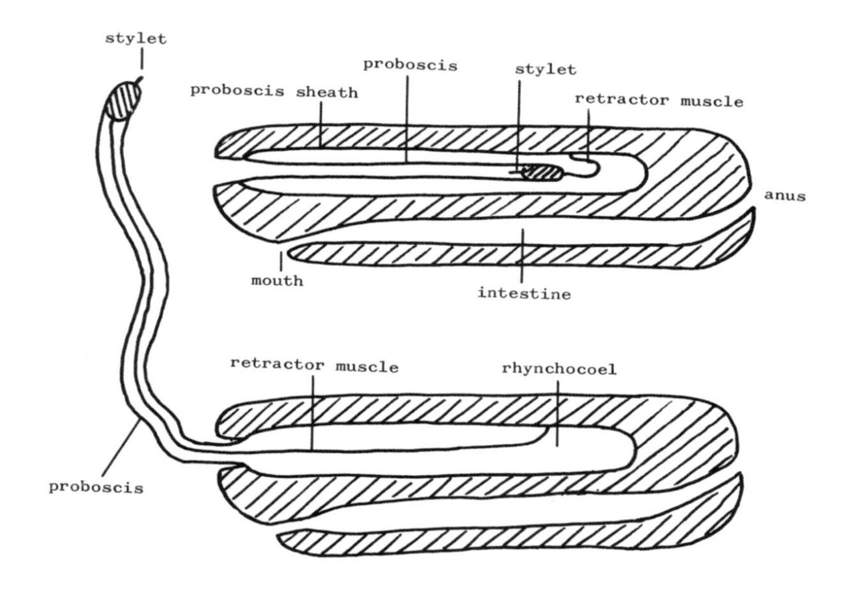

eversion of proboscis

6 Pseudocoelomate Animals

The development of a fluid-filled space separating the body wall of an animal from its gut confers a number of advantages. First, it enables the gut to move independently of the body as a whole and thus to pass food along its length by peristalsis while the animal is otherwise quiescent. Secondly, it may provide a relatively constant environment for the germ cells, which develop from the mesoderm, and a space in which they can be kept until spawning. Thirdly, such a perivisceral space surrounded by the circular and longitudinal muscles of the body wall serves as a hydrostatic skeleton which can be changed in shape by these muscles without change in volume. This makes possible a new type of locomotion where the body is either alternately shortened and lengthened, or the body curved from side to side giving rise to a whipping movement.

In many metazoan animals the perivisceral space is a coelom, that is to say it is a space within the mesoderm, so that the mesoderm not only forms a major part of the body wall, but also a layer providing muscles around the gut. The cavity is lined by an epithelial peritoneum and is formed either by a central split in the mesoderm (schizocoelic) or, during the embryonic formation of the mesoderm, as an outpouching from the gut, which thus encloses a cavity within the pouch (enterocoelic). The annelids, arthropods, molluscs and their allies are schizocoelic, while the chordates and their lower relatives are enterocoelic. But in a number of primitive metazoa a perivisceral space forms in various other ways not within the mesoderm but between the mesoderm and the endoderm of the gut wall, which thus does not have muscles. This type of perivisceral space is termed a pseudocoelom. It has no epithelial lining and is characteristic of a group of phyla some of which are obscure, but others are of great importance.

The most important of the pseudocoelomate phyla are undoubtedly the Nematoda and the Rotifera. The nematodes are in many ways a zoological enigma. They, and the Nematomorpha, are quite unlike any other animal, but within the group are extraordinarily uniform in structure. They seem to have only one environmental requirement which is water and, this satisfied, live in immense numbers wherever there is decaying organic matter for food. A handful of sand from a beach may contain many thousands belonging to perhaps 40 or 50 different species. A large number of nematodes have become parasitic through changes in life history rather than anatomy and, unusually, include both plant parasites and animal parasites, many of considerable agricultural, veterinary and medical importance. Yet for all this we know very little of their origin and relationships. The nematodes have covered their evolutionary tracks with consumate skill.

The rotifers like the nematodes require water, but are not so catholic in their tastes. They are found in fresh-water of all kinds, where they form an important part of the biological economy, and also in the marine littoral and semiterrestrial environments such as the interstices of mosses and the soil. They are minute animals ranging between 100 and 500 microns.

The remaining pseudocoelomate phyla, the Kinorhyncha, Gastrotricha, Endoprocta and Acanthocephala, have little in common apart from the pseudocoelom. Their relationships with other phyla are not understood, nor are they necessarily closely related among themselves. The Pseudocoelomata, therefore, is entirely a grouping of convenience.

Subgrade Pseudocoelomata

Bilateria in which:-

● 1. A perivisceral cavity is present which is not a true coelom.

● 2. The organs are not obviously connected by parenchyma.

3. Flame-cells may or may not be present in the excretory system.

● 4. There is no blood vascular system.

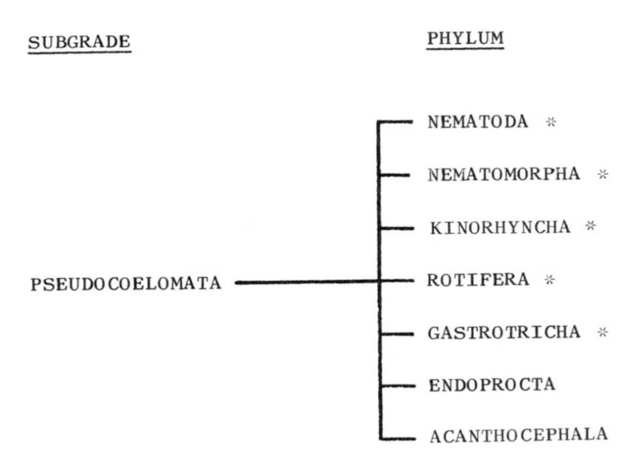

* Sometimes grouped as the Aschelminthes

Phylum Nematoda

Pseudocoelomata in which:-

- ● 1. The body is minute to quite large, elongated and cylindrical.
- ● 2. The anterior end is narrow and contains the mouth, which is characteristically guarded by lips.
- ● 3. The posterior end is usually pointed.
- ● 4. Movement is muscular with a characteristic whipping flexure which is due to the animal possessing only longitudinal muscle fibres. These fibres consist of an inner unmodified region and an outer contractile part immediately beneath the epidermis.

5. The epidermis is syncytial and covered with an elastic cuticle. The epidermis is thickened to form two main lateral lines and less evident mid-dorsal and mid-ventral lines.
6. The gut opens posteriorly through an anus which is subterminal.
7. The nervous system is a network of cells which are aggregated at the anterior end of the body to form a circum-oesophageal ring and one or more non-ganglionated nerve cords.
8. Typically the excretory system comprises two laterally placed intra-cellular tubes. Flame cells are absent.
9. The sexes are usually separate.
10. The gonads and their ducts form continuous tubes.
11. The larvae are very similar to the adults. The life history is often complex and many forms are parasitic either in the adult or in the larval stages, or throughout the entire life cycle.

N E M A T O D A

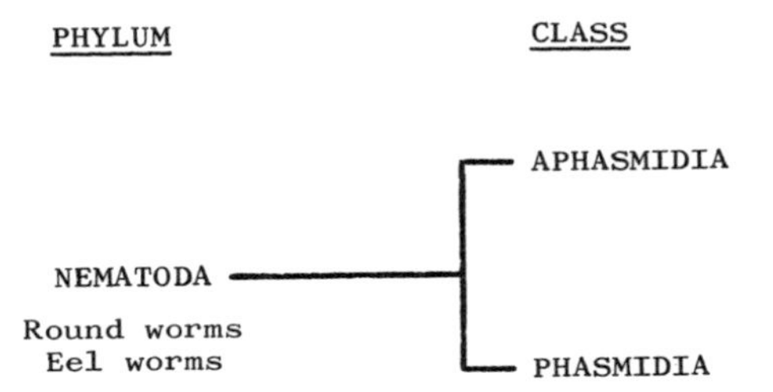

Class Aphasmidia

Nematoda in which:-

1. Forms are usually free living, but a few are parasites.
2. There are conspicuous sensory bristles or papillae on the head.
3. Phasmids are lacking, although caudal glands may be present.

Examples:- *Monhystera*, *Dorylaimus*, *Xiphinema*, *Trichinella*, *Dioctophyme*.

Class Phasmidia

Nematoda in which:-

1. Forms are often parasitic.
2. Sensory bristles or papillae are reduced or wanting.
3. Phasmids are present; caudal glands are absent.

Examples:- *Rhabditis*, *Strongylus*, *Necator*, *Ascaris*, *Enterobius*, *Ditylenchus*, *Heterodera*, *Wuchereria*, *Dracunculus*.

(see pages 80, 81)

PHYLUM NEMATODA

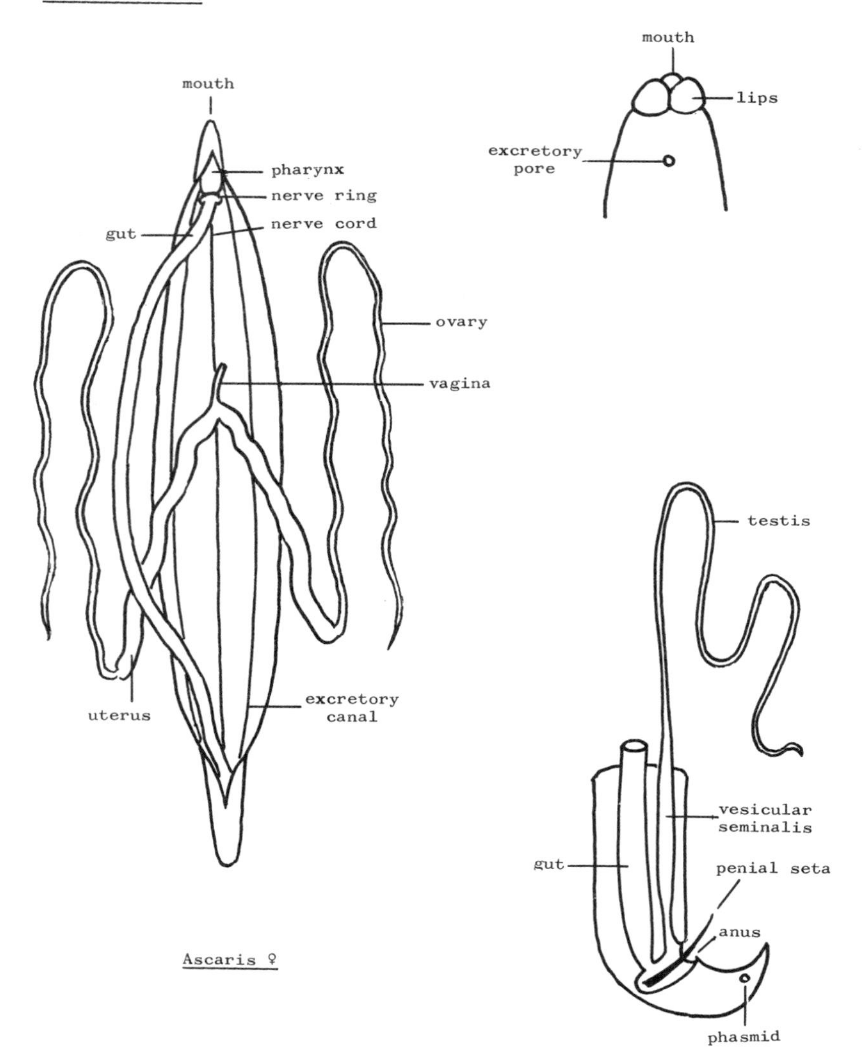

Ascaris ♀

Ascaris ♂

PHYLUM NEMATODA

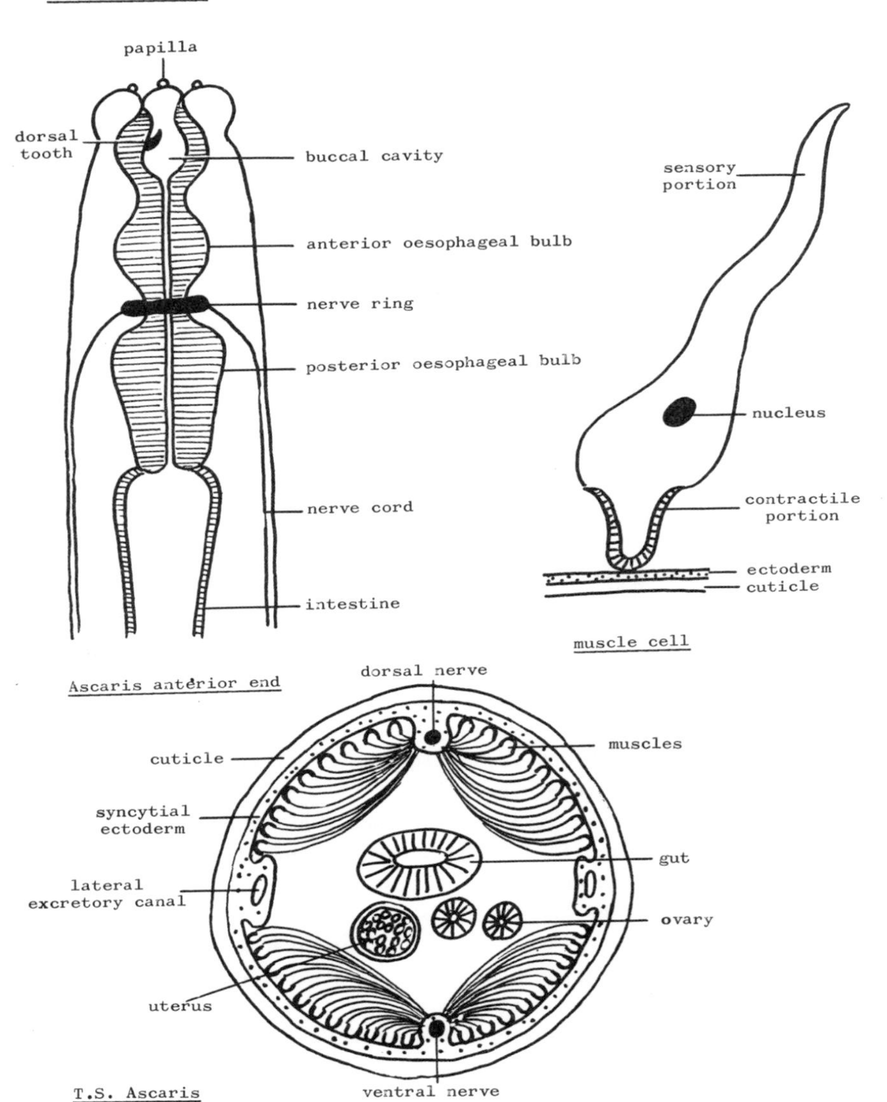

Phylum Nematomorpha

Pseudocoelomata in which:-

- 1. The body is small to quite large, greatly elongated and cylindrical.
2. The anterior end is slender, but has no special features.
3. The posterior end has no special features.
4. Movement is muscular. There are no cilia anywhere in the body. The muscle cells are large with contractile processes below the epidermis.
5. The epidermis is syncytial and is covered by an elastic cuticle, but there are no lateral lines.
6. A through gut is developed, but it tends to become more or less degenerate.
7. The nervous system comprises a thick circum-oesophageal ring and a single ventral nerve cord.
8. There is no excretory system.
9. The sexes are separate.
10. The gonads are developed from laterally placed canals in the body, and the genital ducts open to the hind gut.
11. The larvae are provided with boring organs and are found as parasites in arthropods, while the adults are free-living.

Examples:- Gordius, Nectonema. (horse-hair worms)

(see page 88)

Phylum Kinorhyncha

Pseudocoelomata in which:-

- ● 1. The body is minute and cylindrical.
- ● 2. The head is retractable and covered with circlets of spines.
- ● 3. The posterior end usually bears a terminal spine or spines.
- 4. Cilia are absent. These animals are exclusively marine and often lie buried in sand or mud beneath shallow water.
- ● 5. A chitinous cuticle covers the body and is divided into 'segments' or zonites.
- 6. The gut is straight and has a muscular pharynx. The anus is terminal.
- 7. The nervous system consists of a large dorsal cerebral ganglion and a ganglionated central nerve cord.
- 8. The excretory system consists of a pair of protonephridia with flame cells
- 9. Sexes are separate in some species at least.
- 10. The gonads are simple and have a definite duct.
- 11. Development is through a larva which may moult several times before resembling the adult.

Example:- Echinoderes. (see page 88)

Phylum Rotifera

Pseudocoelomata in which:-

1. The body is extremely minute and variable in form.
2. ● There is typically an anterior retractile trochal disc.
3. ● The posterior end often possesses a mobile bifid tail.
4. Movement is by means of cilia or muscles or both.
5. The epidermis is a syncytium covered by an elastic cuticle.
6. ● The gut opens posteriorly through a dorsally placed anus and has a very characteristic mobile pharynx known as the mastax.
7. The nervous system is reduced to one or two cerebral ganglia and a few short nerves.
8. There is a flame-cell excretory system opening into the hind gut.
9. The sexes are separate with marked sexual dimorphism, the male being degenerate and smaller than the female.
10. The gonads are simple; the ovaries produce more than one kind of egg and discharge via the hind gut.
11. Development is essentially direct, but the adults are very like trochophore larvae in their general organisation.

Examples:- Hydatina, Asplanchna, Floscularia, Rotaria.

(see page 88)

Phylum Gastrotricha

Pseudocoelomata in which:-

1. The body is minute and elongated.
2. There are no special features to the anterior end.
3. ● The posterior end is usually bifurcated.
4. Movement is by ciliary and muscular activity.
5. ● The ectoderm is a syncytium, ciliated in tracts on the ventral surface and forming adhesive papillae, while on the dorsal surface it is covered with a cuticle raised into bristles and scales.
6. The gut is straight and has a simple muscular pharynx. The anus is subterminal.
7. The nervous system comprises a large dorsal cerebral ganglion and a pair of lateral longitudinal nerve cords.
8. There is a flame-cell excretory system discharging on the ventral surface.
9. Individuals are either hermaphrodites or parthenogenetic females.
10. The gonads are simple; the ovary discharges near the anus, the male aperture is variable in position.
11. Development is direct.

Example:- Chaetonotus. (see page 88)

Phylum Endoprocta

Pseudocoelomata in which:-

1. The body is small, sedentary and usually colonial.
2. ● The mouth (and anus) is surrounded by a ring of tentacles that can be covered by a flap of the body wall through the action of a sphincter muscle. An epistome overhangs the mouth.
3. ● A stalk of attachment is found opposite the mouth and anus.
4. Although sedentary, local movements are muscular. There is a ciliary feeding mechanism.
5. The ectoderm is cellular and has no cuticle.
6. The gut is 'U'-shaped so that the anus lies close to the mouth.
7. The nervous system is reduced to a single bilobed ganglion.
8. The excretory system consists of a pair of proto-nephridia with flame cells.
9. The sexes may or may not be separate.
10. The gonads are simple and have a definite duct. Reproduction by budding also occurs.
11. The larva is a trochophore.

Examples:- Pedicellina, Loxosoma. (see page 88)

Phylum Acanthocephala

Pseudocoelomata in which:-

1. The body is small, elongate and cylindrical.
2. ● The anterior end is provided with an eversible proboscis that is covered with rows of hooks.
3. The posterior end is blunt and contains the genital pore.
4. Movement is muscular. There are no external cilia.
5. The epidermis is traversed by lacunae filled with a granular fluid, and is covered by a cuticle.
6. ● There is no gut.
7. The nervous system comprises a large ganglion situated at the base of the proboscis, and two lateral nerve cords.
8. A modified flame-cell excretory system may be present.
9. The sexes are separate.
10. The gonads are contained in a tubular suspensory ligament traversing the body.
11. The larvae are usually parasitic in arthropods and the adults are gut parasites of vertebrates.

Example:- Echinorhynchus. (see page 88)

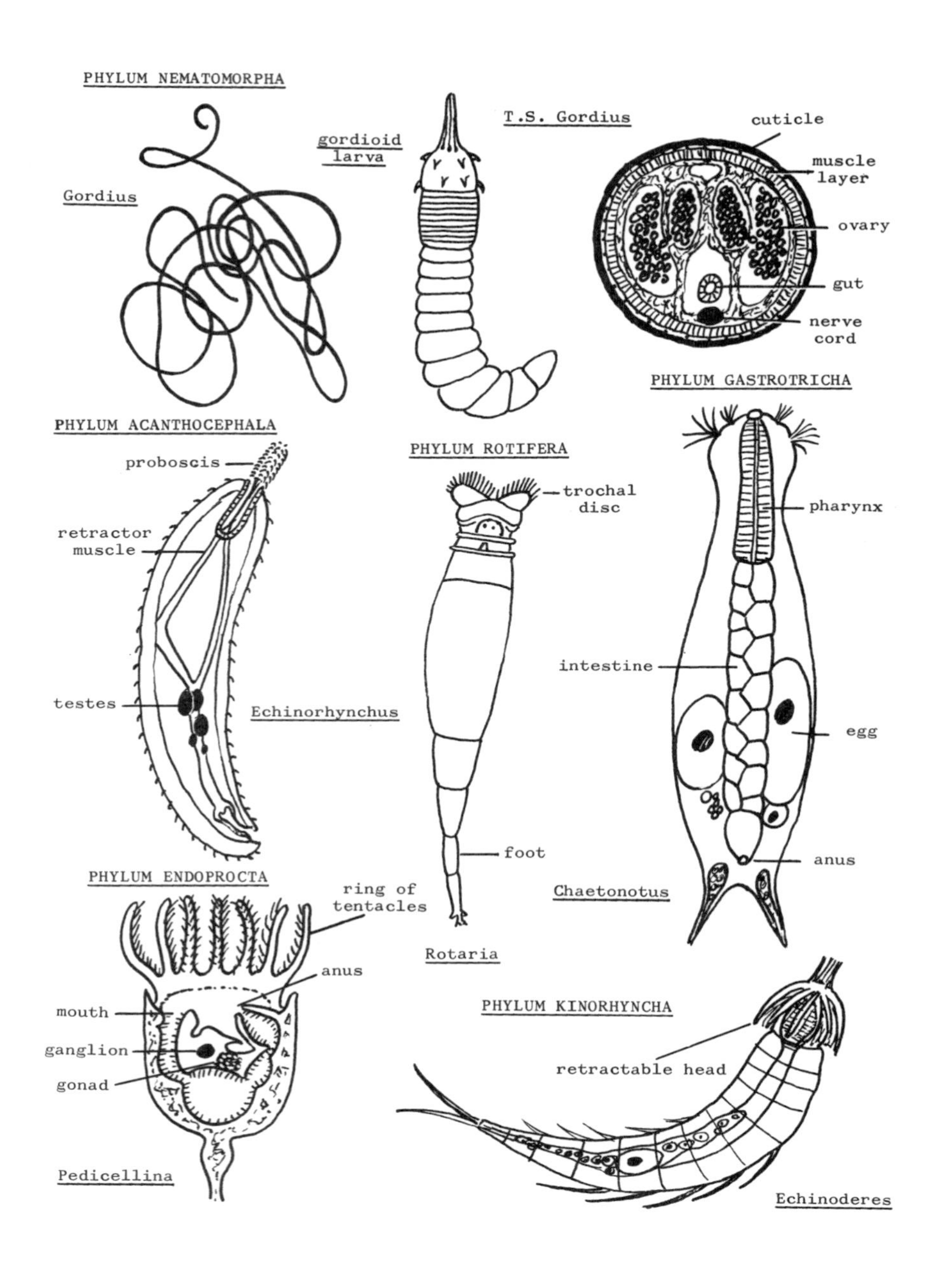

PHYLUM NEMATOMORPHA
Gordius
gordioid larva
T.S. Gordius
cuticle
muscle layer
ovary
gut
nerve cord
PHYLUM GASTROTRICHA
PHYLUM ACANTHOCEPHALA
proboscis
retractor muscle
testes
Echinorhynchus
PHYLUM ROTIFERA
trochal disc
foot
Rotaria
pharynx
intestine
egg
anus
Chaetonotus
PHYLUM ENDOPROCTA
ring of tentacles
anus
mouth
ganglion
gonad
Pedicellina
PHYLUM KINORHYNCHA
retractable head
Echinoderes

7 Eucoelomate Animals Annelida

The Eucoelomata contain the remainder of the Metazoa, that is all the animals with a true coelom surrounded by mesoderm and lined with epithelium. In the higher forms such as the arthropods, molluscs and vertebrates, the coelom loses its function as a hydrostatic, skeletal, perivisceral space and this function is taken over either by an expanded blood system (haemocoel), which is formed from the embryonic cavity of the blastula (blastocoel), or by a skeleton of hard parts, or both. In these cases the coelom becomes reduced to the point where it is finally represented by the cavity of the gonads. But in the more primitive of the Eucoelomata, such as the polychaete worms, the coelom still retains its primitive functions.

The essential feature of the annelid worms is not so much the possession of a capacious coelom, but its division by septa into separate water-tight compartments. This gives much greater control in the use of the hydrostatic skeleton so that changes in shape (shortening, lengthening or bending) can be achieved in one segment without unduly influencing the shape of the adjacent segments. As the septa run right across the body from gut wall to epidermis (except where there has been secondary reduction of septa), the division into coelomic compartments has resulted in a corresponding division of the muscles into blocks, and the nervous system into segments controlled by ganglia. There is also repetition of other essential body components such as blood vessels and excretory organs and the marking off of the epidermis by annuli, although these do not always correspond with segmental boundaries. This is metameric segmentation. It is likely to have arisen in the first place in conjunction with a need for improved locomotion either by burrowing or swimming.

The most primitive of the annelids are small marine worms, simple in structure and with a regular metamerism. They are classed as the Archiannelida and some such forms probably gave rise separately to both the polychaetes and the oligochaetes. The difficulty about simplicity of structure as a taxonomic characteristic is that it may be primitive or it may be the result of the degeneration of an advanced form, and often we cannot tell. This is the same problem posed by the hydrozoan coelenterates in chapter four. It is probable that both primitive and degenerate worms are included among the archiannelids and to this extent the group is one of convenience.

The Polychaeta also are difficult to classify. They are all marine and some are more or less free swimming while others live in tubes of one sort or another. The worms that are free swimming tend to be uniformly segmented while the tube dwellers have the body regionally differentiated to perform different functions within the tube. Differentiation involves external modification of both the anterior processes (usually for feeding or tube building) and the parapodia, which are characteristic of polychaetes. Internally, there is a loss of some or most of the septa. Now it is quite probable that adaptations for tube dwelling have arisen separately on a number of occasions and indeed that various archiannelid ancestors have given rise to polychaete-like descendants. The polychaetes, therefore, are probably polyphyletic and the division into the Errantia (free swimming) and Sedentaria (tube dwelling) is again one largely of convenience. In common with some of the molluscs they typically have a ciliated planktonic larva, the trochophore.

Whereas the polychaetes represent one branch of annelid evolution, the oligochaetes and their relatives the leeches are a second. In the polychaetes the parapodium has become diversified for various functions. Sometimes it forms a kind of limb, or it may serve as a gill, or as a fan creating a water current, with the musculature and allied systems modified accordingly. The oligochaetes, on the other hand, are essentially burrowers living mainly in terrestrial and freshwater habitats. They have never developed the parapodium nor multiplied the number of chaetae and consequently the muscular system has retained the continuous bands of circular and longitudinal muscle fibres which are the primitive condition. Burrowing has suppressed the head appendages and the septa are essentially complete. The oligochaetes are specialised, however, in their reproductive system and loss of a free-swimming larva and also in their methods of osmoregulation, all in accordance with a fresh-water or terrestrial life.

The Hirudinea or leeches, originally predators of small invertebrates, have gone some way to becoming blood-sucking ectoparasites. The primitive members have a sucker at the posterior end only. The more advanced leeches have also an anterior sucker and have developed a new type of locomotion, looping from sucker to sucker. Associated with this may be considered the loss of chaetae and septa and the great reduction of the perivisceral coelom. They are found commonly in freshwater and the sea and also on land in damp forests in the tropics.

Subgrade Eucoelomata

Bilateria in which:-

- ● 1. A perivisceral coelom is characteristically present though it may be partly or wholly replaced by a perivisceral haemocoel.
- ● 2. There is no parenchyma, the organs usually being suspended in the coelom by folds of the coelomic epithelium.
- 3. Solenocytes may or may not be present in the excretory system, but flame cells are absent.
- ● 4. A blood vascular system is almost always present.

E U C O E L O M A T E   A N I M A L S

SUBGRADE		PHYLUM	
EUCOELOMATA		ANNELIDA	annulate phyla
		TRILOBITOMORPHA	
		CHELICERATA	
		CRUSTACEA	
		UNIRAMIA	
		TARDIGRADA	
		PENTASTOMIDA	
		MOLLUSCA	
		ECHIURIDA	minor phyla
		SIPUNCULIDA	
		PRIAPULIDA	
		POGONOPHORA	
		BRACHIOPODA	
		BRYOZOA	
		PHORONIDEA	
		CHAETOGNATHA	
		ECHINODERMATA	
		HEMICHORDATA	
		CHORDATA	

Phylum Annelida

Eucoelomata in which:-

● 1. The body is metamerically segmented.

● 2. There is a single preoral segment called the prostomium.

3. The gut is usually straight and the anus is terminal.

● 4. The nervous system typically comprises preoral ganglia joined by circum-oesophageal commissures to a double ventral ganglionated nerve cord.

5. Organs of special sense are typically present.
6. The epidermis is covered with a thin cuticle.
7. The appendages, when present, are never jointed.
8. The body wall contains an outer circular and an inner longitudinal muscle layer.
9. A spacious perivisceral coelom is typically present.
10. The excretory system is typically a pair of nephridia to each body segment.
11. There is typically a well-defined closed blood vascular system.
12. The products of the gonads are typically passed to the exterior through coelomoducts which may or may not be associated with the nephridia.
13. The sexes may or may not be separate.
14. The larva, when present, is a trochophore.

A N N E L I D A

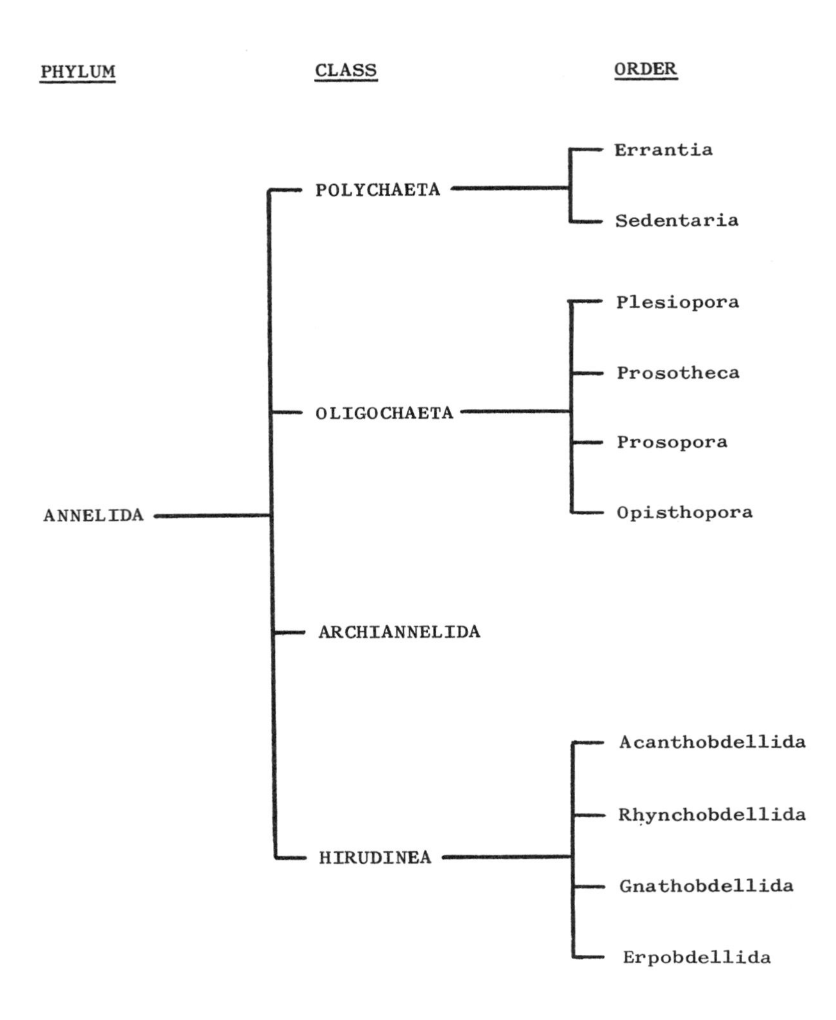
PHYLUM
CLASS
ORDER
Errantia
POLYCHAETA
Sedentaria
Plesiopora
Prosotheca
OLIGOCHAETA
Prosopora
ANNELIDA
Opisthopora
ARCHIANNELIDA
Acanthobdellida
Rhynchobdellida
HIRUDINEA
Gnathobdellida
Erpobdellida

PHYLUM ANNELIDA

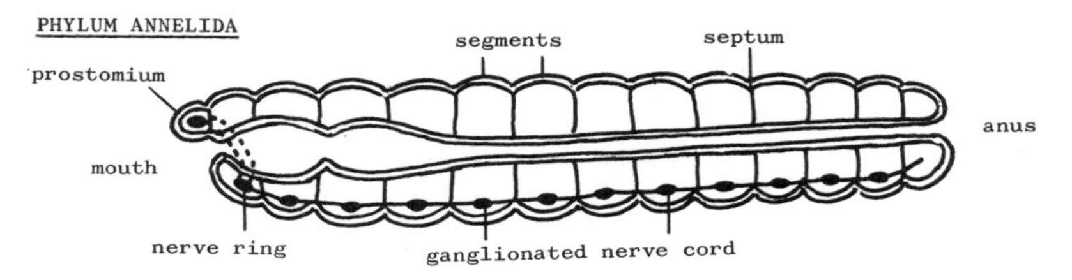

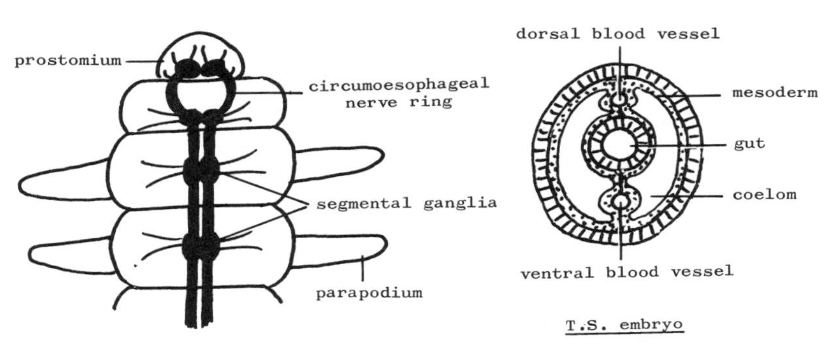

T.S. embryo

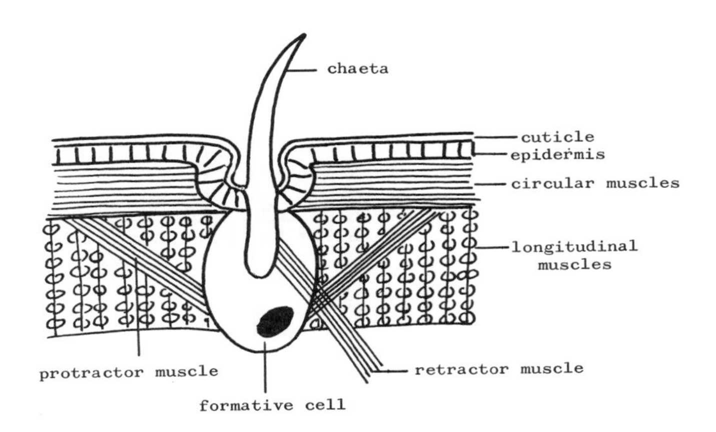

T.S. body wall

A N N E L I D A

Class Polychaeta

Annelida in which:-

- ● 1. The body bears segmentally arranged chaetae, usually numerous arising from ectodermal pits. Parapodia are usually present.
- 2. The coelom is spacious and typically subdivided by septa.
- 3. The vascular system is not in communication with the coelom.
- ● 4. There are no suckers.
- 5. The segments are usually numerous and variable in number.
- 6. The nerve cord is separate from the epidermis and lies internal to the muscle layers.
- ● 7. The sexes are typically separate, the gonads forming in a variable number of segments. There is no clitellum.
- 8. Metamorphosis occurs during development.

Order Errantia - Ragworms etc.

Polychaeta in which:-

- ● 1. The parapodia are well developed, as the animals lead an active life, and possess cirri.
- ● 2. There is a protrusible pharynx usually armed with chitinous jaws.
- ● 3. The segments are more or less alike throughout the body.
- 4. Branchiae, when present, occur throughout the body length
- 5. Although some forms may occupy tubes temporarily, the members are essentially free swimming.

Examples:- Nereis, Aphrodite, Polynoe, Nephthys, Syllis, Glycera, Eulalia, Eunice, Ptomopteris.

(see page 102)

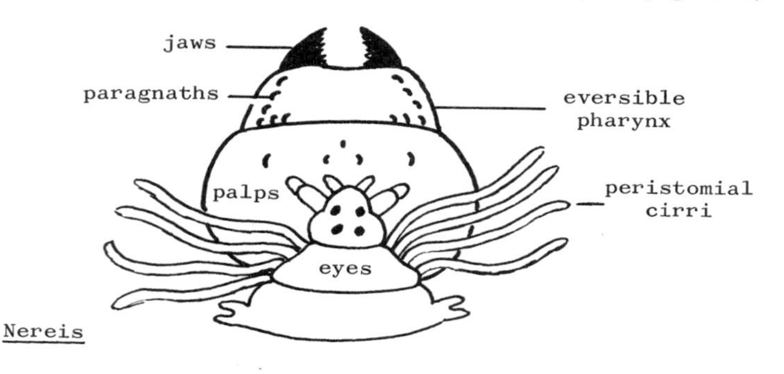

Nereis

A N N E L I D A

Order Sedentaria - Lugworms etc.

Polychaeta in which:-

- 1. Paropodia are poorly developed, or are regionally differentiated, as the animals are essentially sedentary forms. Cirri are usually absent.
- 2. Jaws are absent but an eversible proboscis may be present.
- 3. The segments are different in different parts of the body so that two or three distinct body regions result.

4. Branchiae, when present, are usually confined to the anterior end of the body.
5. The members are either tubicolous or burrow in sand.

Examples:- Chaetopterus, Arenicola, Pomatoceros, Amphitrite, Sabella, Terebella.

(see page 102)

Class Oligochaeta

Annelida in which:-

- 1. Segmentally arranged chaetae are typically present, but are usually few in number. Parapodia are not developed.

2. The coelom is spacious and subdivided by transverse septa.
3. The vascular system is not in communication with the coelom.
4. There are no suckers.
5. There are numerous body segments.
6. The nerve cord is separate from the epidermis and lies internal to the muscle layers.
7. The members are hermaphrodite with one or more pairs of testes and ovaries restricted to a few anterior segments. A cocoon-secreting clitellum is present.
8. Metamorphosis does not occur during development.

Order Plesiopora

Oligochaeta in which:-

1. Excretory system is micronephrostomal.
2. Male gonopores on the segment following the testes.
3. Spermathecae, when present, in the region of the genital segments.

Examples:- Nais, Chaetogaster, Aelosoma, Tubifex.

(see page 102)

A N N E L I D A

Order Prosotheca

Oligochaeta in which:-

1. Excretory system is micronephrostomal.
2. Male gonopores on the segment following the testes.
3. Spermathecae considerably in front of the genital segments.

Examples:- Enchytraeus, Lumbricillus.

Order Prosopora

Oligochaeta in which:-

1. Excretory system is mesonephrostomal.
2. Male gonopores in the same segment as the last pair of testes.
3. Spermathecae in the region of the genital segments.

Example:- Lumbriculus.

Order Opisthopora - Earthworms

Oligochaeta in which:-

1. Excretory system is meganephrostomal.
2. Male gonopores at least one segment behind the last pair of testes.
3. Spermathecae are variable in position.

Examples:- Lumbricus, Glossoscolex, Pheretima.

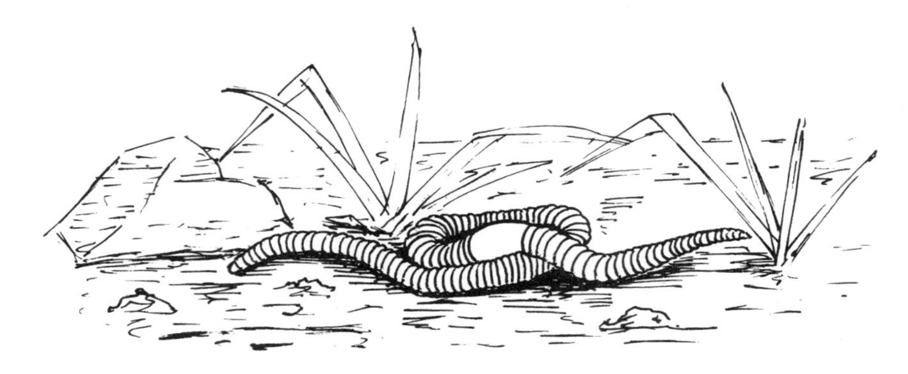

Lumbricus

A N N E L I D A

Class Archiannelida

Annelida in which:-

- ● 1. The chaetae and parapodia are usually reduced or lost.
- 2. The coelom may or may not be reduced.
- ● 3. The vascular system is very simple or absent.
- ● 4. There are no suckers.
- ● 5. The segments are usually comparatively few in number and the segmentation usually indistinct or obliterated.
- 6. The nerve cord is not separated from the epidermis.
- 7. The sexes may be separate or united. There is no clitellum.
- 8. Metamorphosis may or may not occur.

Examples:- Saccocirrus, Nerilla, Histriobdella, Dinophilus, Polygordius, Protodrilus.

(see page 103)

Class Hirudinea - Leeches

Annelida in which:-

- ● 1. The chaetae and parapodia have been lost in almost all forms.
- ● 2. The coelom is reduced by encroachment of botryoidal tissue and typically is not subdivided by transverse septa.
- 3. The vascular system communicates with the coelomic spaces which thus form blood sinuses.
- ● 4. There is always at least one and usually two suckers.
- ● 5. The body consists of a definite number of segments each of which is divided by a varying number of annuli.
- 6. The nerve cord is separate from the epidermis and lies internal to the muscle layers.
- 7. The members are hermaphrodite. A clitellum is present.
- 8. Development is typically direct.

Order Acanthobdellida

Hirudinea in which:-

- ● 1. There is no anterior sucker.
- ● 2. There is a short proboscis.
- 3. Segmental septa are present.
- 4. The members are temporary ectoparasites of fishes.
- ● 5. Chaetae are present on anterior segments.

Example:- Acanthobdella.

ANNELIDA

Order Rhynchobdellida

Hirudinea in which:-

- ● 1. There is an anterior sucker.
- ● 2. There is a protrusible proboscis without jaws.
- 3. Segmental septa are absent.
- 4. The members are temporary ectoparasites of amphibia and fishes or they may be predatory.

Examples:- Pontobdella, Branchellion, Clepsine.

Order Gnathobdellida

Hirudinea in which:-

- ● 1. There is an anterior sucker.
- ● 2. There is no proboscis but the mouth bears two or more (usually three) toothed jaws.
- 3. Segmental septa are absent.
- 4. The members are temporary ectoparasites of vertebrates or they may be predatory.

Example:- Hirudo. (see page 103)

Order Erpobdellida

Hirudinea in which:-

- ● 1. There is an anterior sucker.
- ● 2. There is no proboscis and the mouth does not bear true jaws.
- 3. Segmental septa are absent.
- 4. The members are essentially predatory.

Example:- Erpobdella.

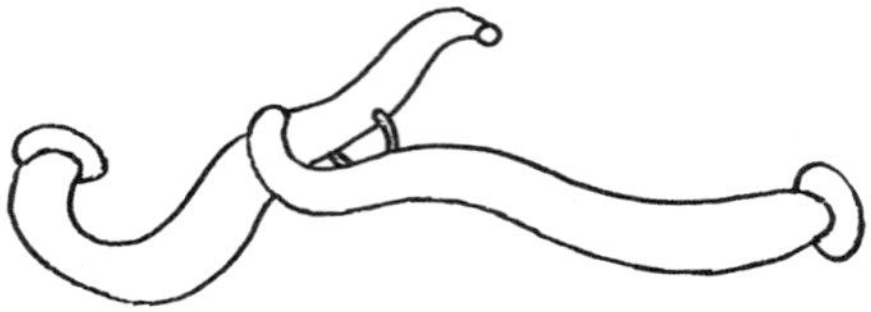

Hirudo copulating

PHYLUM ANNELIDA

CLASS POLYCHAETA

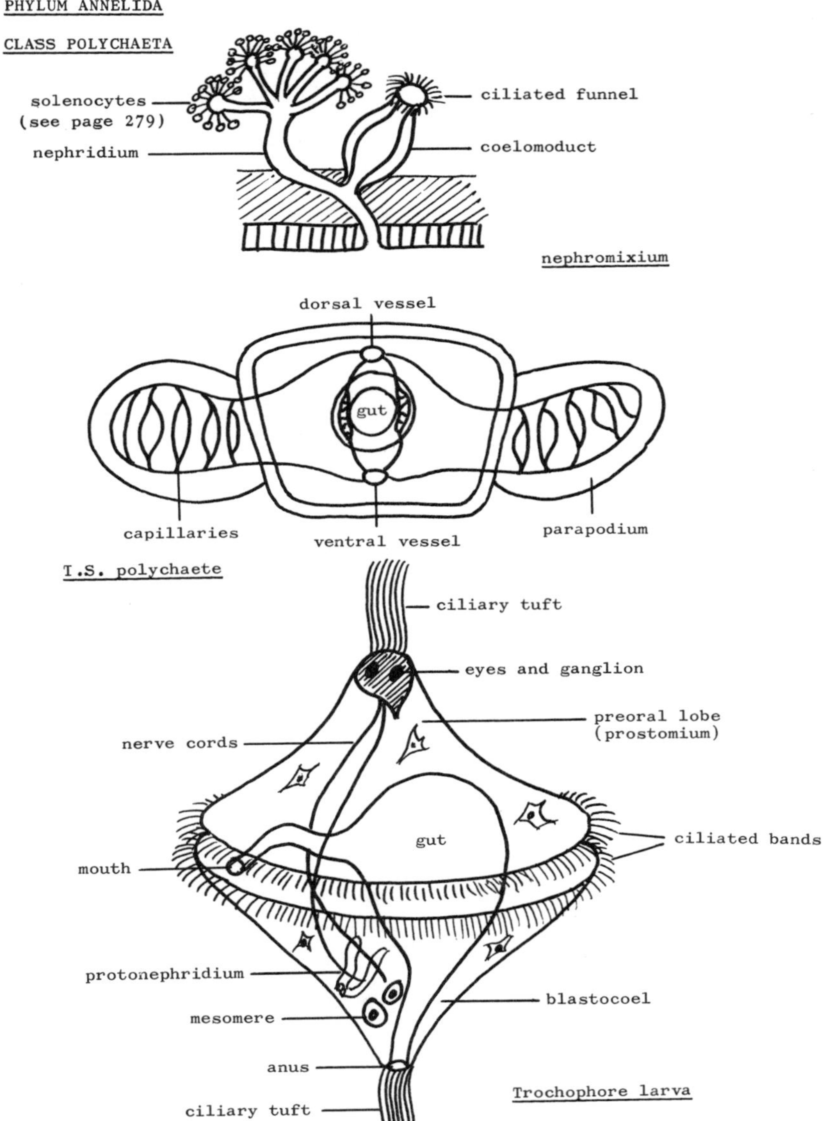

PHYLUM ANNELIDA

CLASS POLYCHAETA

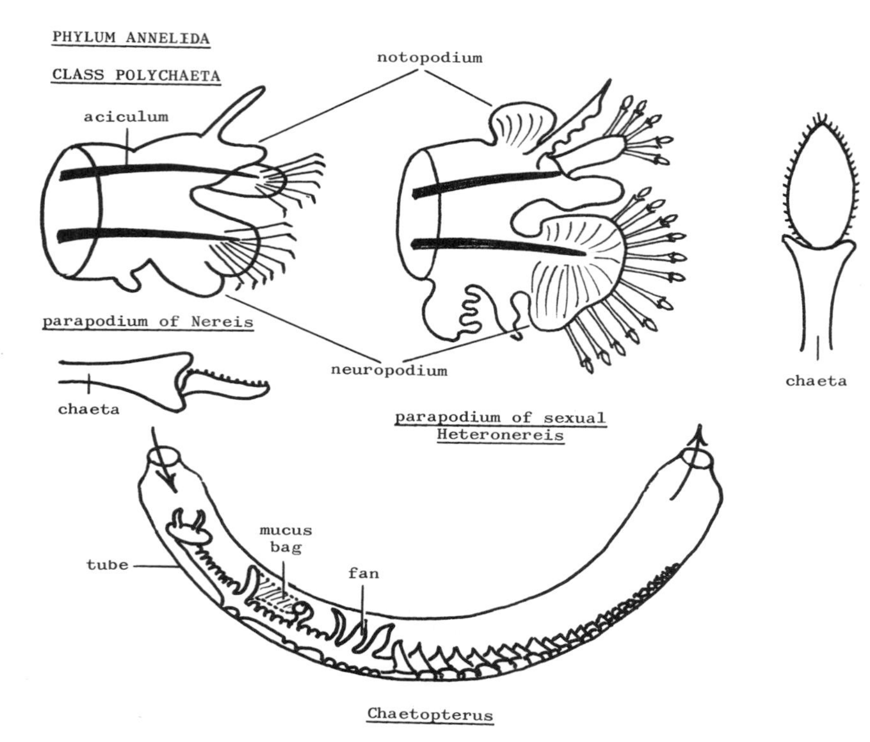

Chaetopterus

CLASS OLIGOCHAETA

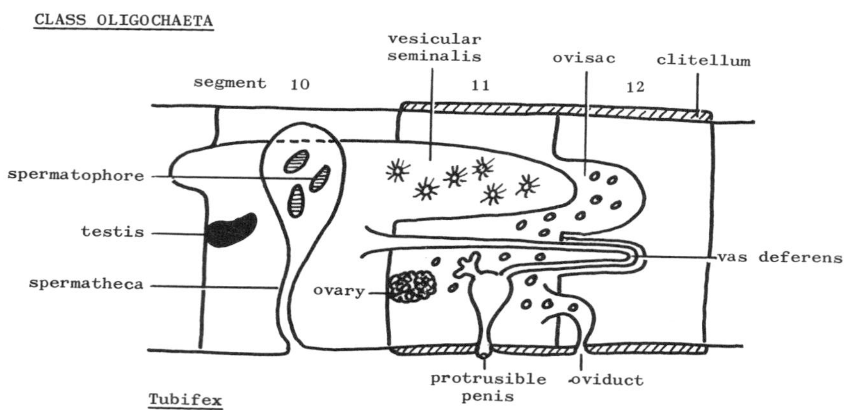

Tubifex

PHYLUM ANNELIDA

CLASS ARCHIANNELIDA

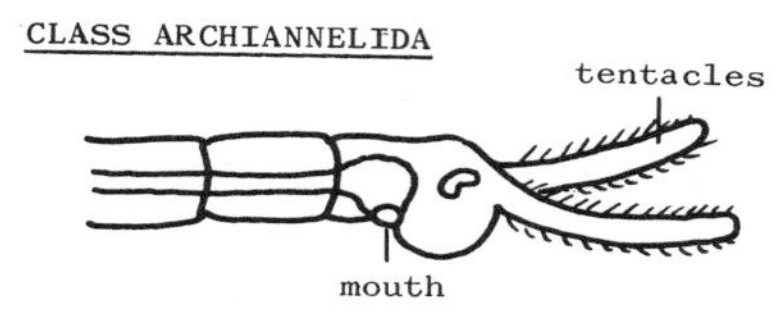

Polygordius

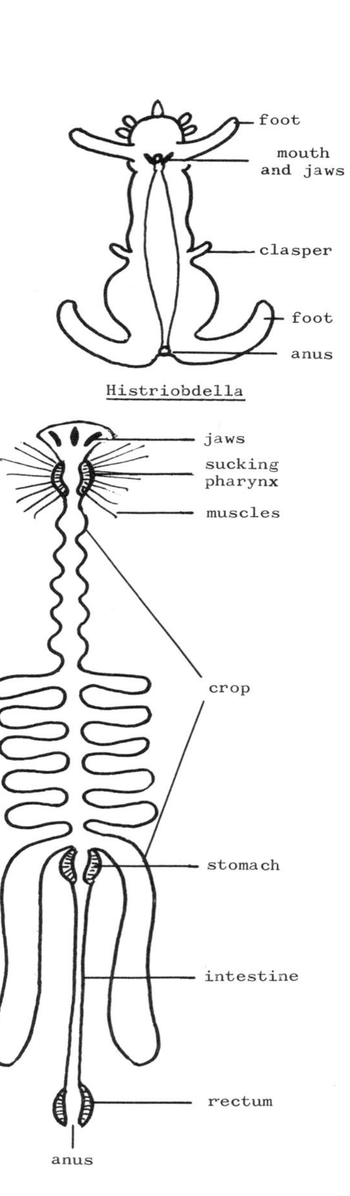

Histriobdella

CLASS HIRUDINEA

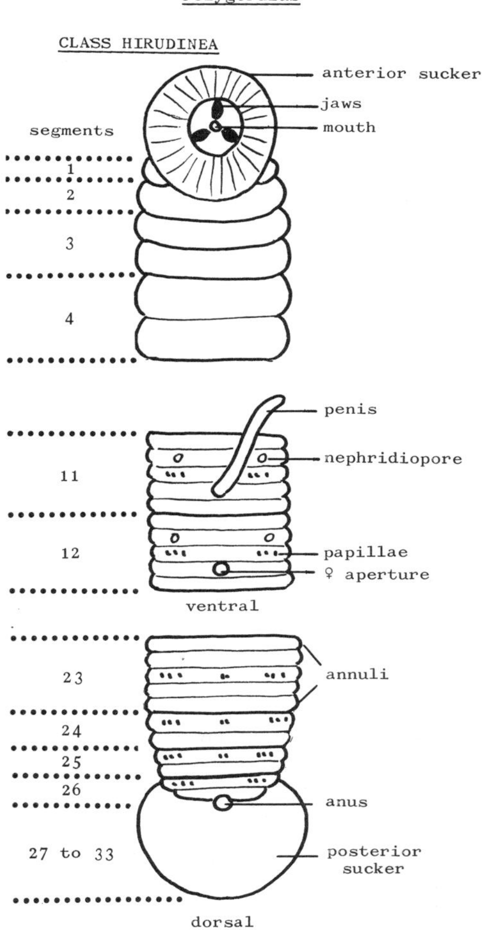

Hirudo

8 Arthropods Trilobites & Chelicerates

The early evolution of the invertebrate groups took place some 500 million years ago and is poorly represented in the fossil record because the majority of invertebrate animals had no hard parts. Many living animals, however, retain evidently primitive structures and modes of organisation of the body, and from these it is possible to speculate on the course that evolution has taken. The structure of annelid worms, for example, seems to suggest that four of their main features may well have foreshadowed developments that were to lead to the most successful of all invertebrate groups, the arthropods. These features are metameric segmentation, the presence of paired parapodial structures on the segments, the protection of the delicate epidermal layer by a thin covering of cuticle and the tendency in free-living forms to develop a distinct head. In the arthropods the segmented body became regionally differentiated into sections, such as head, thorax and abdomen, paired jointed legs appeared for walking and running, and the cuticle thickened to form a jointed exoskeleton essential for this type of locomotion. This is not to say that the annelids were ancestral to the arthropods, but rather to suggest that both may have come from an earlier stock and that the annelids have retained some of the more primitive features.

ARTHROPODS, TRILOBITES & CHELICERATES

A major difference between annelids and arthropods is the replacement of the coelom by the haemocoel as the functional perivisceral space. The reason for this change is not at all clear. It has been suggested that the need for a hydrostatic skeleton disappeared with the advent of a jointed exoskeleton and that the coelom, no longer required for this purpose, was replaced by the cavity of the blood system. A second possibility is that the high fluid pressures used by protoarthropods for digging and similar activities were liable to interfere with the blood flow through the capillary systems. This might arise in a body covered by thickened cuticle or cuticular plates where the consequent expansions due to fluid pressure were limited to the softer regions. The problem could be solved by the abolition of capillaries and the inflation of the vascular system at the expense of the coelom. Whether this or some other process happened we cannot say.

A satisfactory classification to show the supposed evolutionary relationships of the major arthropod groups, the arachnids, crustaceans, myriapods, insects and the Onychophora, has always been difficult to achieve. In many ways the primitive terrestrial onychophoran, *Peripatus*, would seem to be a splendid protoarthropod leading to the myriapods and insects. But it doesn't fit at all with the more primitive of the aquatic crustaceans and neither group seems to link up with the scorpions and their allies which have an immensely long fossil history and are certainly very early in origin. Then there is the extinct group of arthropods, the trilobites, which also seems to be separate.

As recently as 1972 Dr. S.M. Manton (*Zool. J. Linn. Soc.*, 51: 203-400 and *J. Zool. Lond.*, 171, 111-130) has provided an elegantly satisfying answer to the problem. As might be expected she postulates polyphylectic origins for the group. She suggests that arthropod-like animals have evolved at least three and probably four times and that the separate lines can be distinguished by the jaw mechanisms and the nature of the limbs and, indeed, other characters. The limbs in arthropods are either a single strut (uniramous), or a pair of processes arising from a common base (biramous). The Onychophora, Myriapoda and Hexapoda (insects) all have uniramous limbs and are grouped together as the phylum Uniramia. The Crustacea are treated as a separate phylum of biramous arthropods. The Chelicerata (arachnids) show signs of origin from a biramous ancestor, but appear to be unrelated to the Uniramia or the Crustacea and are also treated as a separate phylum. The position of the fossil Trilobita is uncertain through lack of information, but they too appear to be separate and are so treated. Manton's revision has been followed in this guide, which means that the term Arthropoda disappears in the formal classification. The trilobites and the chelicerates, possibly linked by the king crab, _Limulus_, are perhaps the most closely related of the arthropod phyla and are covered in this chapter.

The chelicerates include the king crabs, the arachnids (scorpions, spiders and mites and their allies) and a peculiarly isolated group, the pycnogonids or sea spiders. In all of these the body is divided into two parts, the prosoma and the opisthosoma, with the limbs carried by the prosoma. In this they are quite distinct from all other arthropods. The arachnida are a highly diverse and successful group. Among the first animals to colonize land they have culminated in the spiders and mites and challenge the insects in numbers and kinds.

Arachnids are land animals and have either converted the gills of their aquatic ancestors into lungs (lung-books), or have developed tracheal tubes which carry air to various parts of the body. Some arachnids, such as most spiders, use both methods. The great majority of arachnids are carnivores and most are liquid feeders. Thus although many, such as the scorpions and sun spiders (Solifugae), have powerful claws to hold and rend their prey, it is the body fluids they absorb. It would seem to be a short step to blood-sucking and this mode of life has been adopted among arachnids by the ticks and some of the mites.

Arthropods

Eucoelomata in which:-

- ● 1. The body is metamerically segmented.
- ● 2. There is more than one pre-oral segment, three being the typical number
- 3. The gut is usually straight or nearly so, the anus terminal or sub-terminal.
- 4. The nervous system typically comprises preoral ganglia joined by circum-oesophageal commissures to a double ventral ganglionated nerve cord, but may be condensed in some groups.
- ● 5. Organs of special sense are typically present and they may be very elaborate.
- ● 6. The epidermis is covered by a stout chitinous cuticle.
- ● 7. Paired appendages are present on some or all of the segments and are typically jointed and may bear claws.
- 8. The muscles of the body wall occur as bundles or as separate fibres and are rarely in continuous layers.
- 9. The coelom is greatly reduced, the perivisceral cavity being a haemocoel.
- 10. Nephridia of the annelid type are absent; excretory organs are either coelomoducts or tubules associated with the hind gut.
- 11. The blood vascular system is open with few vessels, as they have been largely replaced by the perivisceral haemocoel.
- 12. The products of the gonads are shed through coelomoducts.
- 13. The sexes are almost always separate.
- 14. Larvae of various types occur, but they are never trochophores.

ARTHROPODS

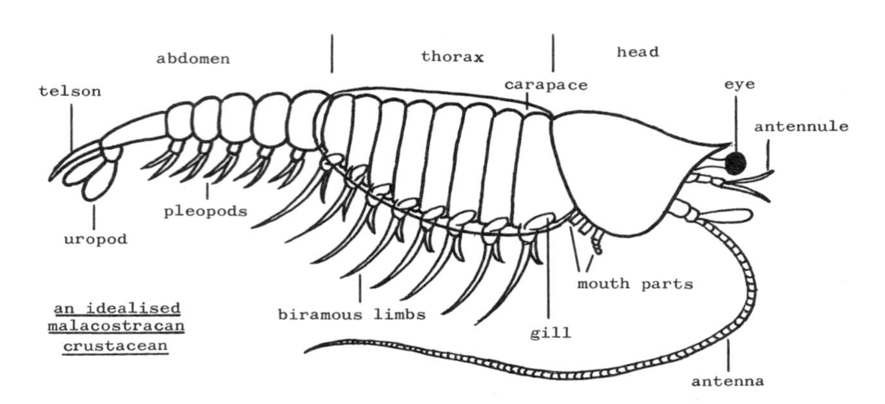

an idealised malacostracan crustacean

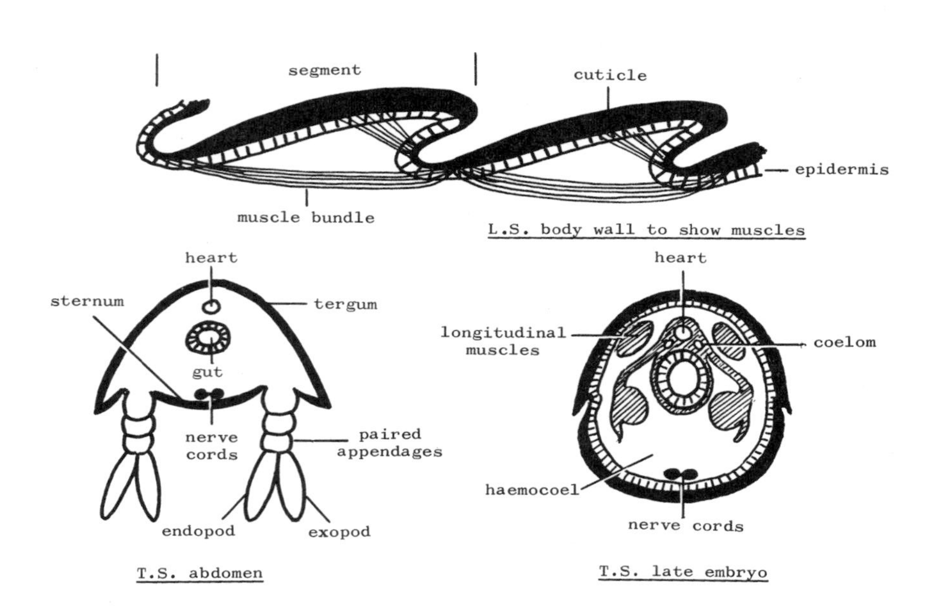

L.S. body wall to show muscles

T.S. abdomen

T.S. late embryo

A R T H R O P O D S

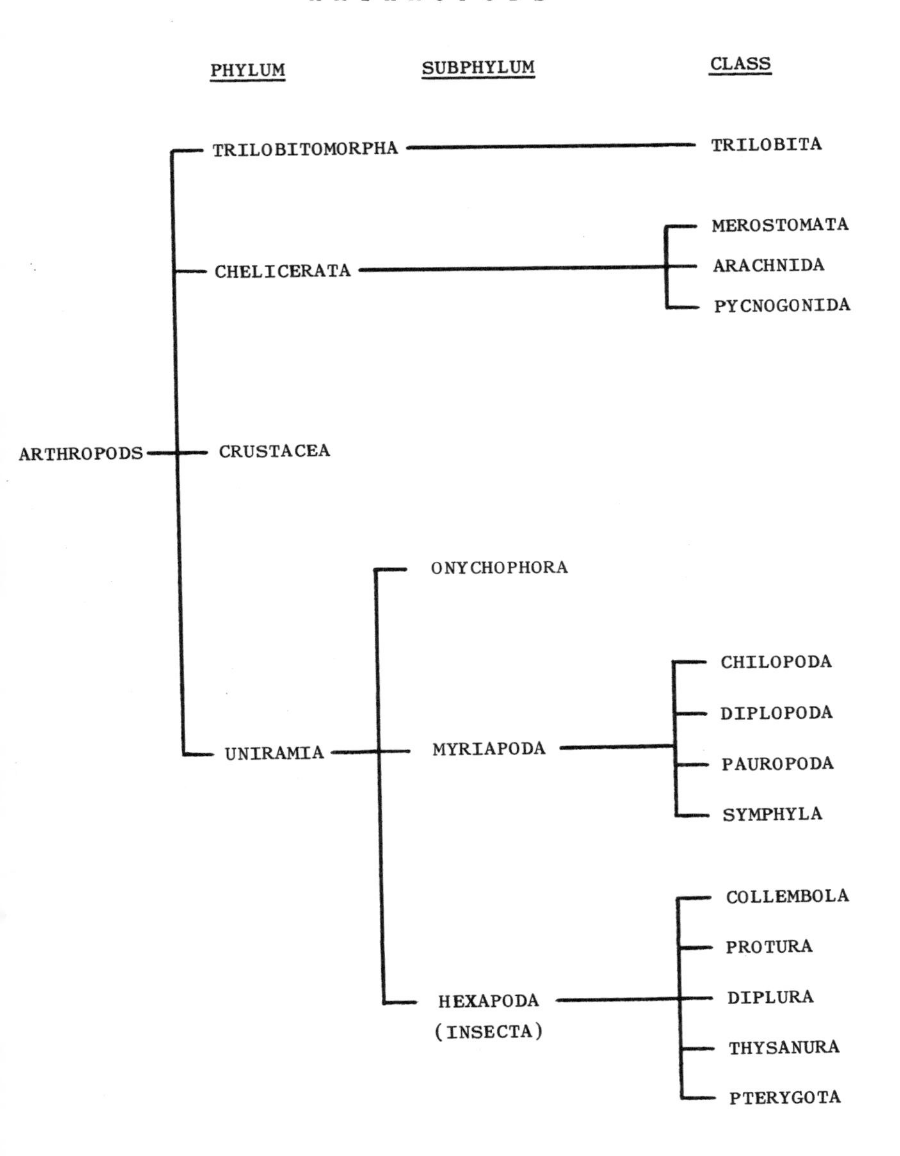

PHYLUM
SUBPHYLUM
CLASS
ARTHROPODS
TRILOBITOMORPHA
TRILOBITA
CHELICERATA
MEROSTOMATA
ARACHNIDA
PYCNOGONIDA
CRUSTACEA
UNIRAMIA
ONYCHOPHORA
MYRIAPODA
CHILOPODA
DIPLOPODA
PAUROPODA
SYMPHYLA
HEXAPODA
(INSECTA)
COLLEMBOLA
PROTURA
DIPLURA
THYSANURA
PTERYGOTA

Phylum Trilobitomorpha

Arthropods in which:-

● 1. There is one pair of pre-oral appendages which are antenniform.

2. The mode of action of the mandible is not known.

● 3. The body is divided into three (more rarely two) regions, head, thorax and abdomen (or head and trunk).

4. The post-oral appendages of the head are not specially modified as mouth parts. They are foliaceous and used for swimming though they may possess gnathobases.

● 5. The appendages posterior to the head are biramous and foliaceous for swimming, and usually extend in an uninterrupted uniform series down the length of the body.

Class Trilobita

Trilobitomorpha in which:-

● 1. The body is divided into a head covered by a cephalic shield, a thorax and an abdomen, and bears throughout its length an elevated median ridge with depressed lateral regions giving the trilobed appearance.

● 2. There is a single pair of uniramous antennae.

● 3. All the post-antennal segments bear similar biramous limbs consisting of a six-jointed telopodite, a pre-epipodite fringed with bristles and a protopodite bearing a gnathobase.

4. The larva, known as the 'Protaspis' has been likened to the 'Nauplius' larva of the Crustacea, and to the early larva of *Limulus*.

5. The members are known only as fossils from Palaeozoic rocks.

Example:- *Triarthrus*. (see page 111)

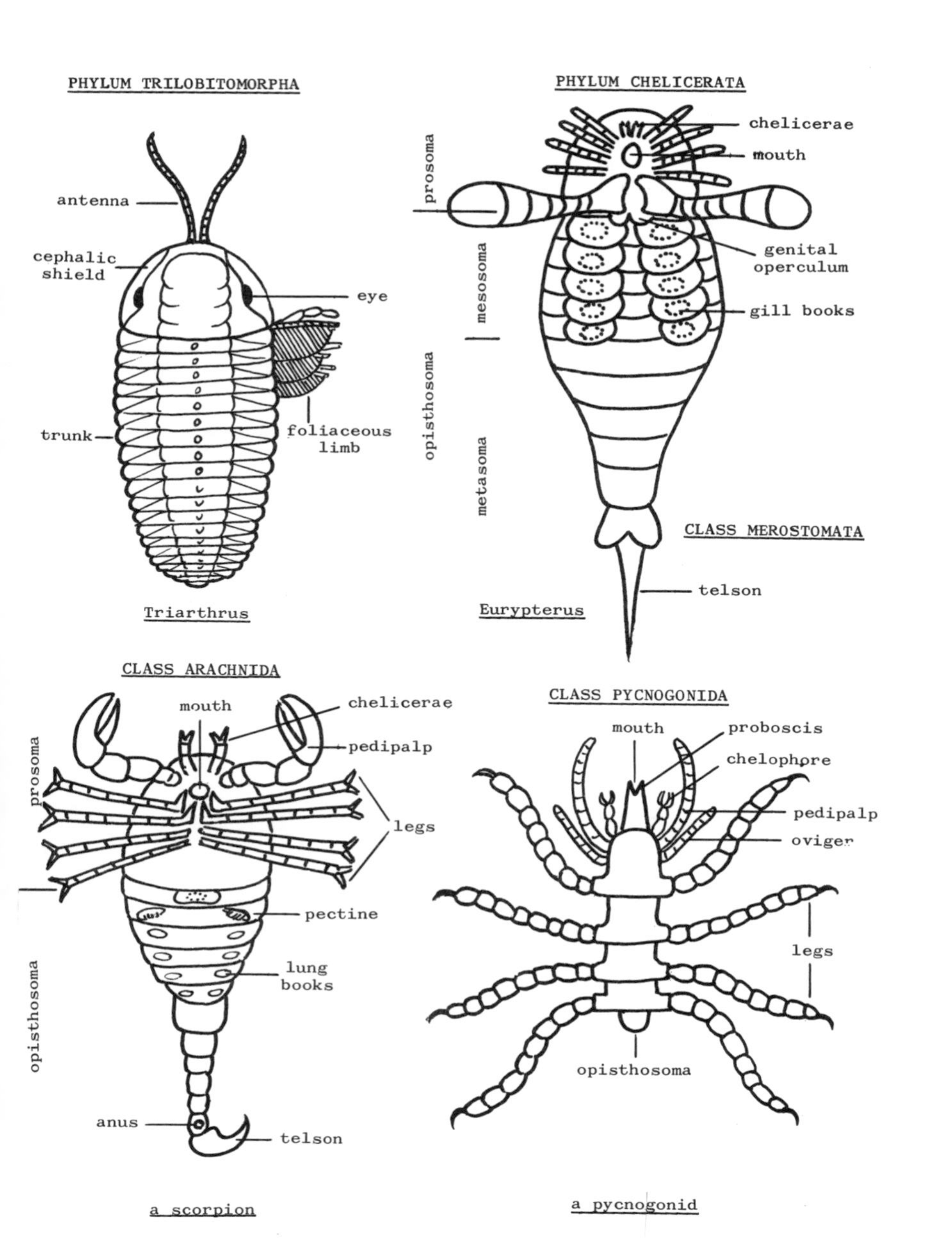
PHYLUM TRILOBITOMORPHA
antenna
cephalic shield
eye
trunk
foliaceous limb
Triarthrus
PHYLUM CHELICERATA
chelicerae
mouth
prosoma
genital operculum
mesosoma
gill books
opisthosoma
metasoma
CLASS MEROSTOMATA
telson
Eurypterus
CLASS ARACHNIDA
mouth
chelicerae
pedipalp
prosoma
legs
pectine
lung books
opisthosoma
anus
telson
a scorpion
CLASS PYCNOGONIDA
mouth
proboscis
chelophore
pedipalp
oviger
legs
opisthosoma
a pycnogonid

Phylum Chelicerata

Arthropods in which:-

- ● 1. There is one pair of pre-oral appendages (chelicerae) which act as mouth parts. They are never antenniform.
- 2. The chelicerae bite in a transverse plane by means of the gnathobase.
- ● 3. The body is divided into two regions, a prosoma and an opisthosoma.
- ● 4. The post-oral appendages of the prosoma comprise an anterior pair of pedipalps, of variable form and function, together with the walking legs of which there are usually four pairs.
- 5. The opisthosoma may or may not bear greatly modified appendages. When present, these are basically of a biramous type.

Class Merostomata

Chelicerata in which:-

- ● 1. The prosoma is undivided and bears a pair of chelicerae and five pairs of limb-like appendages.
- ● 2. The opisthosoma is divided into a mesosoma and a metasoma.
- 3. Excretion takes place through coxal glands.
- 4. Respiration is by gill books which are located on overlapping plate-like mesosomatic appendages.
- 5. The members are, or were, aquatic.
- 6. The gonads are located within the body (not in the legs).
- 7. Development is through a pelagic 'trilobite' larva.

C H E L I C E R A T A

Order Eurypterida (Extinct)

Merosomata in which:-

- ● 1. The prosoma was covered by a thin carapace and was rounded anteriorly.
- ● 2. The differentiation of the opisthosoma was slight, the metasoma comprised six segments and a telson.
- 3. The chelicerae were 3-jointed and leg-like or chelate.
- ● 4. The last pair of legs were large and paddle-shaped.
- ● 5. The first and second mesosomatic appendages form the genital operculum.
- 6. The members were widespread in the Palaeozoic era.

Example:- Eurypterus. (see page 111)

Order Xiphosura - King crabs

Merostomata in which:-

- ● 1. The prosoma is broad and has a semicircular carapace.
- ● 2. The opisthosoma comprises six segments of the mesosoma, a vestigial metasoma and a long spine-like telson.
- 3. The chelicerae are 3-jointed, small and chelate.
- ● 4. The legs are biramous and the last pair are not paddle-shaped.
- ● 5. The first pair of mesosomatic appendages form the genital operculum.
- 6. The members are marine with a restricted and discontinuous distribution.
- 7. The young are planktonic larvae ('Trilobite' stage).

Example:- Limulus.

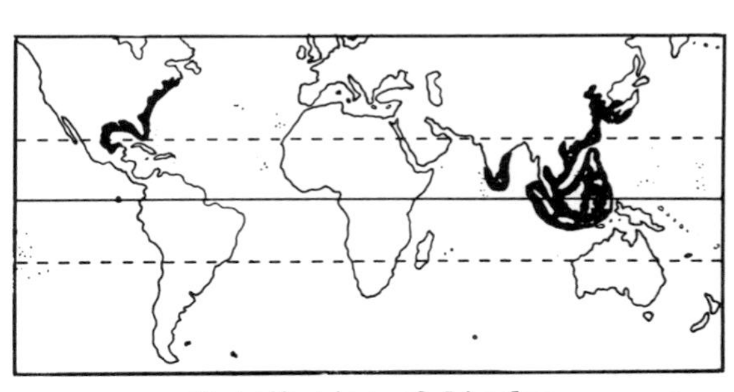

distribution of Limulus

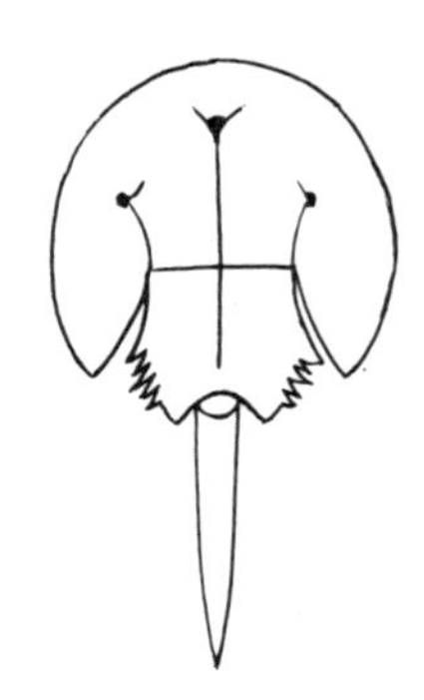

C H E L I C E R A T A

Class Arachnida

Chelicerata in which:-

- ● 1. The prosoma is undivided and bears six pairs of appendages (chelicerae, pedipalps and 4 pairs of walking legs).
- ● 2. The opisthosoma is well developed and usually clearly segmented.
- 3. Excretion is characteristically effected by nephrocytes, coxal glands and by Malpighian tubules of endodermal origin.
- 4. Respiration is typically by means of tracheae and/or lung books.
- 5. The members are mainly terrestrial forms though some are secondarily aquatic.
- 6. The gonads are located within the body (not in the legs).
- 7. Development is almost always direct.

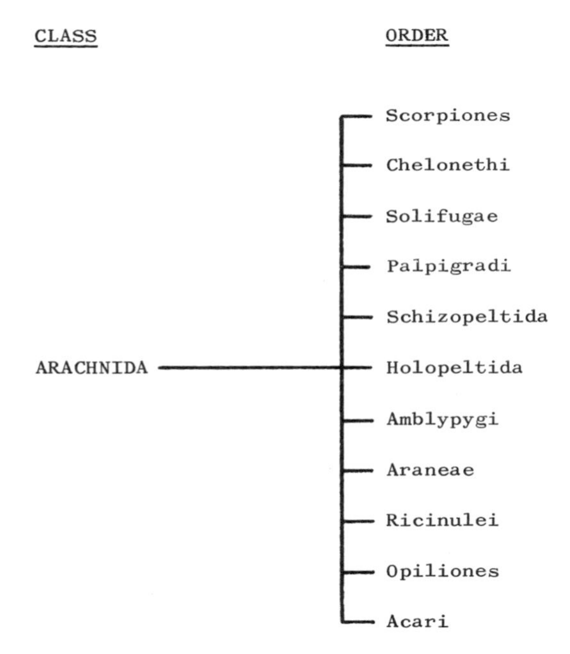

C H E L I C E R A T A

Order Scorpiones - Scorpions

Arachnida in which:-

1. The prosoma is uniform.
- ● 2. The opisthosoma is differentiated into a mesosoma and metasoma, the former of seven segments, the latter of five. There is no pedicel.
- ● 3. The telson is modified to form a sting.
4. The chelicerae are 3-jointed, small and chelate.
- ● 5. The pedipalpi are 6-jointed, large and chelate.
6. The legs are 7-jointed and bear 3 tarsal claws.
- ● 7. There are four pairs of lung books situated on opisthosomal segments three, four, five and six.
8. There is a median pair of eyes and two groups of direct, lateral eyes on the prosoma.
- ● 9. A pair of sensory pectines are borne on the second mesosomatic somite.

Examples:- Buthus, Pandinus. (see pages 111, 116)

Order Chelonethi - False scorpions

Arachnida in which:-

1. The prosoma is uniform.
- ● 2. The opisthosoma is 12-segmented and is not joined to the prosoma by a pedicel.
- ● 3. There is no telson.
4. The chelicerae are 2-jointed, small and chelate.
- ● 5. The pedipalpi are 6-jointed large, chelate and provided with poison glands.
6. The legs are 5 to 7-segmented and bear two claws.
7. The third and fourth opisthosomatic segments bear spiracles.
8. There are not more than two pairs of lateral eyes on the prosoma.

Example:- Chelifer. (see page 126)

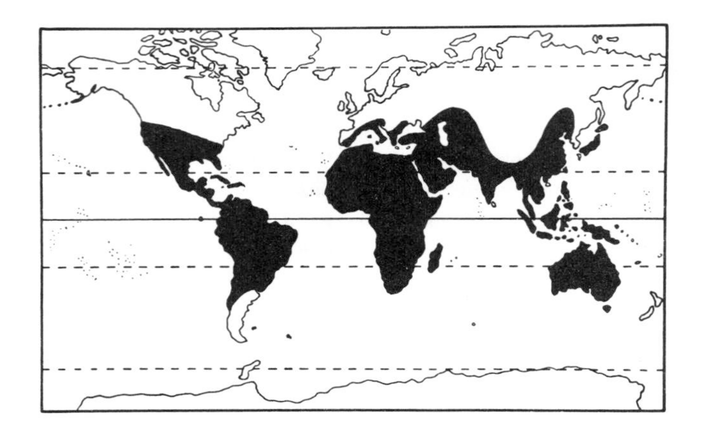

distribution of the Scorpiones

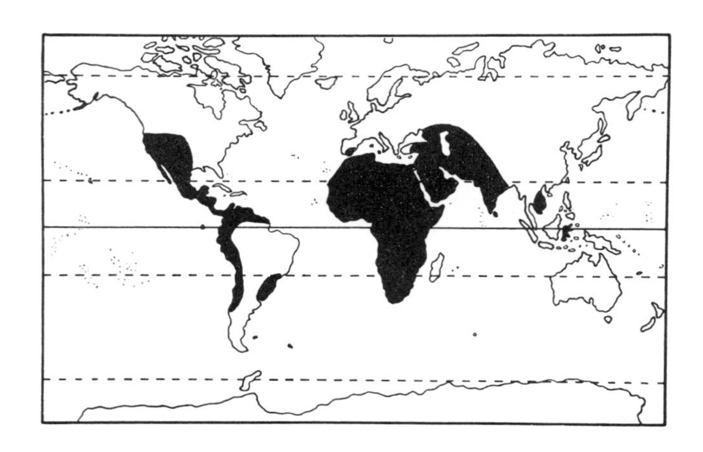

distribution of the Solifugae

C H E L I C E R A T A

Order Solifugae - Sun spiders

Arachnida in which:-

- 1. The last three segments of the prosoma are free.
- 2. The opisthosoma is 10-segmented and is not joined to the prosoma by a pedicel.

3. There is no telson.

- 4. The chelicerae are 2-jointed, large and chelate.
- 5. The pedipalpi are 6-jointed, simple, and very long.
- 6. The first pair of legs are tactile organs with one claw, the remaining pairs ambulatory with two claws. The fourth pair of legs carry racquet-organs on the ventral surface.

7. A tracheal system is present.
8. There is a pair of direct eyes on the prosoma.

Examples:- Galeodes, Solpuga. (see pages 116, 126)

Order Palpigradi - Micro-whip-scorpions

Arachnida in which:-

- 1. The last two segments of the prosoma are free.
- 2. The opisthosoma is segmented.
- 3. There is a long jointed telson.
- 4. The chelicerae are 3-jointed and chelate.
- 5. The pedipalpi are 6-jointed, simple and bear a small tarsal claw.

6. The legs are of 12, 7, 7 and 8 joints respectively and bear two claws.
7. There are three pairs of lung books on the 4th-6th opisthosomatic somites or none.
8. There are no eyes.

Example:- Koenenia. (see page 119)

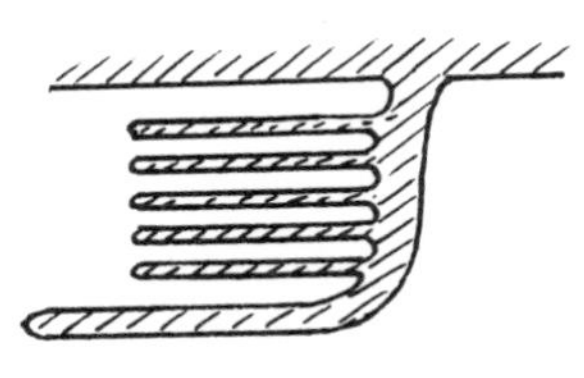

gill book

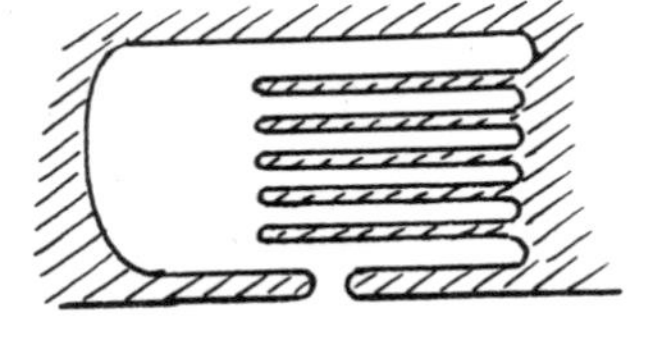

lung book

C H E L I C E R A T A

Order Schizopeltida

Arachnida in which:-

- 1. The prosoma is 3-segmented.
- 2. The opisthosoma is 12-segmented and is joined to the prosoma by a pedicel.
- 3. A pygidium, with a short terminal flagellum, is formed from the posterior three opisthosomatic segments.
- 4. The chelicerae are 2-jointed and sub-chelate.
- 5. The pedipalps are large and raptorial.
- 6. The first pair of legs are tactile, long and whip-like, with a segmented tarsus but no claws; the other legs have segmented tarsi and 3 claws.

7. There is a pair of lung books with spiracles on the second opisthosomatic segment.
8. Eyes are lacking.

Example:- Schizomus.

Order Holopeltida - Whip-scorpions

Arachnida in which:-

1. The prosoma is uniform.

- 2. The opisthosoma is 12-segmented and is joined to the prosoma by a pedicel.
- 3. A pygidium, with a long terminal flagellum, is formed from the posterior three opisthosomatic segments.
- 4. The chelicerae are 2-jointed and sub-chelate.
- 5. The pedipalps are large and raptorial.
- 6. The first pair of legs are tactile, long and whip-like, with a 9-segmented tarsus and no claws; the other legs have a 3-segmented tarsus.

7. There are two pairs of lung books with spiracles on the second and third opisthosomatic segments.
8. Eyes may or may not be present.

Example:- Thelyphonus. (see pages 119, 126)

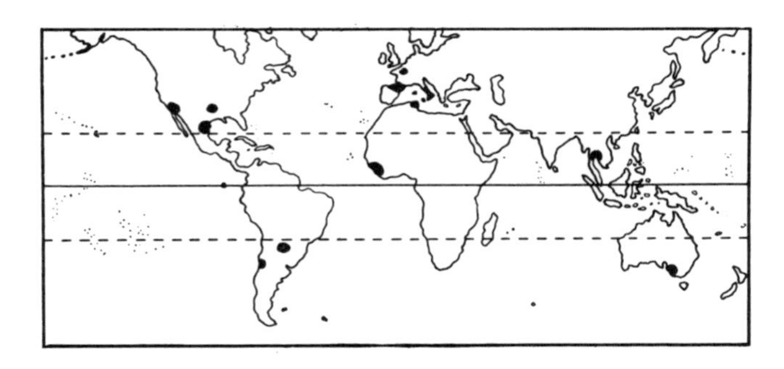

distribution of the Palpigradi

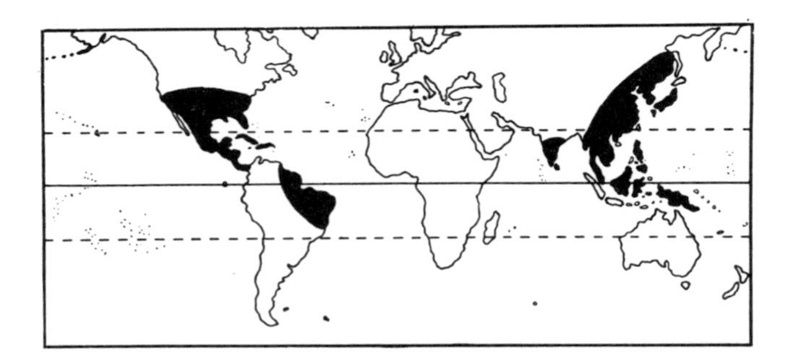

distribution of the Holopeltida

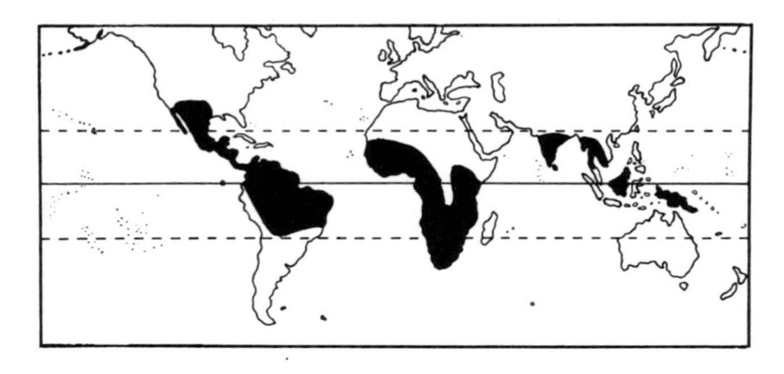

distribution of the Amblypygi

C H E L I C E R A T A

Order Amblypygi - Scorpion spiders

Arachnida in which:-

1. The prosoma is uniform with a carapace that is broader than long.
2. ● The opisthosoma is 12-segmented and broadly joined to the prosoma.
3. ● The posterior segments of the opisthosoma are rounded and there is no telson.
4. ● The chelicerae are 2-jointed, non-chelate, and the second joint is produced into a fang, as in the spiders.
5. ● The pedipalps are large and raptorial.
6. ● The first pair of legs are long, tactile, and their tarsus and metatarsus are segmented with no claws. The other legs also have segmented tarsi but bear three claws.
7. There are two pairs of lung books with spiracles on the second and third opisthosomatic segments.
8. Median and lateral eyes are usually present.

Examples:- Phrynichus, Charinus. (see page 119)

Order Araneae - Spiders

Arachnida in which:-

1. The prosoma is uniform.
2. ● The opisthosoma is rarely segmented and is joined to the prosoma by a pedicel.
3. The telson is absent.
4. ● The chelicerae are 2-jointed, subchelate, and contain a poison gland.
5. ● The pedipalpi are 6-jointed and simple, and in the male are modified for transmission of sperm.
6. The legs are 7-jointed and bear two or three claws.
7. Lung books or tracheae or most often both are present.
8. ● The prosoma bears not more than eight eyes.

(see page 127)

C H E L I C E R A T A

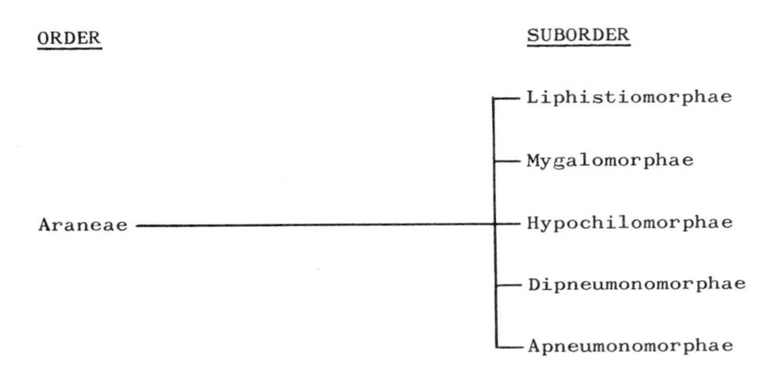

Suborder Liphistiomorphae

Araneae in which:-

- ● 1. The opisthosoma is segmented.
- ● 2. The spinnerets are not terminal.
- ● 3. The chelicerae are so placed that the fangs move up and down.
- 4. There are two pairs of lung-books.

Example:- _Liphistius_. (see page 122)

Suborder Mygalomorphae

Araneae in which:-

- ● 1. The opisthosoma is unsegmented.
- ● 2. The spinnerets are terminal.
- ● 3. The chelicerae are so placed that the fangs move up and down.
- 4. There are two pairs of lung-books.

Examples:- _Atypus_, _Mygale_.

(see pages 122, 127)

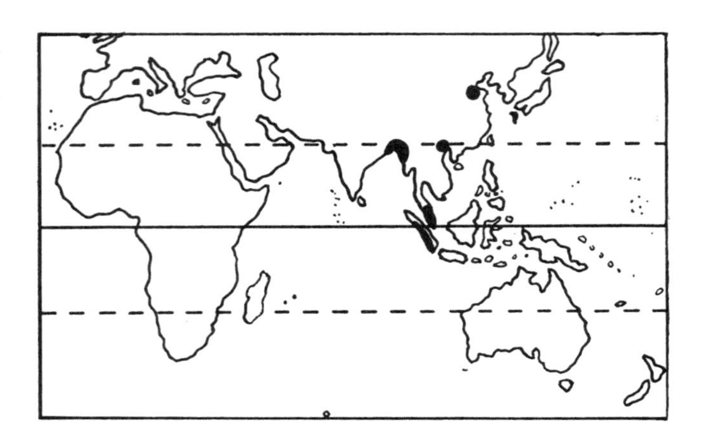

distribution of the Liphistiomorphae

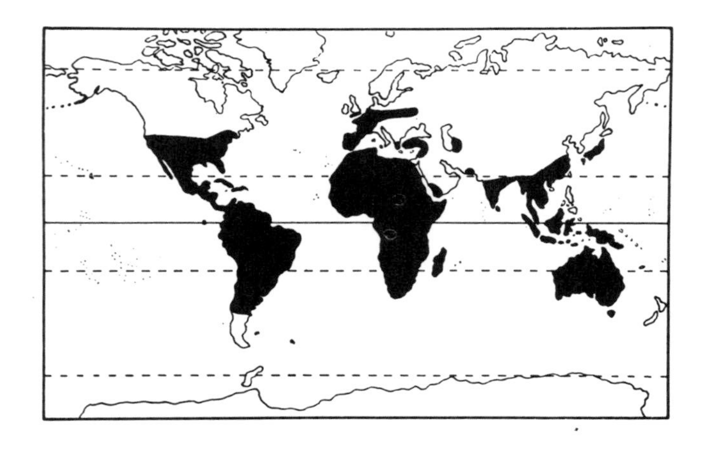

distribution of the Mygalomorphae

Suborder Hypochilomorphae

Araneae in which:-

1. The opisthosoma is unsegmented.
2. The spinnerets are terminal.
● 3. The chelicerae are so placed that the fangs move transversely.
● 4. There are two pairs of lung-books.

Example:- Hypochilus.

Suborder Dipneumonomorphae

Araneae in which:-

1. The opisthosoma is unsegmented.
2. The spinnerets are terminal.
● 3. The chelicerae are so placed that the fangs move transversely.
● 4. There is one pair of lung-books.

Example:- Latrodectus, Tegenaria, Lycosa.

Suborder Apneumonomorphae

Araneae in which:-

1. The opisthosoma is unsegmented.
2. The spinnerets are terminal.
● 3. The chelicerae are so placed that the fangs move transversely.
● 4. There are no lung-books.

Example:- Telema.

C H E L I C E R A T A

Order Ricinulei

Arachnida in which:-

- ● 1. The prosoma is uniform and bears anteriorly a movable plate, the cucullus.
- ● 2. The opisthosoma is of nine (apparently four) segments and is joined to the prosoma by a pedicel.
- 3. There is no telson.
- 4. The chelicerae are 2-jointed, small and chelate.
- 5. The pedipalpi are 6-jointed and chelate.
- ● 6. The legs are of 7, 11 or 12 segments and bear two claws: The metatarsus and tarsus of the third leg are modified in the male to form a sexual organ.
- 7. Tracheae are present and open on the prosoma.
- 8. There are no eyes.

Examples:- Cryptocellus, Ricinoides.

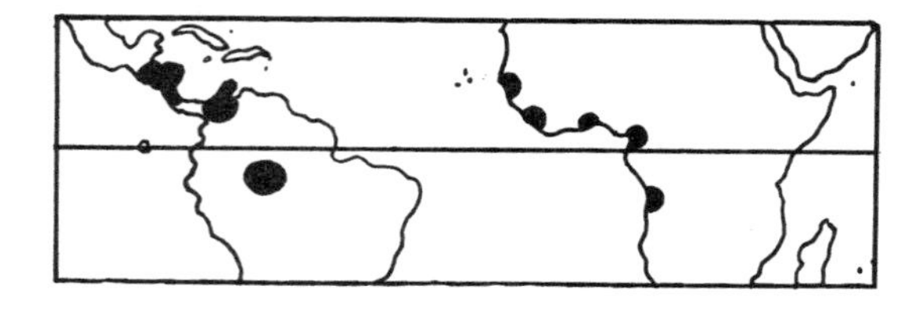

distribution of the Ricinulei

Order Opiliones - Harvestmen

Arachnida in which:-

- 1. The prosoma is uniform.
- ● 2. The opisthosoma is 10-segmented and continuous with the prosoma.
- 3. There is no telson.
- 4. The chelicerae are 3-jointed, small and chelate.
- 5. The pedipalpi are 6-jointed, usually small, and simple.
- ● 6. The legs are 7-jointed and generally very long and bear from 1-3 claws.
- 7. There is a pair of spiracles on the second sternite of the opisthosoma.
- 8. The prosoma bears a pair of simple eyes.

Example:- Phalangium. (see page 126)

C H E L I C E R A T A

Order Acari - Mites and Ticks

Arachnida in which:-

1. The prosoma is uniform.
● 2. The opisthosoma is unsegmented, or indistinctly so, and is continuous with the prosoma.
3. There is no telson.
● 4. The chelicerae are small and modified for piercing and sucking and in some forms for biting and grinding.
● 5. The pedipalpi are small, simple and associated with the mouth parts.
6. The legs are 7-jointed and usually bear two claws.
7. A tracheal system and spiracles may be present or absent.
8. The prosoma may bear simple eyes.

Examples:- Tyroglyphus, Sarcoptes, Argas, Ixodes, Amblyomma.

(see page 127)

Class Pycnogonida - Sea spiders

Chelicerata in which:-

● 1. The prosoma is divided into an anterior part, the 'head', which typically bears chelicerae, palps and ovigers, and a posterior 'thoracic' region bearing 4, 5 or even 6 pairs of walking legs.
● 2. The opisthosoma is reduced to a small knob and is non-segmented.
3. No organs of excretion have been described.
4. Respiration is cutaneous.
5. The members of the group are exclusively marine.
6. The gonads are located in the fourth joint of the legs.
7. Development is through a larval stage somewhat like a nauplius, but the chelicerae are chelate.

Examples:- Pycnogonum, Phoxichilus. (see page 111)

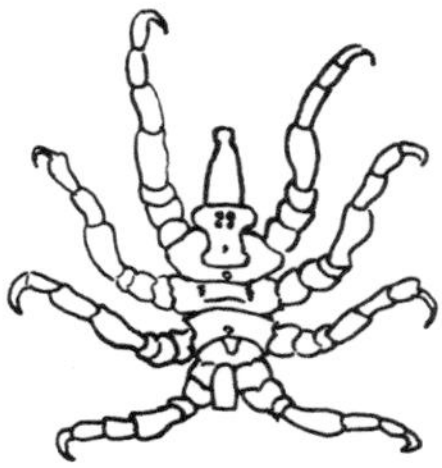

Pycnogonum

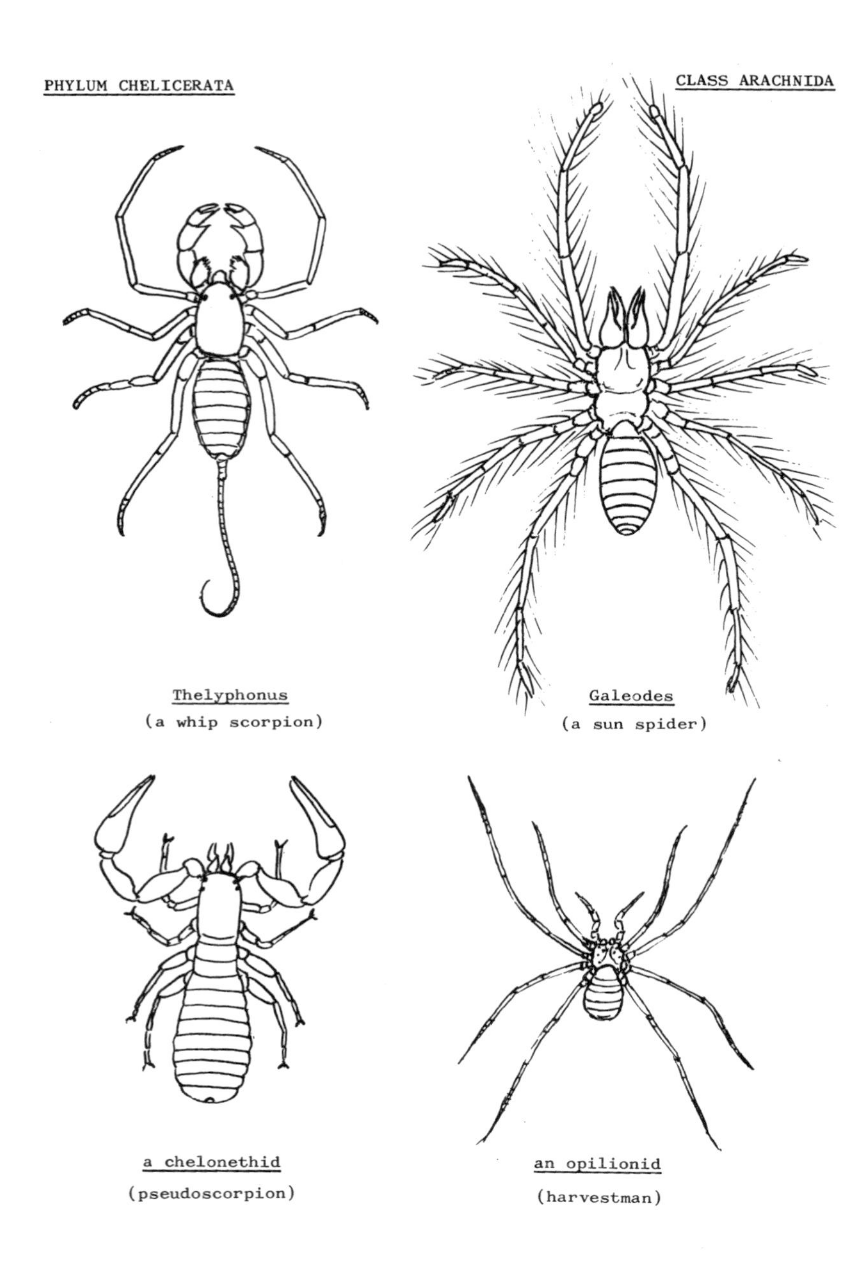

Thelyphonus (a whip scorpion)

Galeodes (a sun spider)

a chelonethid (pseudoscorpion)

an opilionid (harvestman)

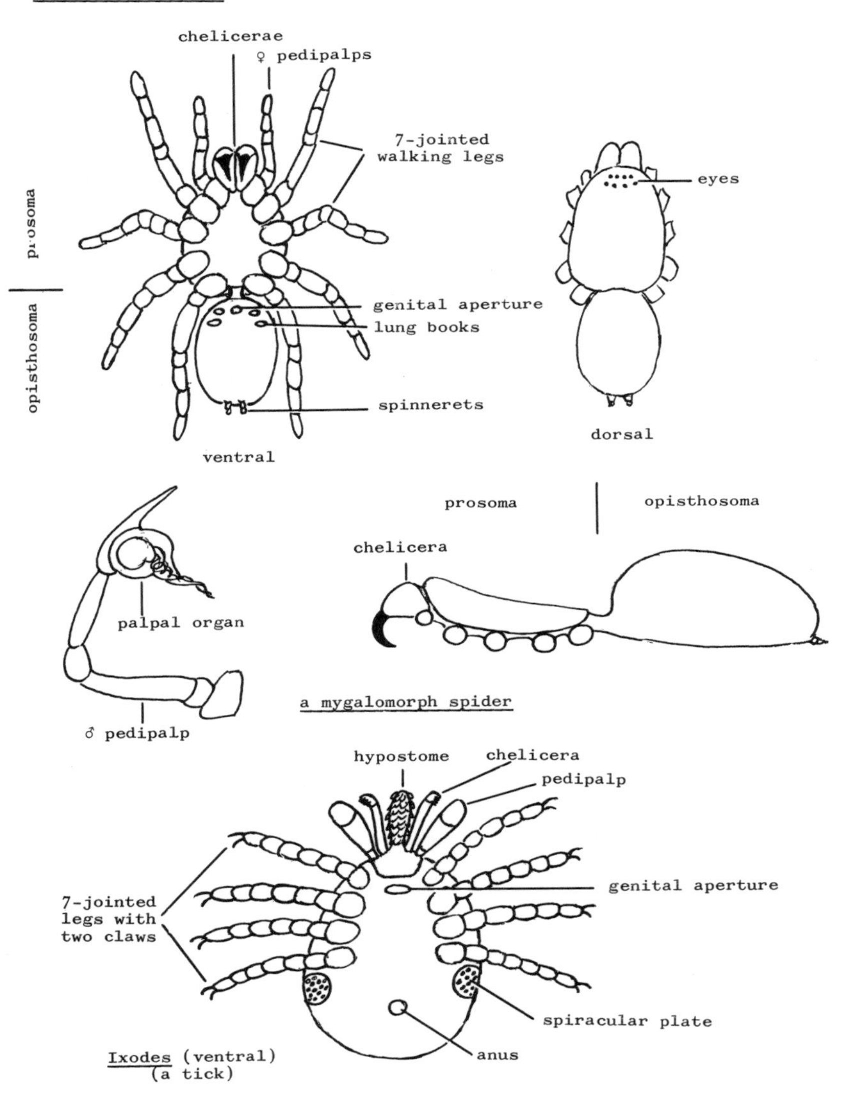

a mygalomorph spider

Ixodes (ventral) (a tick)

9 Biramous Arthropods
Crustaceans

Whereas the chelicerate and uniramous arthropods are primarily land animals, the crustaceans are the dominant aquatic arthropods with an enormous range of structure, and hence of habitat. They occur in vast numbers particularly in the sea. They are not therefore in competition with the even more numerous insects and arachnids. Basically the Crustacea have the body divided into three regions, head, thorax and abdomen, with biramous limbs present throughout. The head is well supplied with the major sense organs and characteristically has two pairs of antennae, although one or both pairs may be reduced.

The key to crustacean classification lies in the modification and distribution of the limbs and the presence and form of a coat-like covering to the thorax, the carapace. The crustacean biramous appendage, particularly in the most primitive forms such as the Cephalocarida, could very well be a polychaete parapodium strengthened by a thickened cuticle and rotated from the lateral to a ventral position for walking, with muscles to move it backward and forward. The limb consists of a basal joint, the protopod, from which arise two branches or rami, the inner endopod and the outer exopod. The basal part may have lateral lobes pointing mesially and called endites, or pointing outward when they are called exites. The endites are often used to manipulate food and as such are termed gnathobases. The exites often act as gills.

In a number of crustacean orders, notably those included in the class Branchiopoda, the limbs are leaf-like or foliaceous and are not used for walking at all, but for swimming or maintaining a respiratory or feeding current. In many of the crustacean groups the limbs become modified along the body in a variety of ways to serve different functions. At the front of the head they become elongated and sensory, around the mouth they form powerful jaws and food-handlers, in the thorax they are for walking and some may be armed with pincers. The abdominal appendages are often used for swimming and in the males may form copulatory structures, but may be absent from some of the segments. Many crustacean limbs are not obviously biramous since one of the rami is reduced or lost. When this happens it is usually the endopod that is enlarged and the exopod reduced.

Most Crustacea have a carapace, a notable exception being the copepods, but its form and extent differ greatly. The carapace arises as a backward extension of the posterior margin of the head. In some, such as the Eucarida, it is fused with the thoracic segments, in others it behaves simply as a loose coat. The carapace may be a single piece or bivalved with an adductor muscle and capable of totally enclosing the body. An extreme modification occurs in many barnacles where, strengthened by calcareous plates, it forms the familiar shell of these animals.

The crustacean embryo hatches as a nauplius larva or, at least, a naupliar stage is recognisable in development. Like the trochophore of the annelids, the nauplius consists of head segments and posterior segments in juxtaposition and growth takes place by the intercalation of segments in the middle. In the more primitive groups, such as the copepods, transition from the larval to the adult form is gradual. But in the Malacostraca and particularly the Eucarida, which represent the peak of crustacean evolution, there is often a sequence of larval forms and transition from one to the next and to the adult involves metamorphosis. On the other hand, many have large yolky eggs and omit some or most of the larval stages.

Phylum Crustacea

Arthropods in which:-

- ● 1. There are two pairs of pre-oral appendages which are antenniform and sensory.
- 2. The mandibles grind the food by a rolling action of the gnathobase.
- 3. The body is divided into three regions, head, thorax and abdomen, but there is a tendency for the anterior thoracic segments to fuse with the head to form a cephalothorax.
- ● 4. There are usually at least three pairs of post-oral appendages acting as jaws (mandibles, maxillules and maxillae).
- 5. The trunk appendages are very variable in form and function and typically occur on every segment of both thorax and abdomen. They are typically biramous.

(see page 108)

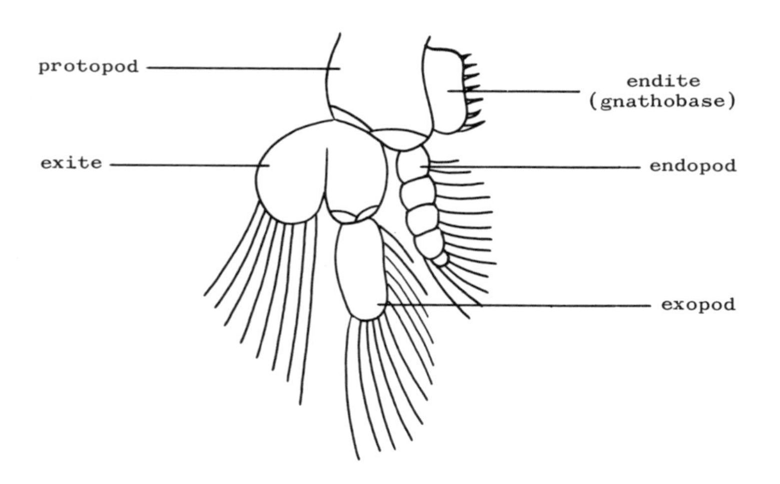

biramous trunk limb of a cephalocarid (Hutchinsoniella)

C R U S T A C E A

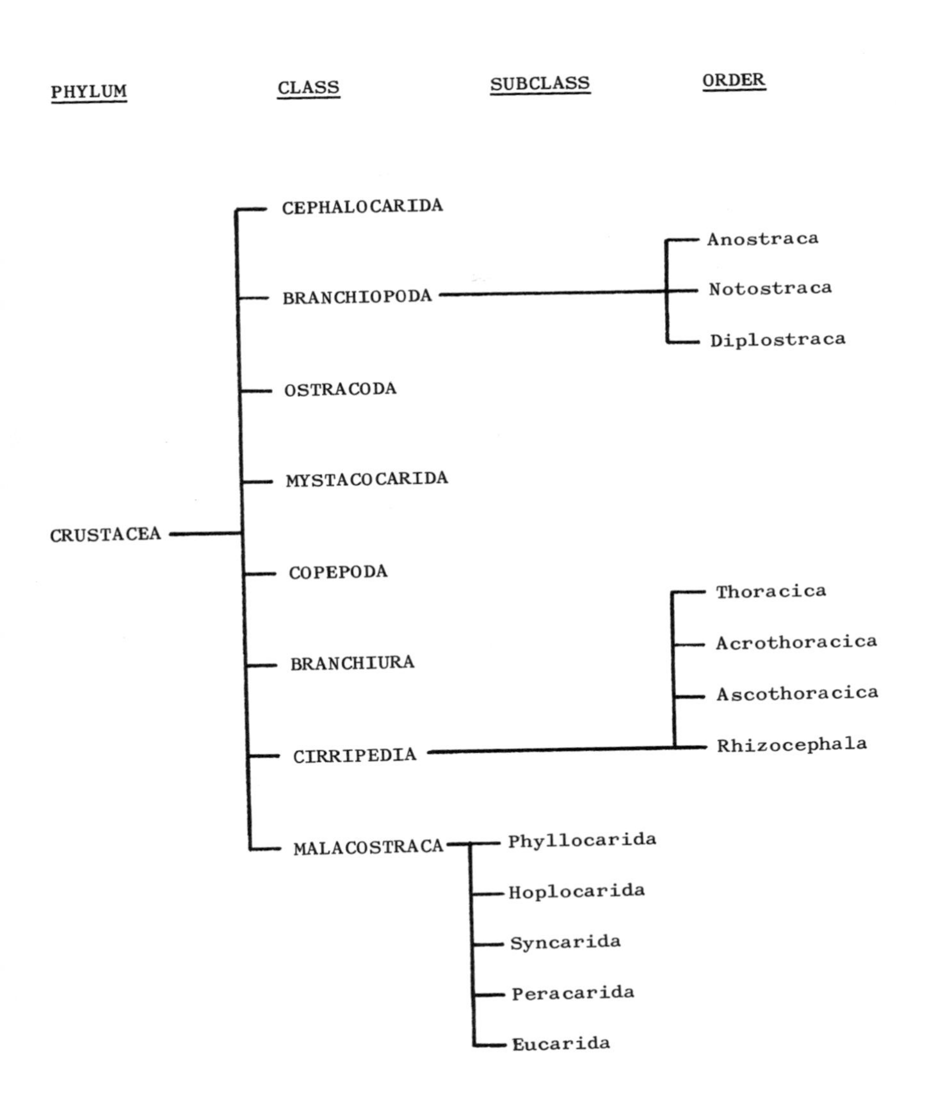
PHYLUM
CLASS
SUBCLASS
ORDER
CEPHALOCARIDA
BRANCHIOPODA
Anostraca
Notostraca
Diplostraca
OSTRACODA
MYSTACOCARIDA
CRUSTACEA
COPEPODA
BRANCHIURA
CIRRIPEDIA
Thoracica
Acrothoracica
Ascothoracica
Rhizocephala
MALACOSTRACA
Phyllocarida
Hoplocarida
Syncarida
Peracarida
Eucarida

C R U S T A C E A

Class Cephalocarida

Crustacea in which:-

● 1. A carapace is present.
2. Eyes are absent.
3. There are two pairs of short antennae.
4. The mandibular palp is absent.
● 5. There are nineteen trunk segments of which only the anterior nine bear appendages.
● 6. The trunk limbs are generally uniform and foliaceous, resembling the second maxillae.
7. A caudal furca with long and short rami is present. A telson is present.
8. The genital opening is on the ninth trunk segment.

Example:- *Hutchinsoniella*. (see page 130)

Class Branchiopoda

Crustacea in which:-

1. The carapace, when present, is variable in form.
● 2. Paired compound eyes are usually present.
● 3. The antennules are reduced or absent.
4. The mandibular palp is absent, or more rarely vestigial.
5. The body has a variable number of distinct segments.
● 6. The thoracic limbs are generally uniform and foliaceous; the abdomen usually lacks appendages.
7. There is a telson with rami.
8. The genital apertures are variable in position.

Order Anostraca - Fairy shrimp and Brine shrimp

Branchiopoda in which:-

● 1. The carapace is absent.
● 2. The paired eyes are stalked.
● 3. The antennae in the male are uniramous and prehensile, but in the female they are reduced.
4. The appendages of the body segments are 11, 17 or 19 pairs
● 5. The caudal rami are unsegmented.
6. Development occurs by metamorphosis.

Examples:- *Branchipus*, *Chirocephalus*, *Artemia*.

(see page 150)

C R U S T A C E A

Order Notostraca

Branchiopoda in which:-

● 1. The carapace forms a dorsal shield.
● 2. The paired eyes are sessile.
3. The antennae are uniramous and vestigial.
4. The appendages of the body segments number 40-63 pairs.
● 5. The caudal rami are many-jointed.
6. Development occurs by metamorphosis.

Examples:- Triops, Lepidurus. (see page 150)

Order Diplostraca

Branchiopoda in which:-

● 1. The carapace is bivalved and laterally compressed and usually encloses the trunk and limbs.
● 2. The paired eyes are sessile and either apposed or fused.
● 3. The antennae are large and biramous.
4. The appendages of the trunk segments do not exceed 27 pairs.
● 5. The caudal rami are claw-like.
6. Development may or may not be direct.

Suborder Conchostraca

Diplostraca in which:-

● 1. The bivalved carapace is provided with an adductor muscle and a hinge.
● 2. The carapace usually encloses the head.
3. The appendages of the trunk segments number 10-27 pairs.
4. There is nearly always a nauplius larva.

Example:- Estheria.

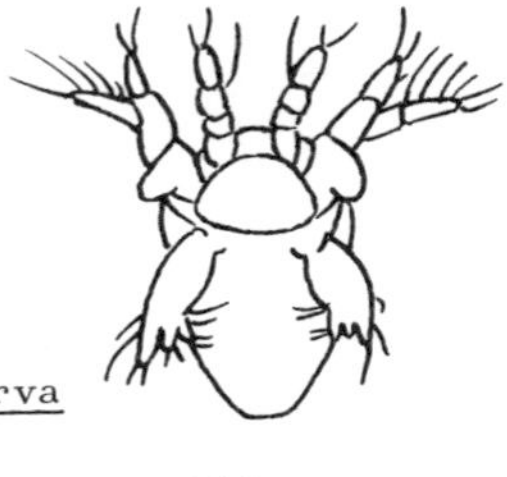

nauplius larva

CRUSTACEA

Suborder Cladocera - Water fleas

Diplostraca in which:-

- 1. The bivalved carapace is provided with neither an adductor muscle nor a hinge.
- 2. The carapace does not cover the head.
- 3. The appendages of the trunk segments number 4-6 pairs.
- 4. There is rarely a nauplius larva.

Examples:- Daphnia, Leptodora, Sida.

(see page 150)

Class Ostracoda

Crustacea in which:-

- 1. The carapace is bivalved and possesses an adductor muscle.
- 2. Paired compound eyes may or may not be present.
- 3. The antennules and antennae are large and are used for locomotion.
- 4. There is a mandibular palp.
- 5. The body is indistinctly segmented.
- 6. There are usually two, and not more than four, pairs of distinct thoracic limbs which are not foliaceous. The abdomen lacks appendages.
- 7. There is a telson with rami.
- 8. The genital aperture is behind the last pair of limbs.

Example:- Cypris.

(see page 150)

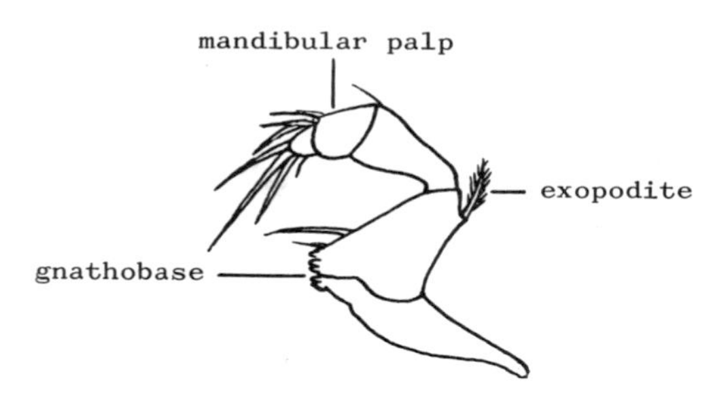

ostracod mandible

C R U S T A C E A

Class Mystacocarida

Crustacea in which:-

- ● 1. There is a carapace, the body being divided into a head, 5-segmented thorax and 6-segmented abdomen.
- ● 2. Only a naupliar eye is present.
- ● 3. Antennae are well developed.
- 4. The mandible is biramous and functions as a limb.
- ● 5. The last four thoracic segments and all the abdominal segments are free.
- ● 6. Thoracic appendages are reduced, and there are no abdominal appendages except on the last segment which carries a pair of caudal styles.
- 7. A telson with rami is lacking.
- 8. The genital aperture is on the first free thoracic segment.

Example:- Derocheilocaris.

Class Copepoda

Crustacea in which:-

- ● 1. There is no carapace.
- 2. Compound eyes are absent.
- ● 3. The antennules and antennae are generally well developed.
- 4. The mandibular palp may be present or absent.
- ● 5. There are typically nine free trunk segments.
- ● 6. There are typically six pairs of thoracic limbs of which the first and sometimes the last are uniramous: the abdomen lacks appendages.
- 7. There is a telson with rami.
- 8. The genital apertures are on the seventh thoracic segment.

Examples:- Calanus, Cyclops, Lernaea, Chondracanthus.

(see page 150)

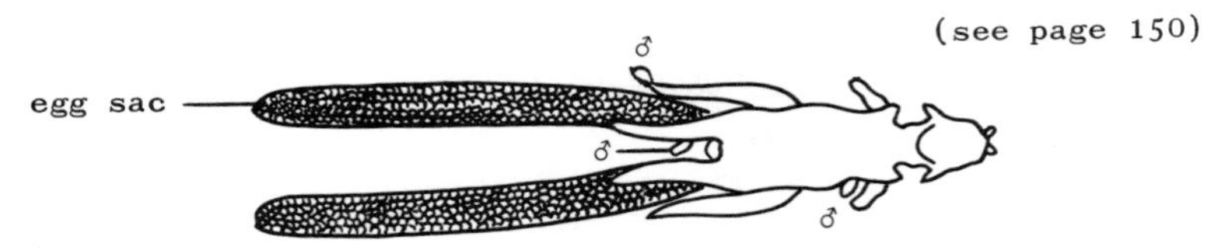

Chondracanthus female parasitic on fish gills with attached males

C R U S T A C E A

Class Branchiura - Fish louse

Crustacea in which:-

1. There is no true carapace, but carapace-like lateral expansions of the head are present.
2. ● There are paired compound eyes.
3. Small antennules and antennae are present.
4. ● The mandibles are reduced, the mouth being suctorial.
5. The body is not distinctly segmented.
6. ● There are four pairs of biramous thoracic limbs with usually a proximal extension of the exopodite: the small, bilobed, unsegmented abdomen lacks limbs.
7. The caudal furca is reduced.
8. The genital apertures are on the fifth trunk segment.
9. Development is more or less direct.
10. ● The members are ectoparasites of fish.

Example:- Argulus. (see page 150)

Class Cirripedia

Crustacea in which:-

1. ● There is almost always a carapace completely enclosing the bod and limbs and usually strengthened by calcareous plates.
2. Compound eyes are absent in the adult.
3. The antennules are present in the larva as organs of attachmer but become vestigial in the adult. The antennae usually disappear.
4. There is no mandibular palp.
5. The body is indistinctly segmented.
6. ● There are typically six pairs of biramous thoracic limbs; the abdomen is limbless and rudimentary.
7. There is usually a caudal furca.
8. The members are usually hermaphrodite with female apertures on the first thoracic segment and the male apertures behind the last pair of limbs.
9. The larva is a nauplius which passes to a cypris stage before final metamorphosis.
10. ● The adults are sessile, non-parasitic or parasitic.

CRUSTACEA

Order Thoracica - Barnacles

Cirripedia in which:-

- ● 1. The adult is non-parasitic and permanently attached by the pre-oral region.
- ● 2. There are six pairs of limbs.
- 3. An alimentary canal is present.
- 4. Hermaphroditism is common or the male and female live in permanent association.

Suborder Pedunculata - Goose barnacles

Thoracica in which:-

- ● 1. There is a stalk of attachment, the peduncle.
- ● 2. The outer plates of the mantle are not fused to form a peripheral 'wall'.

Examples:- *Lepas*, *Scalpellum*. (see page 150)

Suborder Operculata

Thoracica in which:-

- ● 1. There is no stalk of attachment.
- ● 2. The outer plates of the mantle are fused to form a peripheral 'wall', while inner plates, the scuta and terga, form a movable operculum.

Example:- *Balanus*, *Chthamalus*, *Elminia*.

(see page 150)

Order Acrothoracica

Cirripedia in which:-

- ● 1. The adults bore into mollusc shells and are permanently attached by the pre-oral region.
- ● 2. There are less than 6 pairs of limbs of which the first pair is widely separated from the remainder.
- 3. An alimentary canal is present.
- 4. The sexes are separate.

Example:- *Alcippe*.

Order Ascothoracica

Cirripedia in which:-

- 1. The adults are parasitic on Anthozoa and Echinodermata and are not attached by the pre-oral region.
- 2. There are generally 6 pairs of limbs.
3. The mantle contains diverticula of the alimentary canal.
4. The sexes are separate or the animals are hermaphrodite.

Example:- Laura.

Order Rhizocephala

Cirripedia in which:-

- 1. The adults are parasitic on decapod Crustacea and are attached by a stalk having roots which ramify throughout the host body.
- 2. There are no appendages in the adult.
3. There is no alimentary canal.
4. The members are hermaphrodite.

Example:- Sacculina.

Class Malacostraca

Crustacea in which:-

- 1. There is typically a carapace.
- 2. Paired compound eyes are usually present.
- 3. The antennules and antennae are well developed and the former often biramous.
4. A mandibular palp may be present.
- 5. There are typically 14 (rarely 15) trunk segments; the thorax comprises 8 segments, and the abdomen 6 (rarely 7) true segments and a telson.
- 6. There are 8 pairs of thoracic and 6 pairs of abdominal limbs.
7. The telson rarely bears a caudal furca.
8. The female genital apertures are on the sixth and the male on the eighth thoracic segment.
9. Metamorphosis usually occurs but the young rarely hatch as nauplii.

C R U S T A C E A

Subclass Phyllocarida

Malacostraca in which:-

● 1. There is a large carapace which is not fused with any of the thoracic segments. The carapace possesses an adductor muscle.

2. The eyes are pedunculate.

● 3. The protopodite (peduncle) of the antenna apparently comprises 4 (sometimes 3) segments.

4. The mandible lacks a lacinia mobilis.

● 5. The thoracic limbs are similar and foliaceous: the last abdominal segment (seventh) lacks appendages.

6. There are no oostegites (brood plates).

7. The heart is elongated and extends throughout the greater part of the body.

8. The telson bears a caudal furca.

9. There is no free swimming larval stage.

Example:- Nebalia. (see page 151)

Subclass Hoplocarida - Mantis shrimp

Malacostraca in which:-

● 1. The carapace is shallow, is fused with only three thoracic segments and leaves at least four uncovered.

2. There are two free segments in the head bearing pedunculate eyes and antennules respectively.

● 3. The protopodite of the antenna is 2-segmented.

4. There is no lacinia mobilis on the mandible.

● 5. The first five pairs of thoracic limbs are subchelate and the last three biramous.

6. There are no oostegites.

7. The heart is greatly elongated extending through the thoracic and abdominal regions.

8. The abdomen is large with the first five pairs of limbs bearing gills on the exopodites.

9. The sixth pair of abdominal limbs form a tail-fan with the telson.

Example:- Squilla. (see page 152)

C R U S T A C E A

Subclass Syncarida - Tasmanian shrimp

Malacostraca in which:-

- 1. There is no carapace.
- 2. The eyes may be pedunculate, sessile or absent.
- 3. The protopodite of the antenna is 2-segmented.
- 4. The mandible lacks a lacinia mobilis.
- 5. The first thoracic segment is usually fused with the hea most of the thoracic limbs possess exopodites, but none of the limbs is chelate or subchelate.
- 6. There are no oostegites.
- 7. The heart is elongated, extending throughout the greater part of the body.

Examples:- Anaspides, Koonunga, Bathynella.

(see page 151)

Subclass Peracarida

Malacostraca in which:-

- 1. The carapace, when present, leaves at least four thoraci segments free.
- 2. The eyes may be pedunculate or sessile.
- 3. The protopodite of the antenna is 3-segmented.
- 4. The mandible bears a lacinia mobilis.
- 5. The first thoracic segment is fused with the head: the thoracic legs are flexed between their fifth and sixth segments.
- 6. Oostegites are present on all or some of the thoracic limbs of the female, forming a brood pouch.
- 7. The heart is generally elongated.
- 8. Development is direct within the brood pouch.

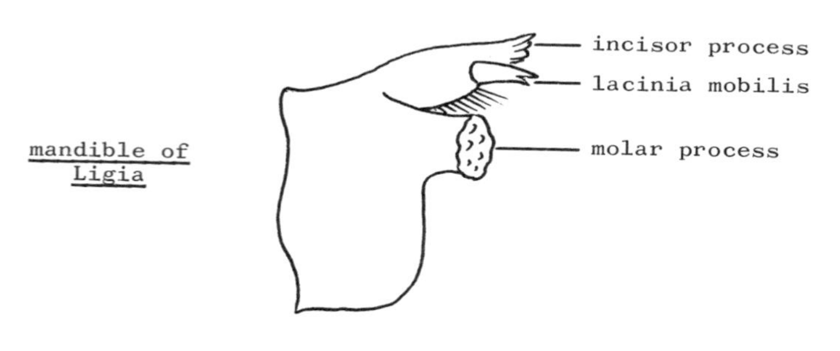

C R U S T A C E A

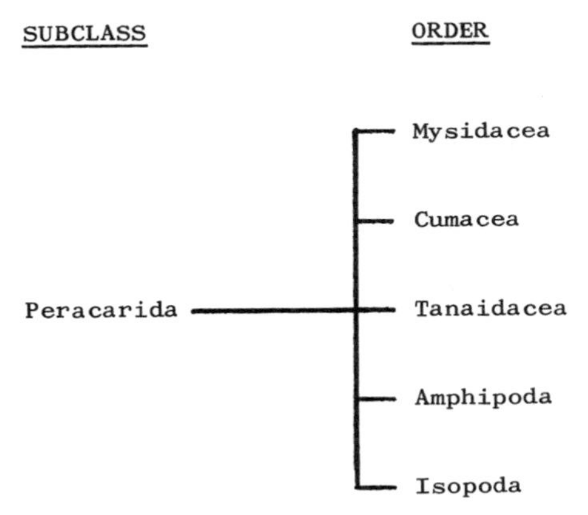

SUBCLASS
ORDER
Mysidacea
Cumacea
Peracarida
Tanaidacea
Amphipoda
Isopoda

C R U S T A C E A

Order Mysidacea - Opossum shrimps

Peracarida in which:-

- ● 1. The carapace covers all or most of the thoracic segments, but does not fuse dorsally with more than three.
- ● 2. The eyes, when present, are pedunculate and movable
- 3. The antennules are biramous and the antennae usuall possess a large scale-like exopodite.
- ● 4. Most or all of the thoracic limbs possess swimming exopodites.
- 5. The first, and sometimes the second, thoracic limbs are maxillipedes.
- ● 6. The uropods form a tail-fan.
- 7. The pleopods may be well developed or reduced and are not specially modified.
- 8. The heart is thoracic.

Example:- Mysis. (see page 151)

Order Cumacea

Peracarida in which:-

- ● 1. The carapace covers only three or four thoracic segments, but is inflated on each side to form a branchial chamber and is drawn out anteriorly into a pseudo-rostrum.
- ● 2. The eyes when present are sessile and usually coalesced.
- 3. The antennules may be biramous and the antennae lac an exopodite.
- ● 4. Some of the thoracic limbs possess swimming exopodites.
- 5. The first three pairs of thoracic limbs are maxillipedes.
- ● 6. The uropods are styliform.
- ● 7. The pleopods are absent in the female and often reduced in the male.
- 8. The heart is thoracic.
- 9. The body is not flattened.

Example:- Diastylis. (see page 151)

CRUSTACEA

Order Tanaidacea

Peracarida in which:-

- ● 1. The carapace covers and fuses with only two thoracic segments and encloses on each side a branchial cavity.
- 2. The eyes, when present, are pedunculate but the peduncles are short and immovable.
- 3. The antennules may be biramous and the antennae may possess a small exopodite.
- ● 4. The exopodites of the thoracic limbs are absent or vestigial.
- 5. The first pair of thoracic limbs are maxillipedes, the second pair are chelate.
- ● 6. The uropods are slender.
- 7. The pleopods are usually present and biramous.
- 8. The heart is thoracic.
- 9. The body is not flattened.

Examples:- Apseudes, Tanais. (see page 151)

Order Amphipoda - Sand hoppers

Peracarida in which:-

- ● 1. The carapace is absent.
- 2. The eyes are sessile.
- 3. The antennules are often biramous and the antennae lack an exopodite.
- ● 4. The thoracic limbs lack exopodites.
- 5. The first pair of thoracic limbs are maxillipedes without epipodites, the second and third pairs usually prehensile and the remainder variously modified.
- ● 6. The uropods do not form a tail-fan.
- ● 7. The first three pairs of pleopods bear multi-articulate rami and the last two pairs are similar to the uropods.
- 8. The heart is thoracic.
- ● 9. The body is usually laterally flattened.

Examples:- Orchestia, Gammarus, Caprella, Cyamus, Phronima.

(see page 152)

Order Isopoda - Slaters, Woodlice

Peracarida in which:-

● 1. The carapace is absent.
2. The eyes are sessile or are set on immovable processes of the head.
3. The antennules are uniramous (except Bathynomus) and the antennae may possess a minute exopodite.
● 4. The thoracic limbs lack exopodites.
5. The first pair of thoracic limbs are maxillipedes and the remainder usually alike.
● 6. The uropods are variable but usually do not form a tail-fan.
● 7. The pleopods are typically biramous with lamellar branchial rami: the second and sometimes the first pair of pleopods in the male are modified as copulatory appendages.
8. The heart lies wholly or partly in the abdomen.
● 9. The body is usually dorso-ventrally flattened.

Examples:- Ligia, Armadillidium, Asellus, Idotea, and highly modified parasitic forms such as Bopyrus, Cryptoniscus.

(see pages 140, 152)

Subclass Eucarida

Malacostraca in which:-

● 1. The carapace is fused with all the thoracic segments forming a cephalo-thorax.
2. The eyes are pedunculate.
● 3. The protopodite of the antenna never has more than two distinct segments.
4. The mandible in the adult lacks a lacinia mobilis.
● 5. The thoracic legs are flexed between the fourth and fifth segments of the limb.
6. There are no oostegites.
7. The heart is short and thoracic.

C R U S T A C E A

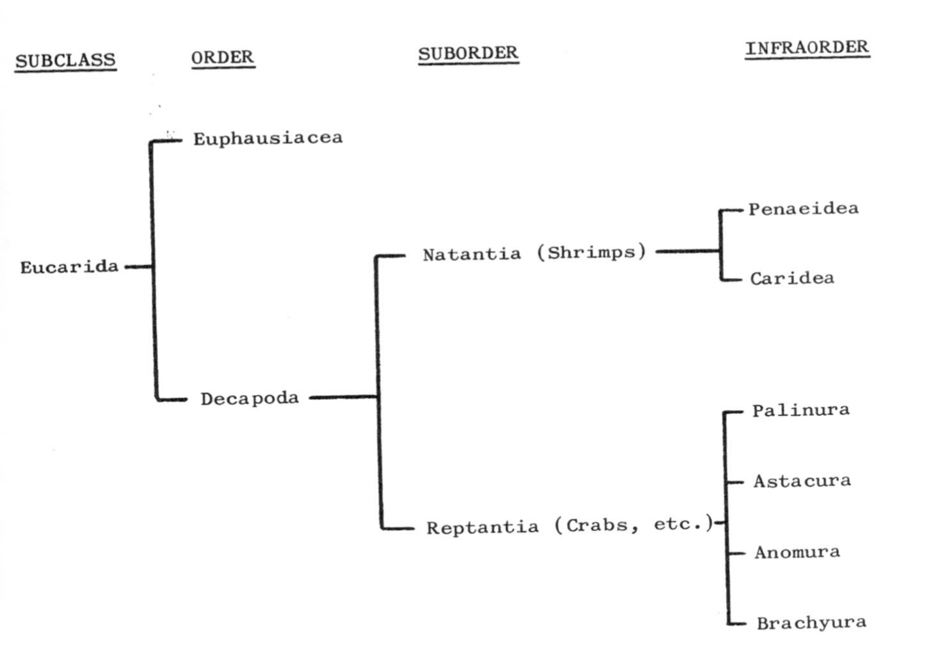

Order Euphausiacea - Krill

Eucarida in which:-

1. The exopodite of the maxilla is small.
2. None of the thoracic limbs is modified as a maxillipede.
3. There is a single series of gills (podobranchiae) attached to the coxopodites of the thoracic limbs.
4. The young are hatched as nauplii.

Examples:- Euphausia, Nyctiphanes. (see page 152)

C R U S T A C E A

Order Decapoda

Eucarida in which:-

1. The exopodite of the maxilla is very large (scaphognathite).
● 2. The first three pairs of thoracic limbs are maxillipedes.
● 3. There is usually more than one series of gills, e.g some are attached to the coxopodites of the thoraci limbs (podobranchiae), some to the joint-membranes at the bases of the limbs (arthrobranchiae), and oth to the lateral walls of the thoracic segments (pleurobranchiae).
4. The young are rarely hatched as nauplii.

Suborder Natantia - Shrimps and Prawns

Decapoda in which:-

1. The body tends to be laterally compressed, wit a prominent saw-toothed rostrum.
● 2. A large, plate-like antennal scale is used as a rudder in swimming.
● 3. The thoracic legs are slender; a cheliped, if present, is one of the first 3 pairs of legs.
4. First abdominal somite is not reduced
● 5. There is a full set of well-developed swimming pleopods.

Infraorder Penaeidea

Natantia in which:-

● 1. The pleura of the second abdominal segmen do not overlap those of the first.

Examples:- Penaeus, Leucifer.

Infraorder Caridea

Natantia in which:-

● 1. The pleura of the second abdominal segmen overlap those of the first.

Examples:- Crangon, Palaemon.

C R U S T A C E A

Suborder Reptantia - Crabs and Lobsters

Decapoda in which:-

1. The body is never laterally compressed, although it may be depressed dorsally; the rostrum is lacking in some cases.
- ● 2. The antennal scale is vestigial or lacking.
- ● 3. Thoracic legs are strong, and almost always with the first pereiopod modified into a strong cheliped.

4. First abdominal somite reduced.
- ● 5. The pleopods are often reduced and not used for swimming.

Infraorder Palinura

Reptantia in which:-

1. The body is either not compressed or is dorso-ventrally compressed.
- ● 2. The abdomen is long and extended, well-armoured and ending in a tail-fan.
- ● 3. The pleura of the second abdominal segment do not usually overlap those in front.

4. The carapace is fused at the sides with the epistome.
- ● 5. The rostrum is generally small or absent.

Examples:- Palinurus, Panulirus.

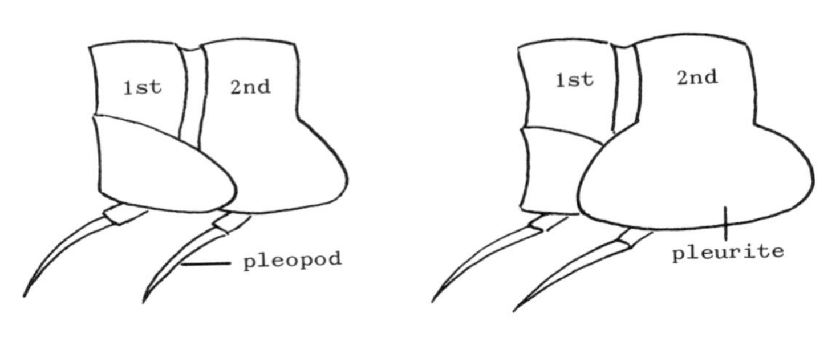

overlap of the pleurites of 1st and 2nd abdominal segments

Infraorder Astacura - Lobsters and Crayfish

Reptantia in which:-

- 1. The body is essentially sub-cylindrical in shape.
- 2. The abdomen is long and extended, well-armoured and ending in a tail-fan.
- 3. The pleura of the second abdominal segmen do not overlap those in front.
- 4. The carapace is not fused at the sides wi the epistome.
- 5. The rostrum is well developed.

Examples:- *Astacus*, *Homarus*.

Infraorder Anomura - Hermit crabs

Reptantia in which:-

- 1. The body is reduced in varying degree and is sometimes asymmetrical.
- 2. The abdomen is usually more or less reduc often soft or bent upon itself and usuall with a tail-fan.
- 3. The abdominal pleura are usually small or absent.
- 4. The carapace is not fused at the sides wi the epistome.
- 5. The rostrum may be well developed, small or absent.
- 6. The last one or two pairs of thoracic lim are usually smaller and often concealed b the carapace.

Examples:- *Callianassa*, *Porcellana*, *Galathe* *Eupagurus*, *Birgus*, *Hippa*.

(see page 149)

Infraorder Brachyura - True crabs

Reptantia in which:-

- 1. The body is usually dorso-ventrally compressed.
- 2. The abdomen is reduced, permanently bent under the thorax and without a tail-fan.
- 3. The abdominal pleura are greatly reduced or absent.
- 4. The carapace is fused with the epistome at the sides and nearly always in the middle.
- 5. The rostrum is usually small or absent.

Examples:- Cancer, Gelasimus, Ocypoda, Callinectes, Potamon, Grapsus, Carcinus, Maia.

(see page 152)

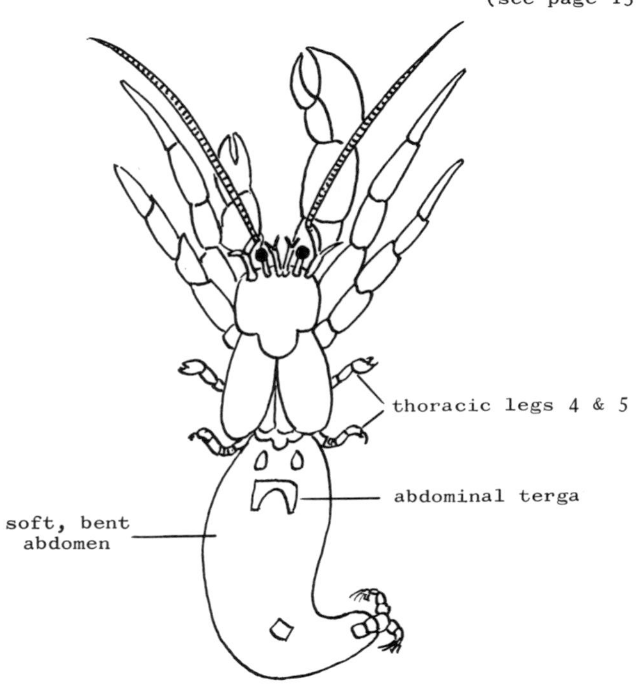

Eupagurus removed from gastropod shell

PHYLUM CRUSTACEA

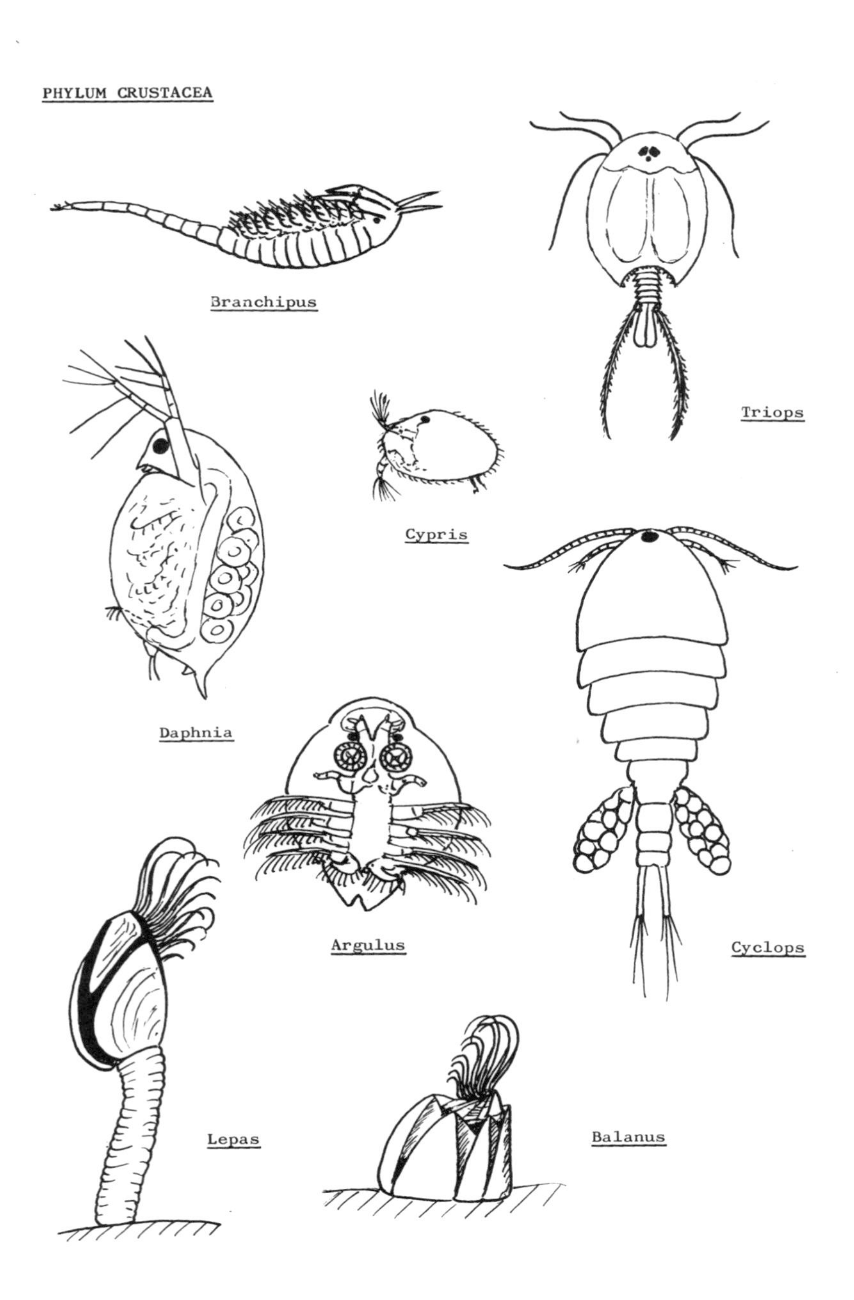

PHYLUM CRUSTACEA

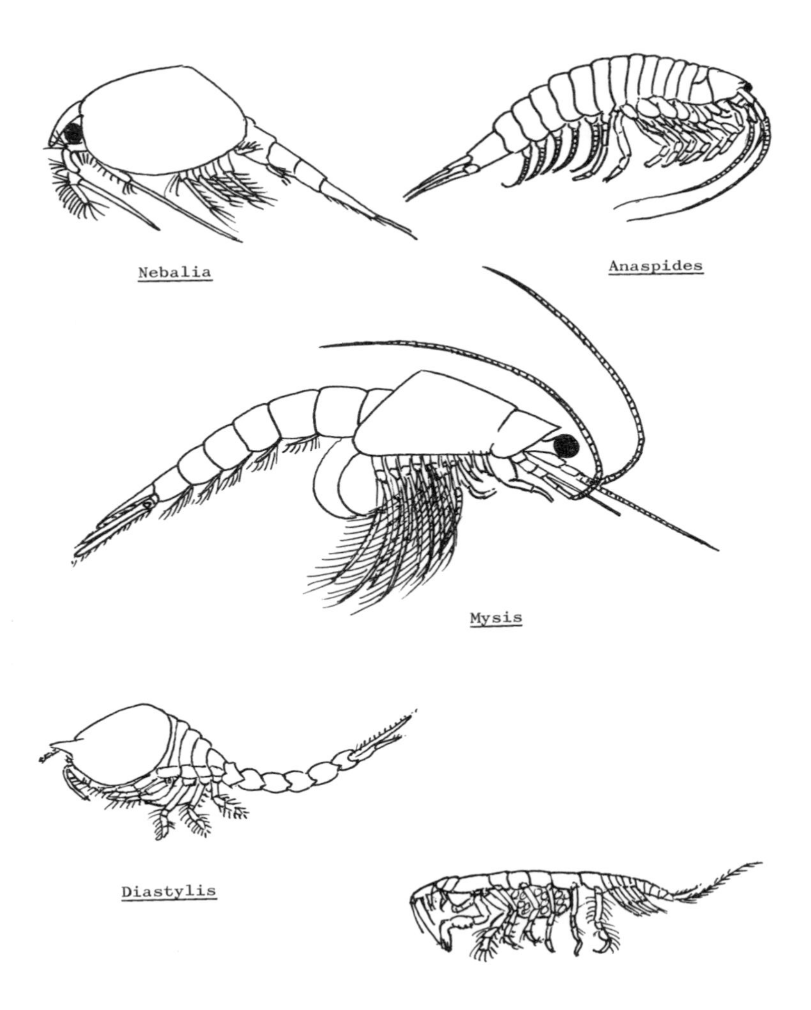

PHYLUM CRUSTACEA

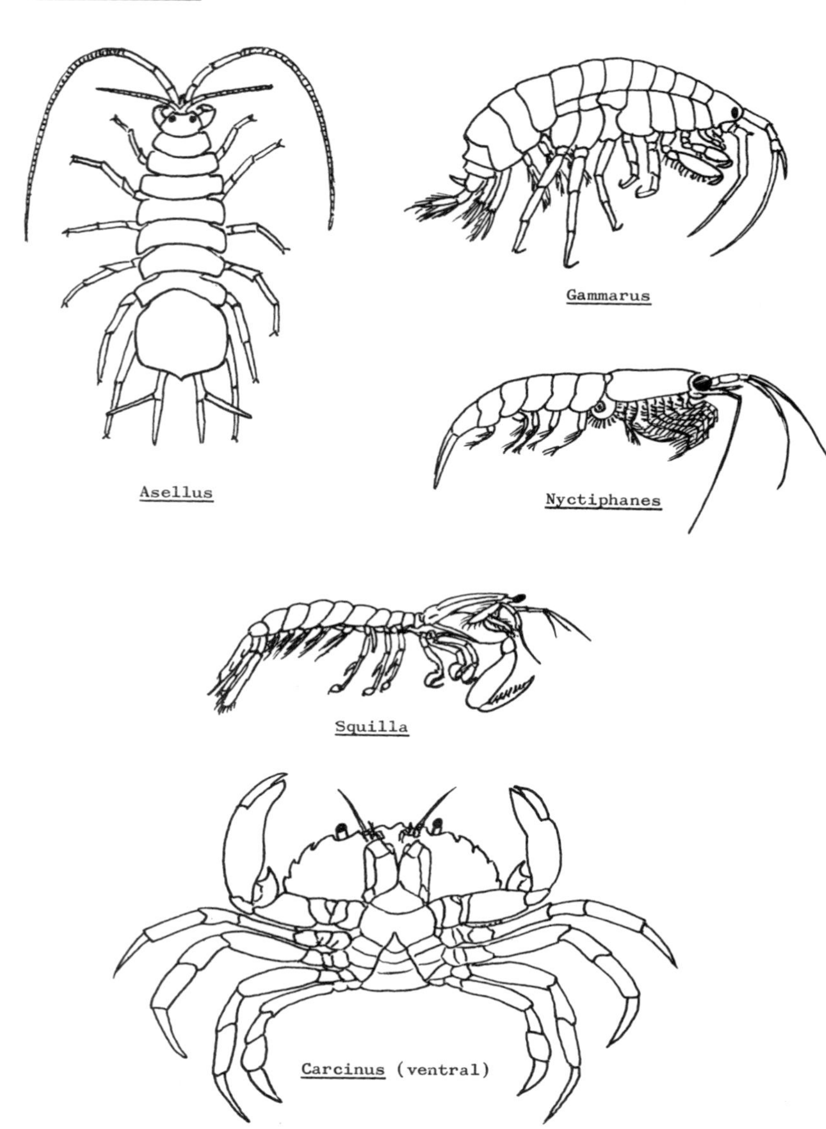

10 Uniramous Arthropods Onychophora, Myriapoda, Hexapoda (Insecta)

Peripatus, the myriapods and the insects, among all the arthropods, seem to be an evolutionary sequence representing increasing complexity within a broad morphological framework. They may well have had common ancestry, but whereas *Peripatus*, retaining many primitive characteristics, represents one line, the myriapods and insects are others that have been long distinct, though remaining relatively close to each other. As the name Uniramia suggests, their appendages are single struts, that is, they do not have an exopod and endopod as, for example, do the crustaceans. This has led to an important difference in the mandibles. In the Crustacea each mandible is a gnathobase arising from the basal protopod of the limb. In the Uniramia, on the other hand, the mandible is an entire limb biting with its tip. This single feature unifies the group and immediately distinguishes them from all other arthropods.

Peripatus is, perhaps, as near as we can get among living forms to the likely general organisation of a protoarthropod. It is soft-bodied with a cuticle, but without jointed exoskeletal plates, and has pairs of stumpy legs along the whole of the body. Myriapods also have limbs throughout the body which is divided into a head and a trunk. Young myriapods resemble the adult, but have fewer segments, new segments being intercalated between two of the hind segments each time the animal moults. This kind of development is said to be anamorphic as distinct from epimorphic where the full number of segments is established before hatching takes place. Anamorphic development in myriapods gives rise to a peculiarity in the position of the genital aperture once thought to be of primary importance in their classification. Centipedes have the genital aperture at the back of the body (opisthogoneate) while in millipedes it is in an anterior position (progoneate). This difference arises from the point at which new segments are formed. Where this point is posterior to the genital segment a progoneate form develops and where it is anterior an opisthogoneate form results. A principal difference between the myriapods and the insects is the division of the insect body into head, thorax and abdomen with the legs, three pairs only, restricted to the thorax. Thus, if an anamorphic myriapod hatching with three pairs of legs were to become epimorphic, then an insect-like creature would result. This is probably the origin of some at least of the primitively wingless hexapods such as the Protura, which may be much more closely related to the myriapods than to the true winged insects or Pterygota.

The Uniramia are essentially land animals. They cope with the terrestrial environment by breathing air through a tracheal system and excreting nitrogenous waste via special tubules (Malpighian tubules in most) capable of concentrating the waste and returning much of the water to the body. Conservation of water is important to all land animals and those Uniramia capable of living under dry conditions, such as the insects, have developed a highly water-proofed cuticle capable of resisting desiccation. In *Peripatus* and the myriapods the cuticle is either relatively permeable to water or is imperfectly water-proofed, so that they are restricted to damp environments.

U N I R A M O U S   A R T H R O P O D S

The most successful of the arthropods are the insects. They far outnumber in individuals and kinds all other animals and include a vast array that are of economic or medical importance. Much of their success is attributable to their powers of flight which they alone among invertebrates have evolved.

The classification of the Pterygota used in this guide is one proposed by Martynov in 1923. It is based on the presence or absence of the anal lobe of the wing and the number of veins that support it. Although it has not been generally adopted in textbooks, this classification has the advantage that it subdivides the hemimetabolous exopterygote insects (17 orders) into three infraclasses, Palaeoptera, Polyneoptera and Paraneoptera, which are well supported by matching characters. Martynov's Oligoneoptera comprises the holometabolous endopterygote insects (11 orders), so that his classification may be considered a useful extension of the commonly accepted division of the Pterygota into Exopterygota (Hemimetabola) and Endopterygota (Holometabola).

Flight in insects is achieved by flapping the wings to create a current of air. The direction of the current depends on the amplitude of the beat and its orientation, so that by changing the stroke some insects can rise vertically, hover, or fly forward or backward. In many insects, such as butterflies, the wing beat is under the control of the nervous system (neurogenic) and its rate is determined by that at which the nerves can carry impulses. It is therefore relatively slow. But in others the wing beat is immensely fast with rates up to about a thousand beats a second. Such insects as the bee or the mosquito when in flight produce a buzz or whine. Here the rate of beat is inherent in the muscles (myogenic) and is then accelerated by a 'click mechanism' arising from the sudden release of stored energy in the elastic thoracic plates under the strain of deformation.

Phylum Uniramia

Arthropods in which:-

- 1. There is one pair of pre-oral appendages which are antenniform and sensory.
- 2. The mandibles bite the food using the tip of the whole limb.
- 3. Except in the Onychophora which show little regional differentiation, the body is divided into two regions (head and trunk) or three regions (head, thorax and abdomen).
- 4. The post-oral appendages of the head all serve as mouth parts; typically there are three pairs, of which the first is usually mandibulate and the remainder assist in feeding.
- 5. The second part of the body (trunk or thorax) always bears the walking legs. The abdomen may or may not bear appendages. The limbs are uniramous.

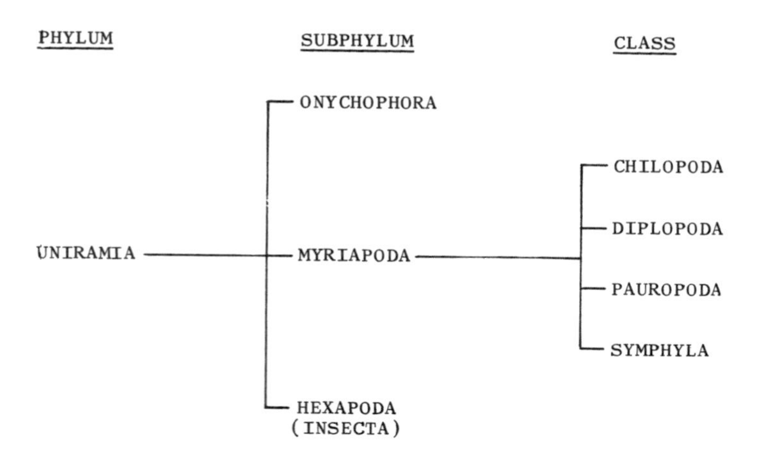

U N I R A M I A

Subphylum Onychophora

Uniramia in which:-

- ● 1. There is a head of three segments which is not clearly separated from the body.
- ● 2. There is a pair of pre-antennae on the first (pre-oral) segment.
- ● 3. The post-oral segments of the head bear a pair of jaws and a pair of oral papillae respectively.
- ● 4. There are numerous pairs of legs.
- 5. There is a pair of excretory tubules to each trunk segment.
- 6. There is a tracheal system with spiracles scattered irregularly over the body surface.
- 7. Development is direct. Many species are viviparous.

Example:- Peripatus. (see page 158)

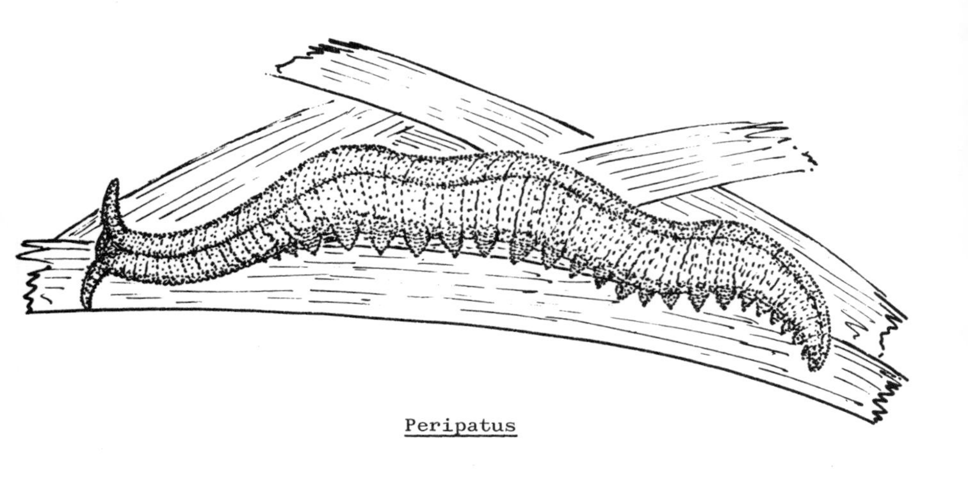

Peripatus

SUBPHYLUM ONYCHOPHORA

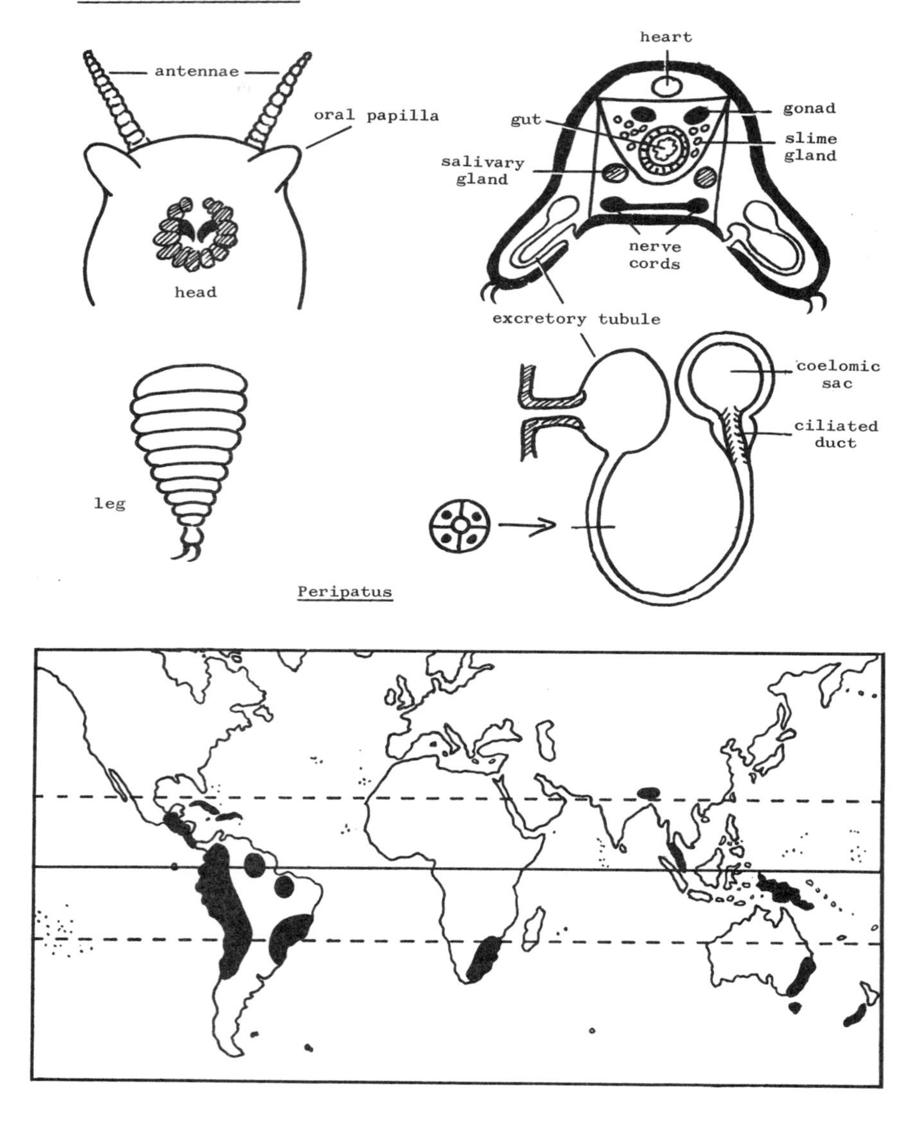

probable distribution of the Onychophora

U N I R A M I A

Subphylum Myriapoda

Uniramia in which:-

- ● 1. There is a distinct head but the trunk is not obviously divided into thorax and abdomen.
- ● 2. There is a single pair of antennae.
- ● 3. There is a mandible without a palp and at least one pair of maxillae.
- ● 4. The body consists of a number of similar segments each bearing either one or two pairs of legs.
- 5. Malpighian tubules are present arising from the hind-gut.
- 6. There is usually a tracheal system with segmentally arranged spiracles.
- 7. The young resemble the adult but possess fewer segments.

Class Chilopoda - Centipedes

Myriapoda in which:-

- ● 1. The trunk segments are numerous (15-177)
- ● 2. Each trunk segment except the last two bears a single pair of legs.
- ● 3. There are two pairs of maxillae; the second pair usually being fused to form a labium.
- 4. The tracheae form an anastomosis.

Examples:- *Lithobius*, *Scolopendra*, *Scutigera*.

(see page 161)

Class Diplopoda - Millipedes

Myriapoda in which:-

- ● 1. The apparent trunk segments are very numerous and each, except the first four, represents two fused somites.
- ● 2. There are two pairs of legs to each apparent segment except the first four, which bear one pair.
- ● 3. There is a single pair of maxillae.
- 4. The tracheae arise in tufts and do not anastomose.

Examples:- *Julus*, *Polydesmus*, *Ophyiulus*.

(see page 161)

U N I R A M I A

Class Pauropoda

Myriapoda in which:-

- 1. There are eleven trunk segments and an anal pygidium.
- 2. Each segment except the last bears a single pair of limbs.
- 3. There is a single pair of maxillae.

4. There is no tracheal system.

Example:- Pauropus. (see page 161)

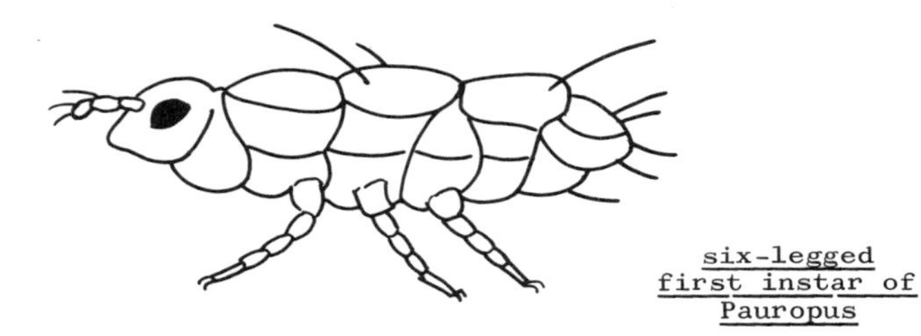

six-legged first instar of Pauropus

Class Symphyla

Myriapoda in which:-

- 1. There are not more than twelve leg-bearing segments.
- 2. Each leg-bearing segment has a single pair of limbs.
- 3. There are two pairs of maxillae.

4. There is a single pair of tracheal tufts opening to the exterior on the head.

Examples:- Scolopendrella, Scutigerella. (see page 161)

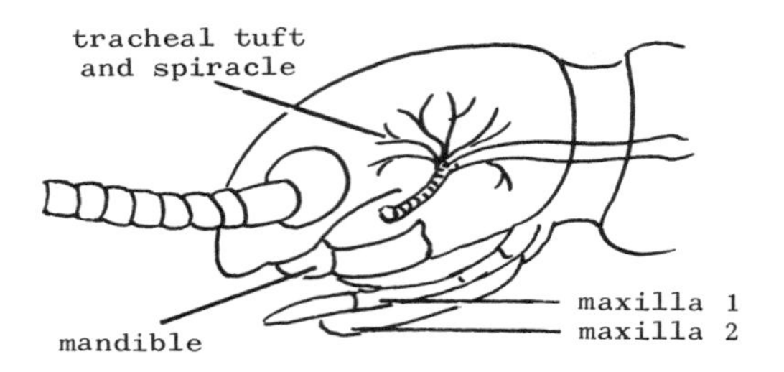

head of a symphylid

SUBPHYLUM MYRIAPODA

CLASS DIPLOPODA

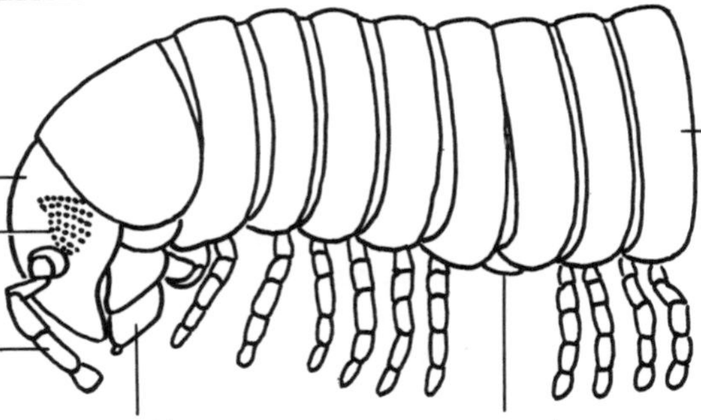

trunk

trunk segment with two pairs of legs

head

eye

antenna

maxilla

gonopod

Ophyiulus

CLASS CHILOPODA

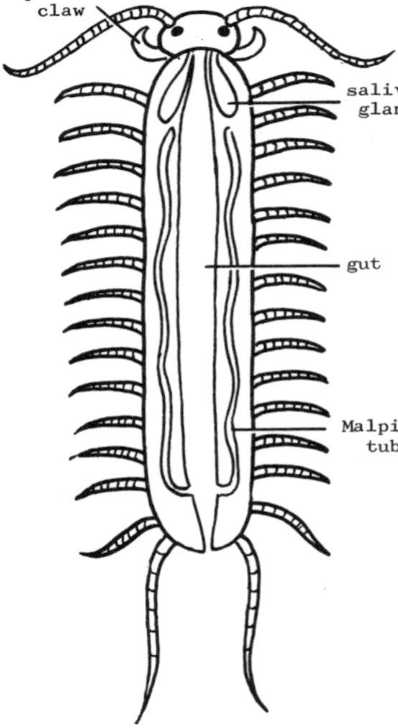

poison claw

salivary glands

gut

Malpighian tubule

Lithobius

CLASS PAUROPODA

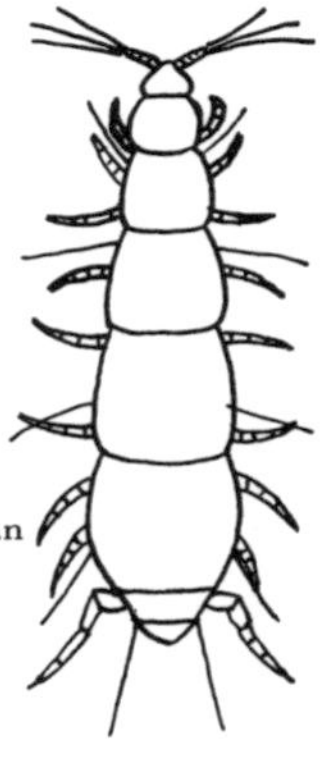

Pauropus

CLASS SYMPHYLA

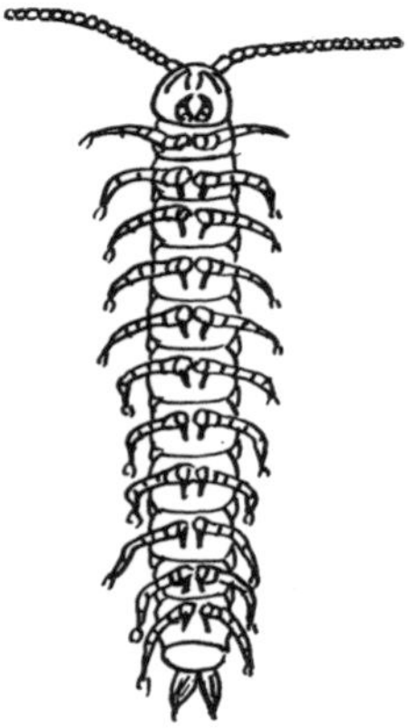

Scutigerella

U N I R A M I A

Subphylum Hexapoda (Insecta)

Uniramia in which:-

- 1. The body is divided into three regions, head, thorax and abdomen.
- 2. There is a single pair of antennae.
- 3. There is typically one pair of mandibles and two pairs of maxillae, the second pair being joined to form the labium.
- 4. There are three pairs of walking legs borne on the thorax in the adult. The abdomen does not bear ambulatory appendages.

5. Malpighian tubules are usually present arising from the hind gut.

6. There is a tracheal system with segmentally arranged spiracles

7. Development may be direct or metamorphosis may occur.

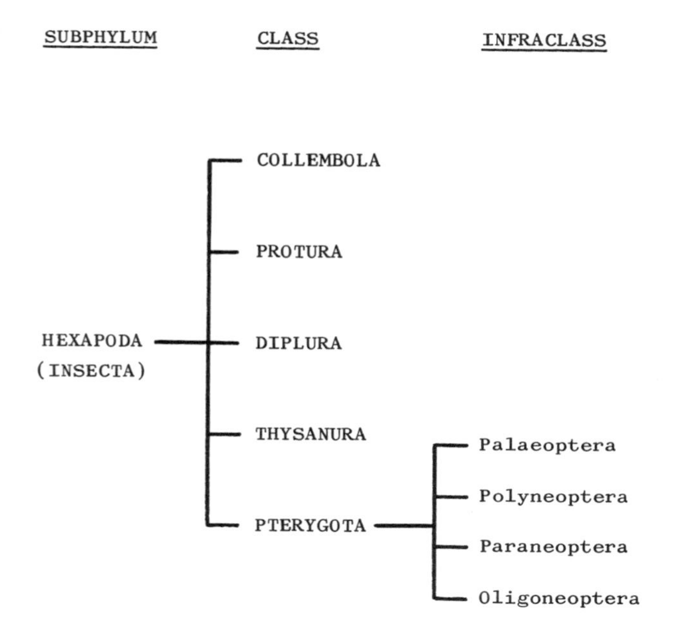

U N I R A M I A

Class Collembola - Springtails

Hexapoda in which:-

- ● 1. The adult is primitively wingless.
- ● 2. There are one or more pairs of abdominal appendages other than genitalia and cerci.
- ● 3. The antennae have 3 to 6 joints.
- 4. The mouth parts are adapted for biting.
- ● 5. There are six segments in the abdomen; the first abdominal segment bears a sucker-like ventral tube, the third a minute hamula and the fourth usually a forked springing organ (furcula); there are no cerci.
- 6. Malpighian tubules are absent.
- 7. Metamorphosis is absent or very slight.
- 8. Development is protomorphic, i.e. the number of post-cephalic embryonic segments (nine) is preserved in the adult.

Examples:- *Podura*, *Sminthurus*. (see page 165)

Class Protura

Hexapoda in which:-

- ● 1. The adult is primitively wingless.
- ● 2. There are one or more pairs of abdominal appendages other than genitalia and cerci.
- ● 3. There are no antennae.
- 4. The mouth parts are adapted for piercing.
- ● 5. There are eleven abdominal segments and a telson; springing organs and cerci are lacking.
- 6. Rudimentary Malpighian tubules are present.
- 7. Metamorphosis is absent or very slight.
- 8. Development is anamorphic, i.e. the number of postcephalic segments increases by proliferation in the hind part of the body. This proliferation is arrested in the adult.

Example:- *Acerentomon*. (see page 165)

U N I R A M I A

Class Diplura

Hexapoda in which:-

- ● 1. The adult is primitively wingless.
- ● 2. There are one or more pairs of abdominal appendages other than genitalia and cerci.
- ● 3. The antennae are many-jointed and each joint is capable of independent movement.
- 4. The mouth parts are adapted for biting.
- ● 5. There are eleven segments on the abdomen; springing organs are absent; cerci are present, either many-jointed or in the form of unjointed forceps.
- 6. Malpighian tubules are absent or rudimentary.
- 7. Metamorphosis is absent or very slight.
- 8. Development is epimorphic, i.e. the number of postcephalic segments increases by proliferation in the hind part of the body following the first embryonic stages, but becomes fixed during the embryonic period. Thus the animal hatches from the egg with the adult number of segments.

Examples:- *Japyx*, *Campodea*. (see page 165)

Class Thysanura - Bristle tails

Hexapoda in which:-

- ● 1. The adult is primitively wingless.
- ● 2. There are one or more pairs of abdominal appendages other than genitalia and cerci.
- ● 3. The antennae are many-jointed and the joints are not capable of independent movement, the antenna being moved as a whole upon its base.
- 4. The mouth parts are adapted for biting.
- ● 5. There are eleven segments on the abdomen, bearing styles and coxal vesicles; springing organs are lacking; a pair of many-jointed cerci and a median cerciform process are present.
- 6. Malpighian tubules are present.
- 7. Metamorphosis is absent or very slight.
- 8. Development is epimorphic.

Examples:- *Petrobius*, *Lepisma*. (see page 165)

SUBPHYLUM HEXAPODA (INSECTA)

CLASS COLLEMBOLA

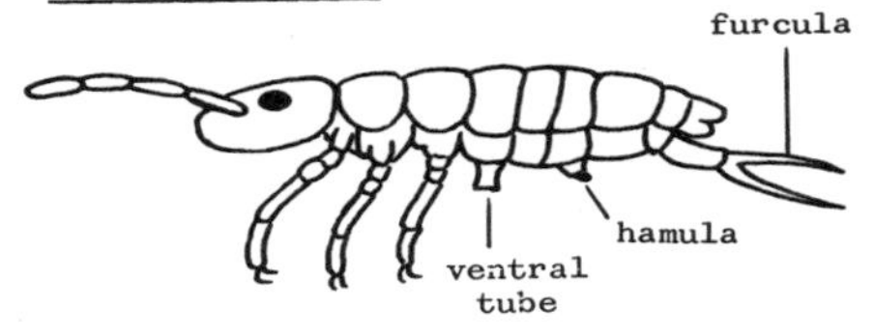

CLASS THYSANURA

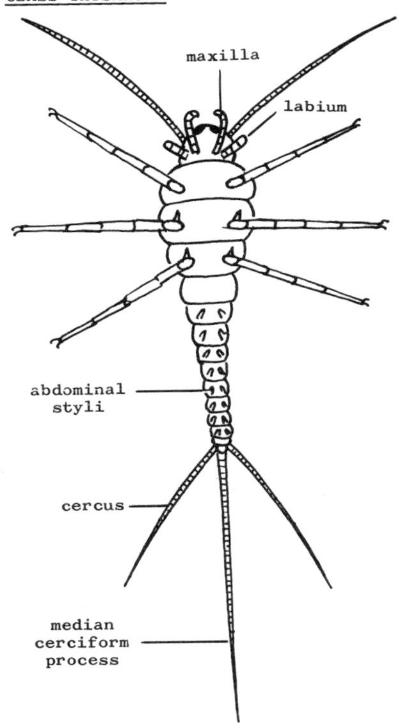

(ventral)

CLASS PROTURA

CLASS DIPLURA

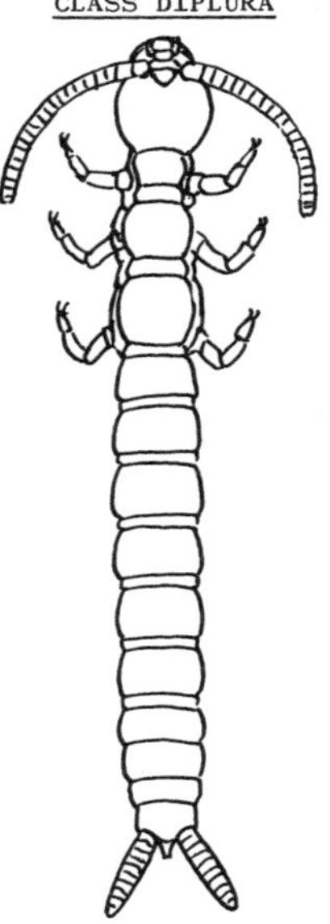

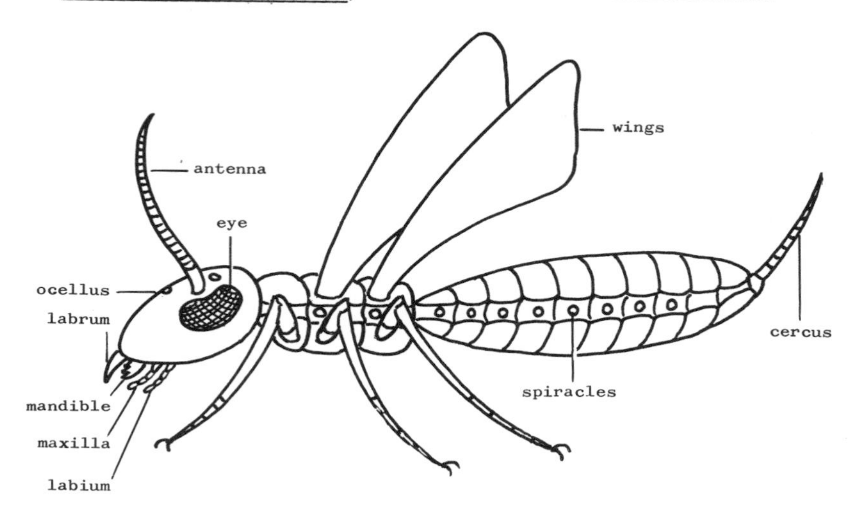

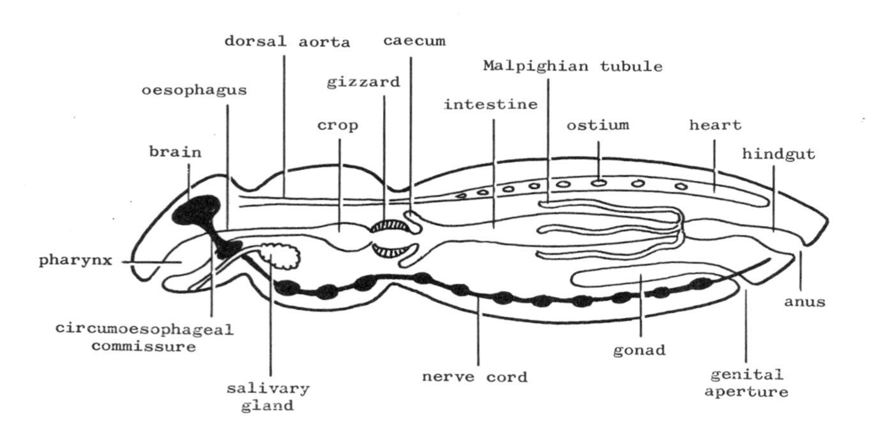

generalised pterygote insect

U N I R A M I A

Class Pterygota

Hexapoda in which:-

- ● 1. The adult is winged although the wings may have become secondarily lost.
- ● 2. There are no abdominal appendages other than genitalia and cerci.
- ● 3. The antennae are many-jointed and variously developed. The joints are not capable of independent movement.
- 4. The mouth parts are variously developed for biting, piercing, grinding, sucking and licking.
- ● 5. There are basically eleven abdominal segments, but these may be secondarily reduced in number; abdominal springing organs are lacking; cerci may or may not be present.
- 6. Malpighian tubules are present.
- 7. Metamorphosis occurs to a greater or lesser extent.
- 8. Development is epimorphic.

Infraclass Palaeoptera

Pterygota in which:-

- ● 1. The wings are held at right angles to the body when at rest, and are incapable of being folded backward over the abdomen.
- ● 2. The wings lack the anal lobe.
- 3. The mouth parts are typically adapted for biting.
- 4. The tarsi are usually less than 5-jointed.
- 5. The Malpighian tubules are very numerous.
- 6. Metamorphosis is incomplete (hemimetabolous) and the wings develop externally (exopterygote).
- 7. Cerci are present except in some Odonata.

(see page 170)

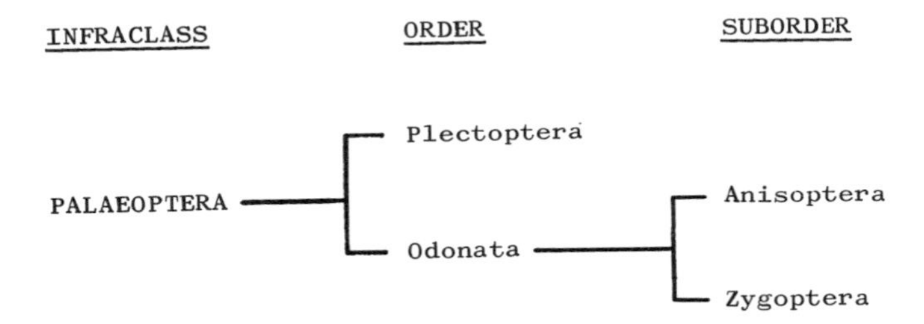

U N I R A M I A

Order Plectoptera - May flies

Palaeoptera in which:-

● 1. The wings are unequal in size, the hind-wing being small and sometimes absent. The venation is very little reduced, numerous intercalary and cross veins being present. There is no pterostigma in the wing. The wings are held vertically above the body when at rest.

2. The mouth parts in the imago are vestigial but of the biting type.

2. The antennae are setaceous.

4. The tarsi are 1- to 5-jointed.

5. The nymphs are aquatic and bear lamellate or plumose tracheal gills. The imago moults prior to mating and is extremely short-lived.

Example:- Ephemera. (see page 170)

Order Odonata - Dragonflies

Palaeoptera in which:-

● 1. The wings are almost equal in size, frequently narrow at the base, and with venation only slightly reduced. A pterostigma is present and also an arrangement of veins known as the 'arculus' and the 'nodus'. When at rest the wings may be held either vertically (damsel flie or horizontally (dragonflies).

2. The mouth parts are adapted for biting.

3. The antennae are very short and filiform.

4. The tarsi are 3-jointed.

5. The nymphs are aquatic and respire by means of rectal or caudal gills. The labium in the nymph is modified to form a prehensile grasping organ, the mask.

Suborder Anisoptera

Odonata in which:-

● 1. The wings are held horizontally when at rest.
● 2. The wings are not greatly constricted at the base; the hind-wings being broader than the fore-wings.
3. The discal cell is divided forming a 'triangle' and a 'supra-triangle'.
● 4. The eyes are close together, i.e. they are not separated by a greater distance than their own diameter.
5. There is one inferior anal appendage in the male.
● 6. The nymphs possess rectal gills.

Example:- *Libellula*.

Suborder Zygoptera - Damsel flies

Odonata in which:-

● 1. The wings are held vertically when at rest.
● 2. The wings are alike and narrow at the base.
3. The discal cell is undivided and is quadrilateral in form.
● 4. The eyes are wide apart, i.e. they are separated by a distance greater than their own diameter.
5. There are two inferior anal appendages in the male.
● 6. The nymphs possess caudal gills.

Example:- *Agrion*, *Lestes*. (see page 170)

SUBPHYLUM HEXAPODA (INSECTA)

CLASS PTERYGOTA

INFRACLASS PALAEOPTERA

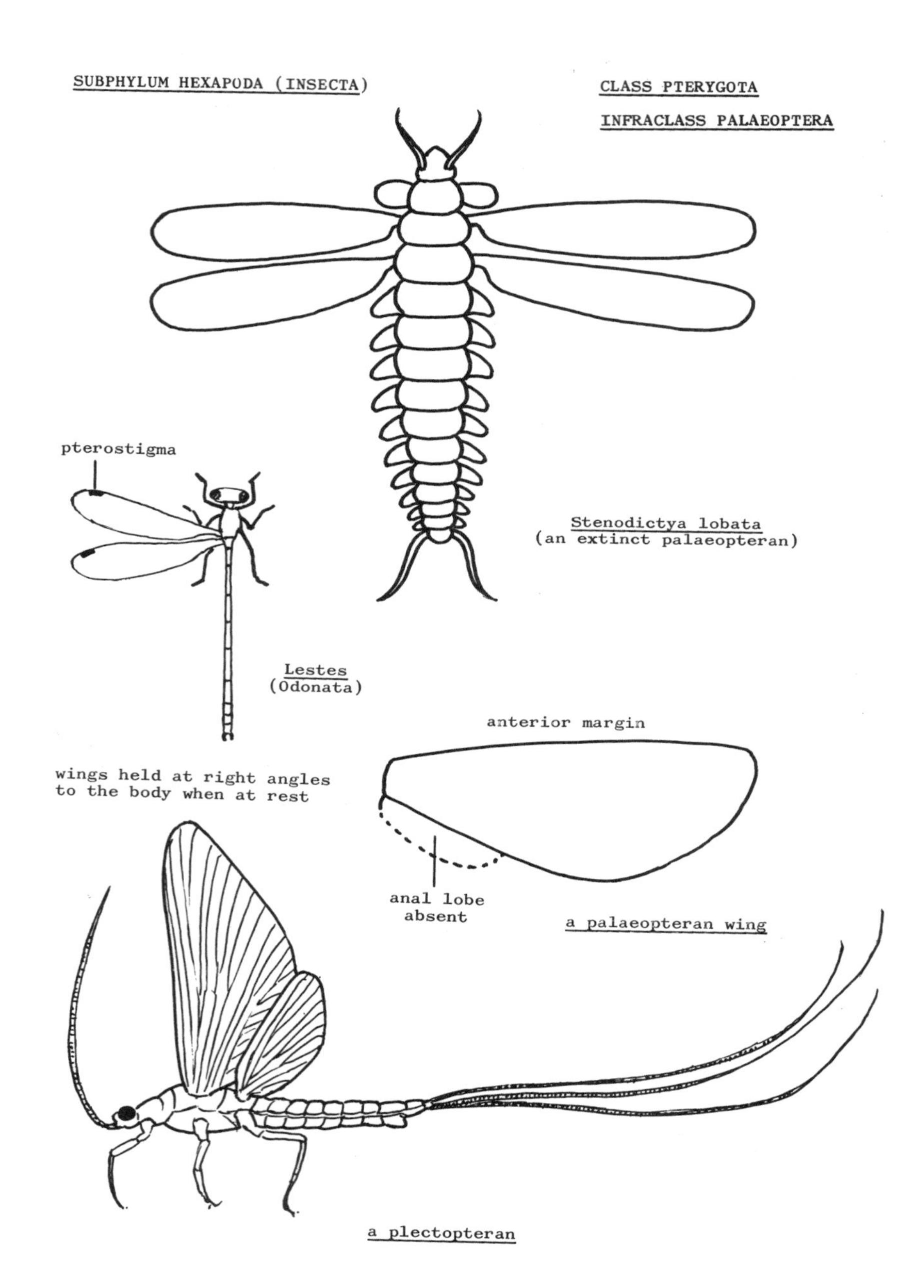

Infraclass Polyneoptera

Pterygota in which:-

1. The wings are folded backward over the abdomen when at rest.
2. There is a fan-shaped anal lobe with numerous veins.
3. The mouth parts are adapted for biting.
4. The tarsi may be 5-jointed or less.
5. The Malpighian tubules are usually numerous.
6. Metamorphosis is incomplete (hemimetabolous) and the wings develop externally (exopterygote).
7. Cerci are present.

(see page 179)

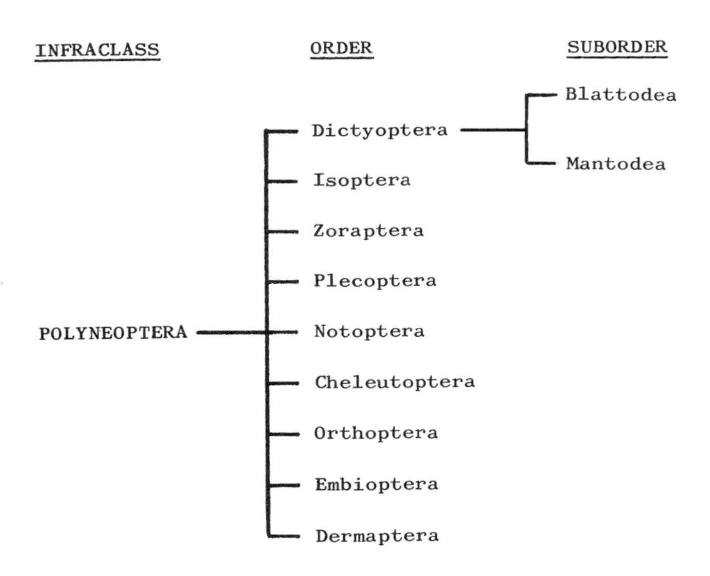

Order Dictyoptera

Polyneoptera in which:-

● 1. The fore-wings are almost always leathery.
● 2. The antennae are very long and filiform.
3. The head is partially covered by the pronotum.
● 4. The legs are adapted for walking. In the Mantids the fore-legs are raptorial and used for food capture.
● 5. The tarsi are 5-jointed.
6. The cerci are multi-articulate.
7. Ovipositor reduced and concealed.
8. The members are solitary, and the eggs are laid in oothecae.

Suborder Blattodea - Cockroaches

Dictyoptera in which:-

1. The fore-limbs are not raptorial.
● 2. The prothorax is shield-like but not elongated.
3. The eyes are of moderate size. There are two ocelli. The head is not conspicuously mobile.
● 4. The body is more or less flattened dorso-ventrally.
● 5. The coxae are very broad and cover the ventral surface of the thorax.
6. The body is not modified to resemble parts of plants.

Examples:- *Blatta*, *Periplaneta*, *Rhyparobia*.

Suborder Mantodea - Mantids

Dictyoptera in which:-

- ● 1. The fore-limbs are subchelate and raptorial.
- ● 2. The prothorax is almost always very long.
- ● 3. The eyes are large and set on an extremely mobile triangular head. There are three ocelli.
- 4. The body is seldom flattened dorso-ventrally.
- 5. The coxae do not cover the ventral surface of the thorax.
- ● 6. The coloration and form of the body is usually adapted to resemble parts of plants.

Examples:- Mantis, Blepharopsis.

Order Isoptera - Termites

Polyneoptera in which:-

- ● 1. Both fore- and hind-wings are slightly leathery and in most forms lack the anal lobe. The wings are borne only by the sexual forms and are shed immediately after the mating flight.
- ● 2. The antennae are monilliform.
- 3. The head is not usually covered by the pronotum.
- 4. The legs are adapted for walking.
- ● 5. The tarsi are almost always 4-jointed.
- 6. The cerci are short and multi-articulate or very short.
- 7. Ovipositor absent or concealed.
- ● 8. The members are polymorphic and social in habit. The eggs are laid in chambers in a complex nest and are cared for by the parents or by the worker caste.

Examples:- Mastotermes, Calotermes, Macrotermes.

(see page 174)

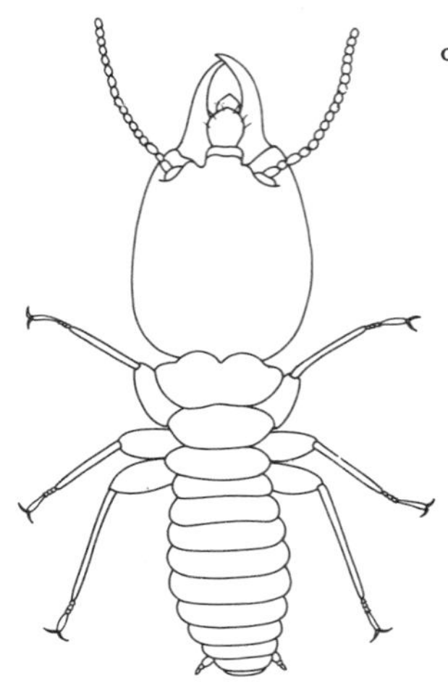

Macrotermes soldier

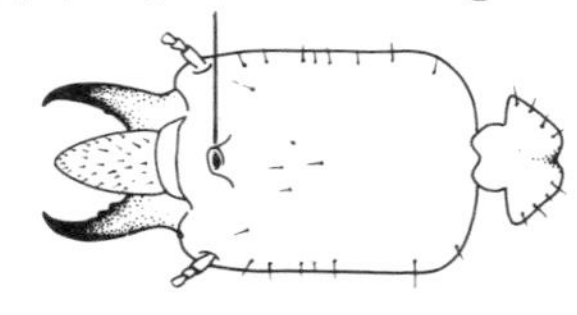

Labiotermes soldier

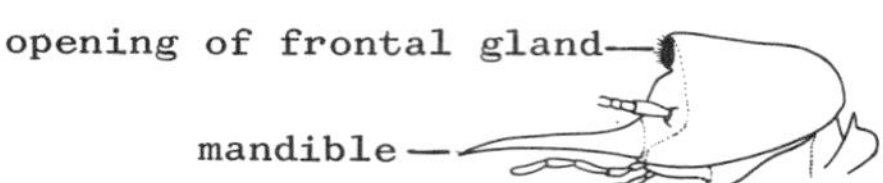

Noditermes soldier (lateral)

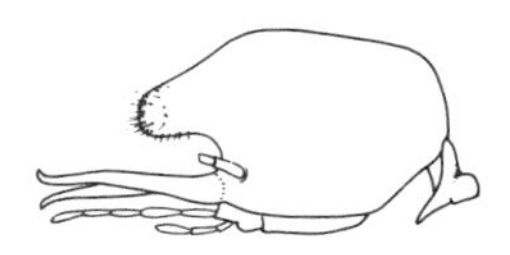

Proboscitermes soldier (lateral)

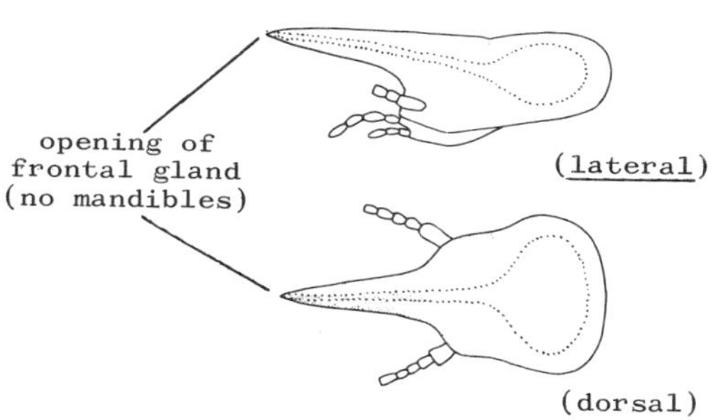

Eutermellus nasutiform soldier

development of the frontal gland and
loss of mandibles in the nasutiform soldi

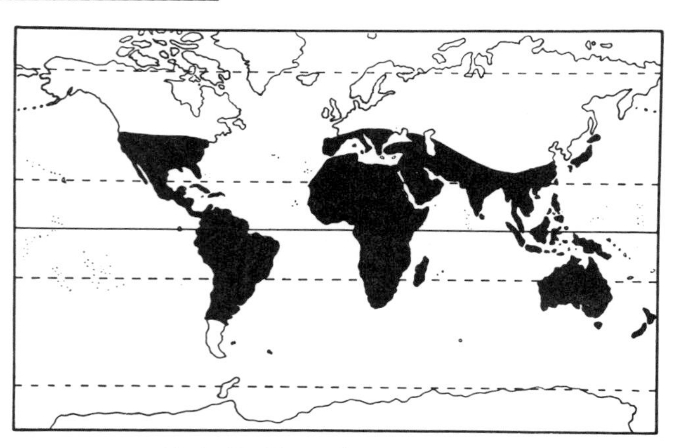

distribution of the Isoptera

U N I R A M I A

Order Zoraptera

Polyneoptera in which:-

- ● 1. In the female the wings are not leathery and are reduced. They may be shed. The male is wing-less.
- ● 2. The antennae are monilliform.
- 3. The head is not covered by the pronotum.
- 4. The legs are adapted for walking.
- ● 5. The tarsi are 2-jointed.
- 6. The cerci consist of a single joint.
- 7. The ovipositor is absent.
- ● 8. The insects are gregarious and are found under bark or stones or in termite nests. Different castes are known.

Example:- Zorotypus.

Order Plecoptera - Stone flies

Polyneoptera in which:-

- ● 1. The wings are more or less alike, without a precostal field and with reduced venation. The anal field is well developed.
- ● 2. The antennae are long and setaceous.
- 3. The pronotum is large but not elongated.
- 4. The legs are adapted for walking.
- ● 5. The tarsi are 3-jointed.
- 6. The cerci are multi-articulate and very long, or they comprise a single joint.
- 7. There is no ovipositor.
- 8. The nymphs are aquatic and campodeiform.

Examples:- Perla, Nemoura. (see page 179)

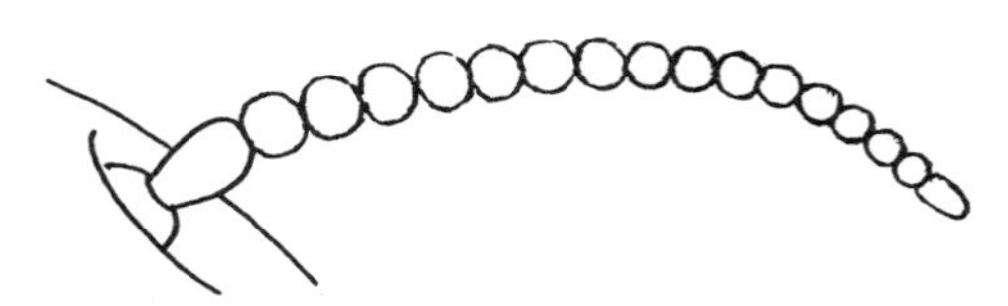

monilliform antenna

U N I R A M I A

Order Notoptera

Polyneoptera in which:-

● 1. There are no wings.
● 2. The antennae are long and filiform.
3. The pronotum is slightly elongated.
4. The legs are adapted for walking.
● 5. The tarsi are 5-jointed.
6. The cerci are multi-articulate and of moderate length.
● 7. An ovipositor is present.
8. The members are rather small insects found in the mountains of North America and Japan.

Example:- Grylloblatta.

Order Cheleutoptera - Stick insects and Leaf insects

Polyneoptera in which:-

● 1. When wings are present the fore-wings are leathery and may be large or, more commonly, very small, while the hind-wings are large and fan-shaped. In many cases the wings simulate the form of leaves very closely.
● 2. The antennae are filiform and usually long.
● 3. The pronotum is short but the mesonotum long.
4. The legs are adapted for walking.
● 5. The tarsi are usually 5-jointed.
6. The cerci are short and comprise a single joint
7. There is a rudimentary ovipositor.
● 8. All forms resemble sticks or leaves and drop single seed-like eggs on the ground beneath the plants on which they are feeding.

Examples:- Carausius, Phyllium.

filiform antenna

U N I R A M I A

Order Orthoptera - Grasshoppers, Locusts and Crickets

Polyneoptera in which:-

- ● 1. The wings are long with a small precostal field. The fore-wings tend to be leathery and the hind-wings have a well-developed anal field. Venation is only slightly reduced.
- ● 2. The antennae are setaceous and either very long (Tettigonidae, Gryllidae) or short and often thick (Acridiidae).
- 3. The pronotum although large is not noticeably elongated.
- ● 4. The posterior legs are modified for jumping.
- ● 5. The tarsi are 3- or 4-jointed.
- 6. The cerci show little sign of segmentation but are very variable in form.
- ● 7. There is a well-developed ovipositor.
- 8. Almost all members have stridulating organs and organs of hearing. The eggs are laid in groups.

Examples:- *Schistocerca*, *Brachytrypes*, *Gryllotalpa*.

(see page 179)

Order Embioptera

Polyneoptera in which:-

- ● 1. The males are winged and the females wingless. The wings are equal in size with very small precostal and anal fields and reduced venation.
- ● 2. The antennae are long and monilliform.
- 3. The pronotum is not elongated.
- 4. The legs are adapted for walking.
- ● 5. The tarsi are 3-jointed with the first joint of the tarsi of the anterior pair of legs conspicuously swollen.
- 6. The cerci are two-jointed and usually asymmetrical in the male.
- 7. There is no ovipositor.
- 8. The insects may be solitary or gregarious and live in silken tunnels under stones or in vegetable debris.

Examples:- *Embia*, *Rhagadochir*.

Order Dermaptera - Earwigs

Polyneoptera in which:-

- ● 1. The fore-wings are reduced to horny elytra below which the large fan-shaped hind-wings are folded. Parasitic forms are wing-less.
- ● 2. The antennae are long and filiform.
- 3. The pronotum is large but not noticeably elongated.
- 4. The legs are adapted for walking.
- ● 5. The tarsi are 3-jointed.
- ● 6. The cerci are unjointed and almost always modified to form horny forceps.
- 7. There is no ovipositor.
- 8. Some members (Hemimerus) are ectoparasites of vertebrates, but most are free living. Species living in temperate regions (earwigs) often hibernate in pairs and lay eggs in special chambers in the soil.

Examples:- Forficula, Adaethetus, Hemimerus.

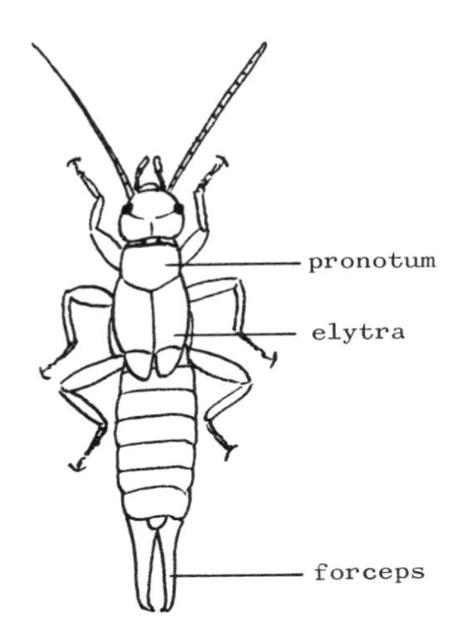

earwig

SUBPHYLUM HEXAPODA (INSECTA)

CLASS PTERYGOTA

INFRACLASS POLYNEOPTERA

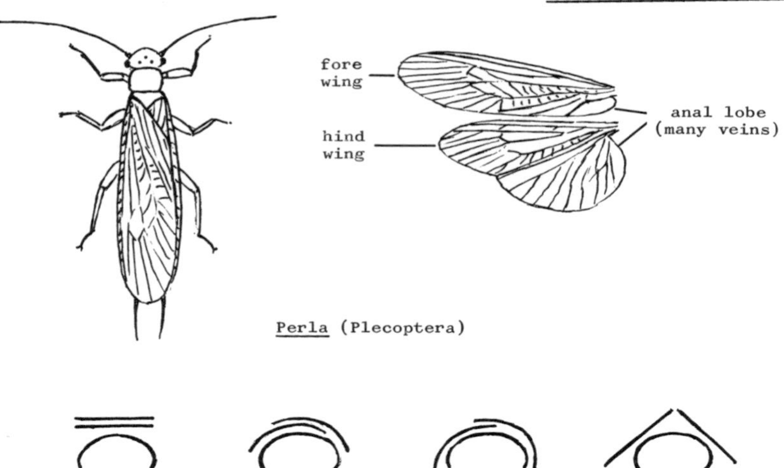

Perla (Plecoptera)

different ways in which the wings are folded over the abdomen

an acridiid grasshopper

U N I R A M I A

Infraclass Paraneoptera

Pterygota in which:-

- ● 1. The wings when present are folded backward over the abdomen. They are often of highly modified form.
- ● 2. The anal lobe is usually greatly reduced or absent.
- 3. The mouth parts may be adapted for biting or for sucking.
- 4. There are never more than three tarsal joints.
- 5. The Malpighian tubules are few (usually four) in number.
- 6. Metamorphosis is incomplete (hemimetabolous) and the wings when present develop externally (exopterygote)
- 7. There are no cerci.

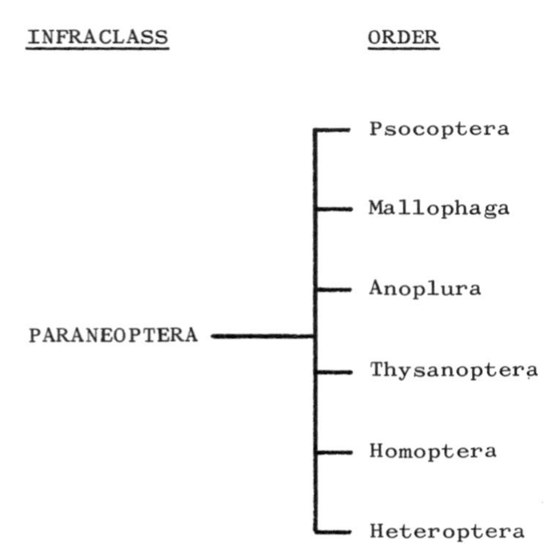

U N I R A M I A

Order Psocoptera - Book lice

Paraneoptera in which:-

1. Winged forms are frequent but apterous forms more common.
2. The mouth parts are adapted for biting.
3. ● The antennae are filiform and are composed of from 13-50 joints.
4. ● The prothorax is reduced and free; the meso- and metathorax are large and fused.
5. The thoracic spiracles are lateral in position.
6. ● The tarsi are 2- or 3-jointed and end in two claws.
7. There is no ovipositor.
8. ● The body is not flattened dorso-ventrally and the abdomen is globular.
9. The insects feed chiefly on algae and fungi or on farinaceous material and are common under the bark of trees or in places where flour or flour-paste is available.

Example:- Psocus. (see page 185)

Order Mallophaga - Biting lice

Paraneoptera in which:-

1. The wings have been lost.
2. ● The mouth parts are adapted for biting.
3. ● The antennae are 3- to 5-jointed.
4. ● The thoracic segments are free or partially free.
5. The thoracic spiracles are lateral in position.
6. ● The tarsi are 1- or 2-jointed (rarely 3-jointed) and end in a single claw (rarely a second weak claw is present).
7. There is no ovipositor.
8. The body is flattened dorso-ventrally.
9. ● The members are obligate ectoparasites of birds and mammals and feed on feathers or skin detritus.

Examples:- Menopon, Trichodectes, Haematomyzus.

U N I R A M I A

Order Anoplura - Sucking lice

Paraneoptera in which:-

1. The wings have been lost.
- 2. The mouth parts are adapted for piercing and sucking.
- 3. The antennae are 3- to 5-jointed.
- 4. The thoracic segments are fused.

5. The thoracic spiracles are dorsal in position.
- 6. The tarsi are 1-jointed and end in a single claw.

7. There is no ovipositor.

8. The body is flattened dorso-ventrally.
- 9. The members are obligate ectoparasites of mammals and feed by sucking blood.

Examples:- Pediculus, Haematopinus.

Order Thysanoptera - Thrips

Paraneoptera in which:-

- 1. The fringed wings are very characteristic but brachypterous and apterous forms are common.
- 2. The mouth parts show extreme asymmetry.
- 3. The antennae are filiform and 6- to 9-jointed.

4. There is a large free prothorax.

5. The first thoracic spiracle is lateral and the second dorsal in position.
- 6. The tarsi are 1- or 2-jointed and terminate in protrusible vesicle.
- 7. An ovipositor may be present (Terebrantia) or absent (Tubulifera).

8. The body is not flattened dorso-ventrally.
- 9. The members are commonly found in flowers but also occur on other parts of plants and in decaying vegetation. They suck the juices from plants and from humus.

Examples:- Thrips, Phloeothrips.

(see page 185)

<u>Order Homoptera</u> - Bugs

Paraneoptera in which:-

- ● 1. The fore-wings are of uniform consistency and, when at rest, generally lie sloping over the sides of the thorax and abdomen.
- ● 2. The mouth parts form a long rostrum adapted for piercing and sucking. The base of the rostrum extends backward between the first pair of coxae. The rostrum clearly arises from the head (Auchenorhyncha) or apparently arises from between the anterior coxae (Sternorhyncha).
- ● 3. The antennae are either very short with a terminal arista (Auchenorhyncha) or usually well developed and without a prominent arista (Sternorhyncha).
- 4. The pronotum is usually small.
- 5. The thoracic spiracles are lateral in position.
- ● 6. The tarsi are 3-jointed (Auchenorhyncha) or 1- or 2-jointed (Sternorhyncha).
- 7. An ovipositor may be present.
- 8. The body may or may not be flattened dorso-ventrally.

Examples:- Cicada, Phromnia, Aphis.

(see page 185)

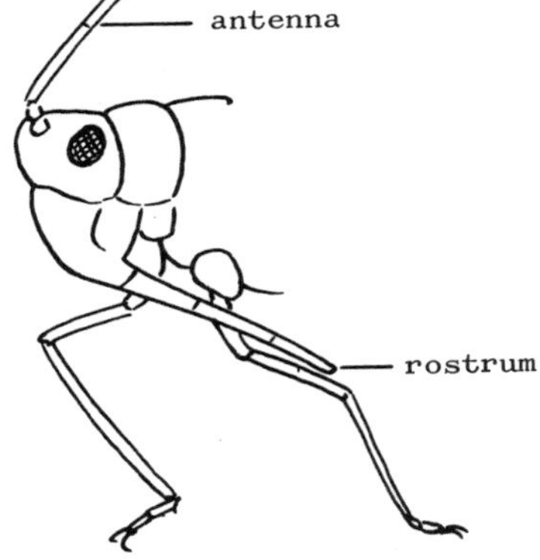

anterior end of an aphid
(left legs removed)

Sternorhyncha

eye
arista
antenna
rostrum

head of a fulgorid

Auchenorhyncha

Order Heteroptera - Bugs

Paraneoptera in which:-

- 1. The fore-wings are not uniform. The proximal portion is hardened and the distal portion membranous. At rest the wings overlap and li flat above the abdomen.
- 2. The mouth parts form a long rostrum adapted fo piercing and sucking. The base of the rostru rarely touches the first pair of coxae.
- 3. The antennae are of different types, long, wel developed and freely movable (Gymnocerata) or short and concealed in fovae on the underside the head (Cryptocerata).
- 4. The pronotum is large.
- 5. The thoracic spiracles are lateral in position
- 6. The tarsi are usually 3-jointed.
- 7. There is frequently a well-developed oviposito
- 8. The body is frequently dorso-ventrally flatten

Examples:- Dysdercus, Cimex, Nepa, Belostoma.

(see page 185)

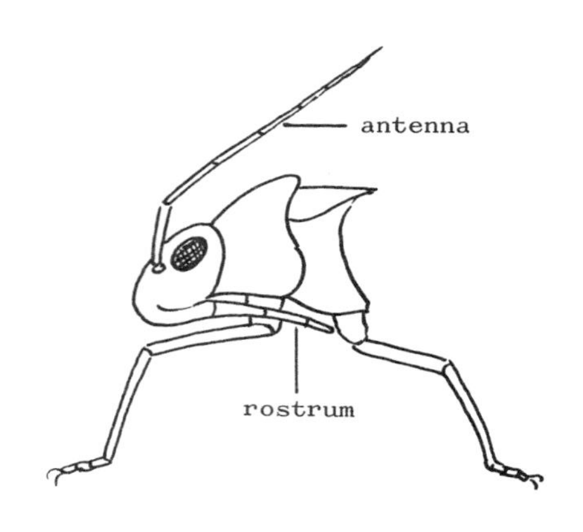

anterior end of capsid bug
(left legs removed)

Gymnocerata

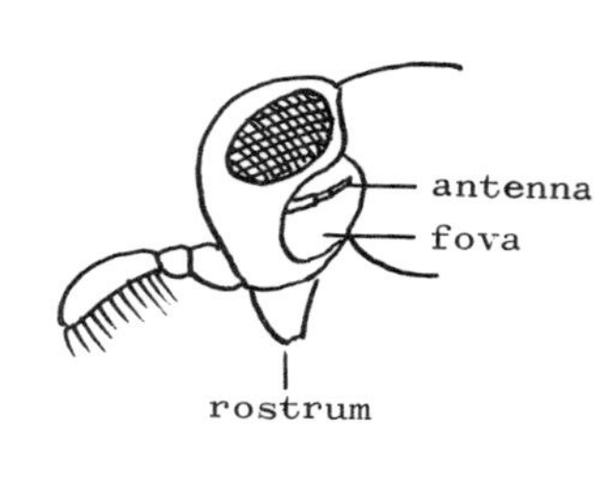

head and right fore limb
of Corixa

Cryptocerata

SUBPHYLUM HEXAPODA (INSECTA)

CLASS PTERYGOTA

INFRACLASS PARANEOPTERA

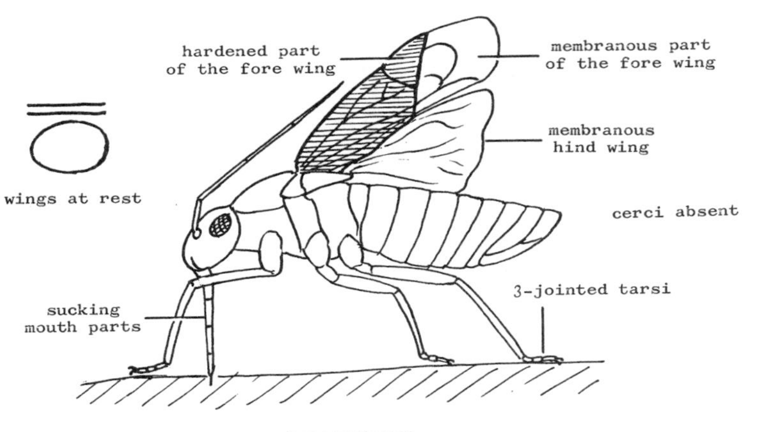

a heteropteran

reduced venation and anal lobe

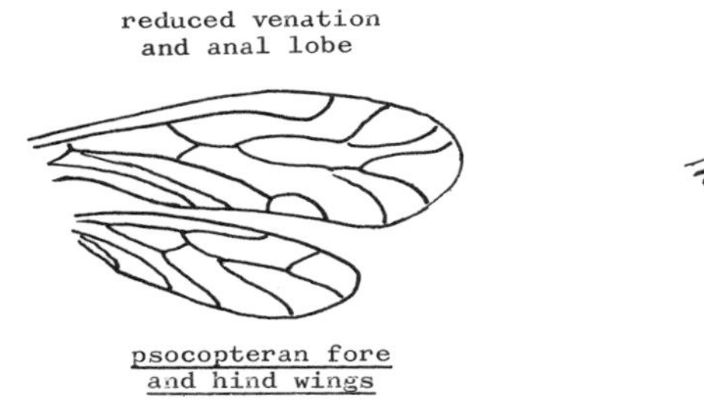

psocopteran fore and hind wings

reduced venation

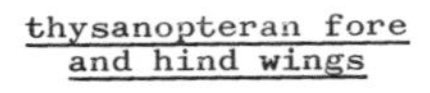

thysanopteran fore and hind wings

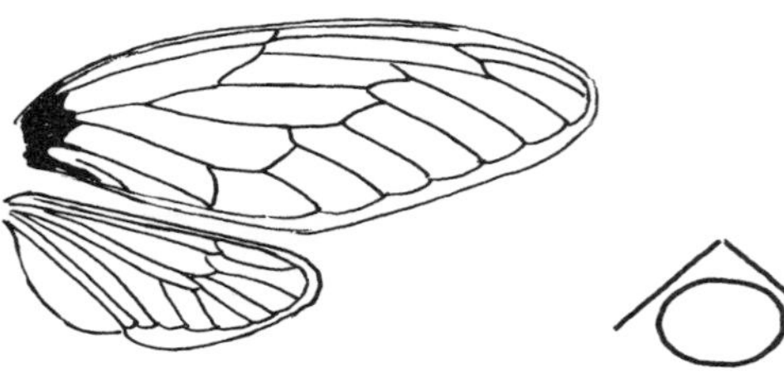

Cicada fore and hind wings

wings at rest

Infraclass Oligoneoptera

Pterygota in which:-

1. The wings are folded backward over the abdomen when at rest.
2. The anal lobe has a single vein which may be simple or branched.
3. The mouth parts may be adapted for biting or for sucking.
4. The tarsi are 5-jointed except in some Coleoptera a some Strepsiptera where there may be less.
5. The Malpighian tubules are few in number except in Hymenoptera where they are numerous.
6. Metamorphosis is complete (holometabolous). The wings develop internally (endopterygote).
7. Cerci are usually absent.

(see page 195)

INFRACLASS	ORDER	SUBORDER
OLIGONEOPTERA	Coleoptera	
	Megaloptera	
	Raphidioptera	
	Planipennia	
	Mecoptera	
	Trichoptera	
	Lepidoptera	
	Diptera	Nematocera
		Brachycera
		Cyclorrhapha
	Siphonaptera	
	Hymenoptera	Symphyta
		Apocrita
	Strepsiptera	

U N I R A M I A

Order Coleoptera - Beetles

Oligoneoptera in which:-

- ● 1. The fore-wings are modified into horny or leathery elytra and when at rest almost always meet to form a straight, mid-dorsal suture. The venation of the wings is reduced. The hind-wings are membranous and are usually folded beneath the elytra or they may be absent.
- 2. The mouth parts are adapted for biting.
- 3. The antennae are of various types.
- ● 4. The prothorax is large, firmly attached to the head, but articulated with the mesothorax.
- 5. There are no cerci.
- 6. There is no true ovipositor.
- 7. The pupa is usually of the exarate type.

Examples:- Goliathus, Dytiscus, Atractocerus, Melolontha.

(see page 195)

Order Megaloptera - Alder flies

Oligoneoptera in which:-

- ● 1. There are two pairs of usually similar membranous wings with primitive venation and many accessory veins and costal veinlets. At rest the wings are usually held roof-like over the abdomen. In flight the fore and hind-wings beat independently of one another. The wings do not possess a pterostigma. The veins rarely bifurcate at their extremities.
- 2. The mouth parts are adapted for biting.
- 3. The antennae are usually long and setiform.
- ● 4. The prothorax is short.
- 5. In the male there are 1-jointed cerci.
- 6. There is no ovipositor.
- 7. The pupa is exarate.

Examples:- Sialis, Corydalis.

Order Raphidioptera - Snake-flies

Oligoneoptera in which:-

● 1. There are two pairs of usually similar membranous wings with primitive venation and many accessory veins and costal veinlets. At rest the wings are usually held roof-like over the abdomen. In flight the fore and hind-win beat independently of one another. The wings possess a pterostigma and some of the veins bifurcate at their extremities.
2. The mouth parts are adapted for biting.
3. The antennae are setiform but rather short.
● 4. The prothorax is very long.
5. The cerci are very reduced.
● 6. There is a long ovipositor.
7. The pupa is exarate.

Example:- *Raphidia*.

Order Planipennia - Lacewings and Ant lions

Oligoneoptera in which:-

● 1. There are two pairs of usually similar membranous wings with primitive venation and many accessory veins and costal veinlets. At rest the wings are usually held roof-like over the abdomen. In flight the fore and hind-win beat independently of one another. The wings do not possess a pterostigma and the great majority of the veins bifurcate at their extremities.
2. The mouth parts are adapted for biting.
3. The antennae are long or rather short, filifor or clubbed.
● 4. The prothorax is not reduced or elongated.
5. There are no cerci.
6. There is usually an ovipositor.
7. The pupa is exarate.

Examples:- *Palpares*, *Mantispa*, *Hemerobius*.

U N I R A M I A

Order Mecoptera - Scorpion flies

Oligoneoptera in which:-

- ● 1. There are two pairs of similar membranous wings held lengthwise over the body when at rest. The venation is primitive with few costal veinlets. The wings are coupled and beat together.
- ● 2. The mouth parts are of the biting type and are borne at the end of a beak-like rostrum projecting downward at a right angle to the body.
- 3. The antennae are long and filiform.
- ● 4. The prothorax is greatly reduced.
- 5. Short jointed cerci are present.
- ● 6. There is no ovipositor. In the male the genital apparatus arches upward over the abdomen and resembles superficially the telson of a scorpion.
- 7. The pupa is exarate.

Examples:- Panorpa, Bittacus.

Order Trichoptera - Caddis flies

Oligoneoptera in which:-

- ● 1. There are two pairs of membranous wings more or less densely covered with hairs and held roof-like over the body when at rest. The venation is predominantly longitudinal with few cross veins. The wings are coupled and beat together.
- 2. The mouth parts are of the biting type but modified in the adult for licking.
- ● 3. The antennae are long and setaceous.
- 4. The prothorax is reduced.
- 5. The cerci are reduced or absent.
- 6. An ovipositor may be present.
- 7. The pupa is exarate.

Example:- Halesus.

U N I R A M I A

Order Lepidoptera - Butterflies and Moths

Oligoneoptera in which:-

- 1. There are two pairs of membranous wings typica covered with broad pigmented scales. When at rest the wings may be held vertically above th body, or roof-like, or more or less horizontal and lengthwise over the body. The venation i predominantly longitudinal with few cross vein The wings are coupled and beat together.
- 2. The mouth parts are either of a modified bitin type (Homoneura) or formed into a spirally coiled suctorial proboscis (Heteroneura).

3. The antennae are of various types.
4. The prothorax is rarely well developed.
5. There are no cerci.
6. An ovipositor is rarely present.
7. The pupa is more or less obtect.

Examples:- Hepialus, Papilio, Protoparce, Pieris

(see page 195)

Order Diptera - Two-winged flies

Oligoneoptera in which:-

- 1. There is one pair of membranous wings, the hin pair being modified to form balancing organs (halteres). The venation is reduced.
- 2. The mouth parts are modified either for pierci and sucking or for licking and are usually formed into a proboscis.

3. The antennae are of various types.
4. The prothorax is greatly reduced.
5. There are no cerci.
6. A true ovipositor is rarely present.
7. The pupa may be exarate or coarctate.

(see page 195)

U N I R A M I A

Suborder Nematocera - Mosquitoes, Sand flies etc.

Diptera in which:-

1. The discal cell of the wing is usually absent and the cubital cell, when present, is widely open.
2. The antennae are many-jointed, longer than the head and thorax and with the majority of the joints alike.
3. The maxillary palpi are 4- or 5-jointed.
4. The larvae have a well developed head and horizontally biting mandibles.
5. The pupa is exarate.

Examples:- Tipula, Anopheles, Bibio, Phlebotomus.

(see page 195)

Suborder Brachycera - Horseflies etc.

Diptera in which:-

1. The discal cell of the wing is almost always present and the cubital cell contracted before the margin of the wing or closed.
2. The antennae are shorter than the thorax, usually 3-jointed and with the last joint prolonged to form a segmented style.
3. The maxillary palpi are 1- or 2-jointed.
4. The larvae have an incomplete head with vertically biting mandibles.
5. The pupa is exarate.

Examples:- Chrysops, Leptis, Empis, Tabanus.

(see page 195)

antennae

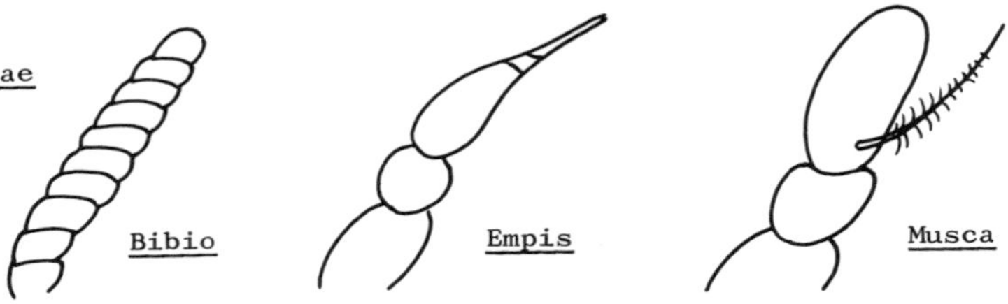

Bibio

Empis

Musca

Suborder Cyclorrhapha - House flies, Tsetse flies etc.

Diptera in which:-

1. The discal cell of the wing is almost always present.
● 2. The antennae are 3-jointed and with a dorsal, bristle-like arista.
3. The maxillary palpi are 1-jointed.
● 4. The larva has a vestigial head.
● 5. The pupa is coarctate.

Examples:- Musca, Glossina, Syrphus, Ornithomyia.

(see pages 191, 195)

Order Siphonaptera - Fleas

Oligoneoptera in which:-

1. The wings have been lost.
● 2. The mouth parts have become adapted for sucking blood.
● 3. The antennae are short and stout and lie in grooves or fovae at the sides of the head.
4. The prothorax is large and the thoracic segments are not fused.
5. There are no cerci.
6. There is no ovipositor.
7. The pupa is exarate in a silken cocoon.
● 8. The members are ectoparasites of birds and mammals. The body is laterally flattened, the hind-limbs are modified for jumping and the coxae are very large.

Examples:- Pulex, Xenopsylla, Tunga.

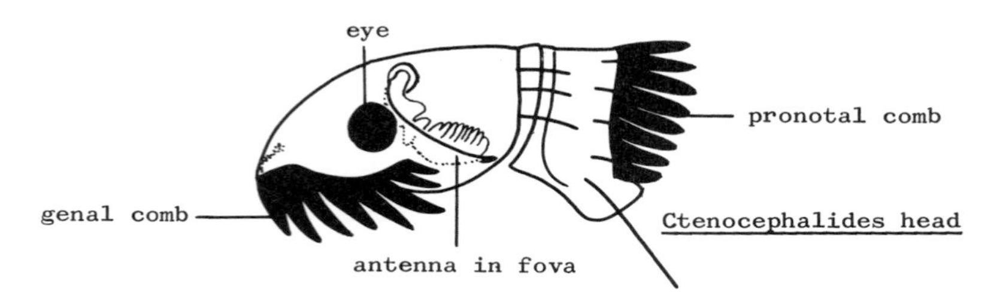

Ctenocephalides head

Order Hymenoptera - Bees, Wasps and Ants

Oligoneoptera in which:-

- ● 1. The hind-wing is smaller than the fore wing and coupled with it by hooks. Apterous forms common.
- 2. The mouth parts, although of the biting or licking type, differ widely throughout the order.
- 3. The antennae are of various types.
- ● 4. The prothorax is small and bears the very mobile head on a distinct neck. The metathorax is fused with the first segment of the abdomen.
- 5. There are no cerci.
- ● 6. An ovipositor is present. It may be very long and may be modified for sawing, piercing or stinging.
- 7. The pupa is exarate.

(see page 195)

Suborder Symphyta

Hymenoptera in which:-

- ● 1. There is no marked constriction between the thorax and the abdomen.
- ● 2. The trochanters are 2-jointed.
- ● 3. The larvae possess thoracic and usually 6 or more pairs of abdominal legs.

Examples:- *Sirex*, *Nematus*, *Cephus*, *Cimbex*, *Oryssus*.

Suborder Apocrita

Hymenoptera in which:-

- ● 1. The abdomen is separated from the thorax by a deep constriction or petiole.
- ● 2. The trochanters are 1- or 2-jointed.
- ● 3. The larvae are apodous.

Examples:- *Apis*, *Sphex*, *Monomorium*, *Mutilla*, *Rhyssa*, *Apanteles*, *Blastophaga*, *Chalcis*, *Cynips*.

Order Strepsiptera

Oligoneoptera in which:-

- ● 1. In the male, the fore-wings are reduced to halteres and the hind wings are membranous, fan shaped and with longitudinal venation only. The female is apterous.
- 2. The mouth parts are of the biting type but are atrophied.
- ● 3. The antennae are flabellate.
- 4. The prothorax is very reduced and the remaining thoracic segments are not fused.
- 5. There are no cerci.
- 6. There is no ovipositor, the female being larviform.
- 7. The pupa is exarate.
- ● 8. The members are internal parasites of other insects and cause parasitic castration of the host.

Example:- Stylops.

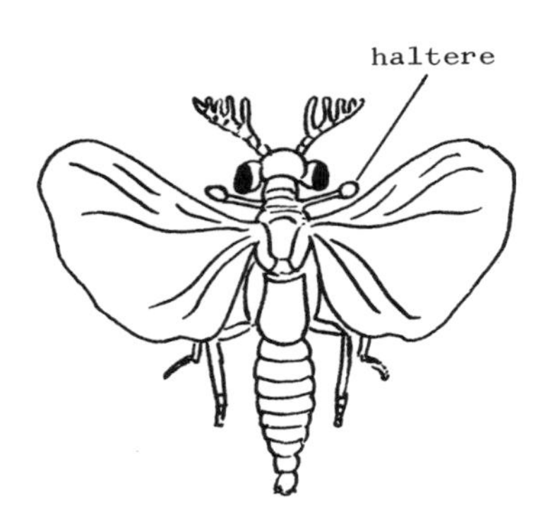

Stylops

anal field
(one vein simple or branched)

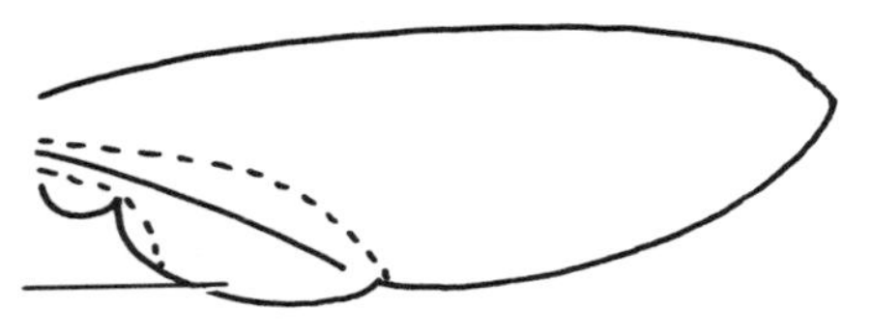

dipteran wing

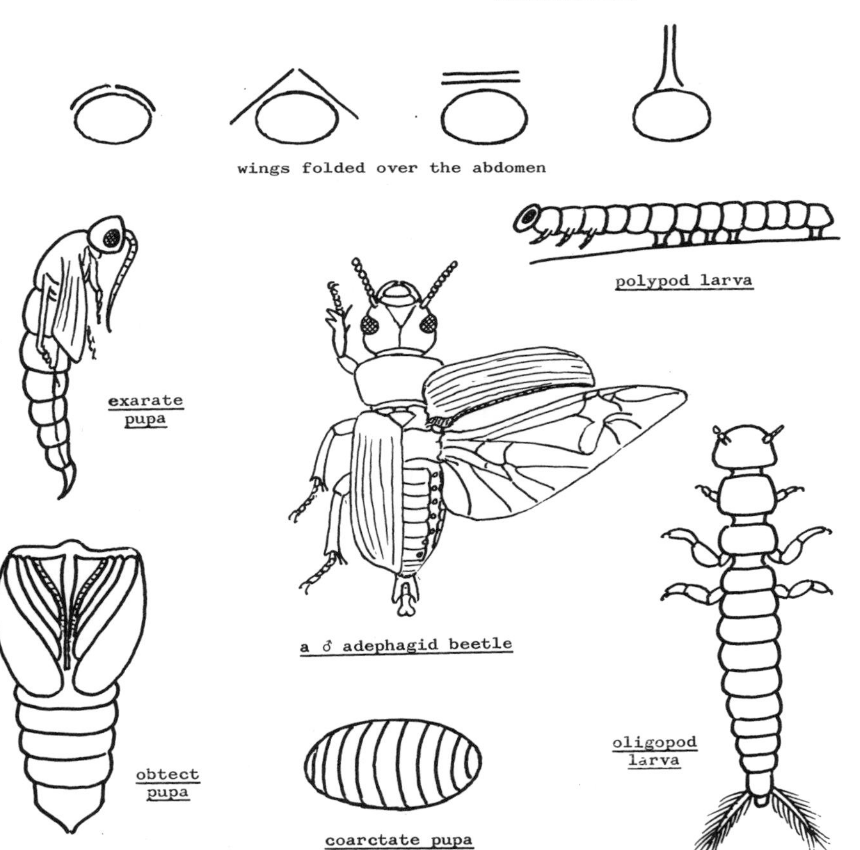

11 Tardigrades and Pentastomids

A number of the smaller invertebrate phyla are isolated groups of animals with obscure or uncertain relationships. Two of these, the Tardigrada and the Pentastomida, probably have distant links with each other and with the arthropods and are therefore included at this point in the Guide. The tardigrades are minute aquatic or semi-aquatic animals with a cuticle and four pairs of stumpy legs. Many live on mosses, lichens and liverworts, others in various freshwater habitats and some are marine with a distribution extending from the interstices of seashore sands down into the deep sea. The semi-aquatic forms, at least, can survive long periods in a desiccated state and return to active life as and when water becomes available. They are evidently very primitive and at a level of organisation appropriate to the annelid-arthropod stem. There are resemblances, perhaps superficial, with the Onychophora.

The pentastomids are parasites of the respiratory passages of vertebrates, particularly reptiles. The body is worm-like with hooked appendages, or hooks alone, for attachment to the host's nasal epithelium or lungs. In some, two pairs of appendages are borne on prominences while the mouth is on a fifth, hence the name 'Pentastomida'. Eggs are voided with the respiratory secretions of the host and are eaten by an intermediate host, usually a small mammal or other small vertebrate. The eggs hatch into larvae which pierce the stomach wall and encyst in the intermediate host's tissues. The larva has two pairs of legs and a strong superficial resemblance to a tardigrade.

Phylum Tardigrada

Eucoelomata in which:-

● 1. The body is not clearly differentiated into regions, although there is some evidence of metamerism.
2. There is no definite head.
3. The gut is straight and the anus is terminal.
4. The nervous system consists of pre-oral ganglia joined by circum-oesophageal commissures to a double ventral nerve cord which has four ganglia along its length.
5. Sense organs consist of eye spots, bristles and spines.
6. The cuticle is non-chitinous.

● 7. There are four pairs of short unjointed legs, each with terminal claws.
8. Muscles of the body wall are single and smooth; they occur in bands.
9. The body cavity is a fluid-filled pseudocoelom.
10. Excretory organs are Malpighian tubules.
11. There is no blood vascular system.
12. The products of the gonads are shed through the terminal part of the intestine.
13. The sexes are separate.
14. The immature stage resembles the adult.

Example:- <u>Macrobiotus</u>. (see page 199)

Phylum Pentastomida

Eucoelomata in which:-

1. Superficial annulations may or may not be present on the body.
2. There is no distinct head, and the body is worm-like.
3. The gut is straight or nearly so, and the anus is terminal.
4. The nervous system is reduced, consisting of a circum-oesophageal commissure, a sub-oesophageal ganglion and a simple nerve cord.
5. Sense organs are restricted to papillae on the body surface.
6. A chitinous cuticle is present.
7. There may be five short prominences anteriorly; one bears the mouth, and the others the claws.
8. Circular and longitudinal muscles are present in the body wall.
9. There is a perivisceral haemocoel.
10. There is no excretory system.
11. There is no circulatory system.
12. The products of the gonads are passed to the exterior by gonoducts.
13. The sexes are separate.
14. The larva develops within the egg and has two or three pairs of rudimentary legs bearing claws.
15. The members are all parasitic chiefly in reptiles, but also in birds and mammals.

Example:- Linguatula. (see page 199)

PHYLUM TARDIGRADA

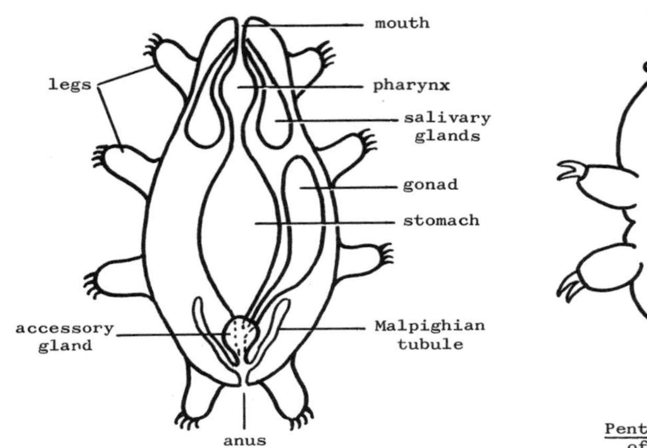

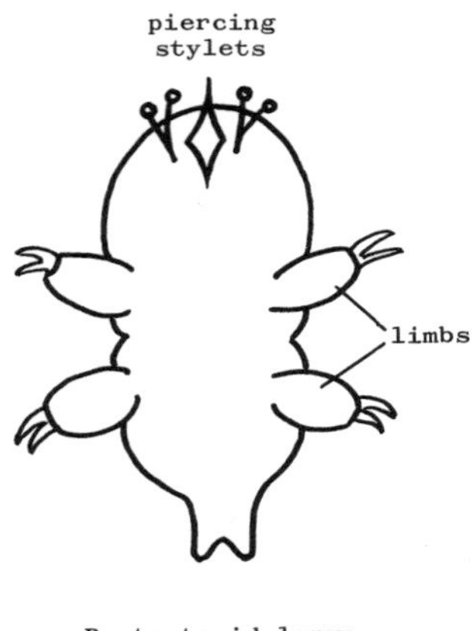

Pentastomid larva of Linguatula

PHYLUM PENTASTOMIDA

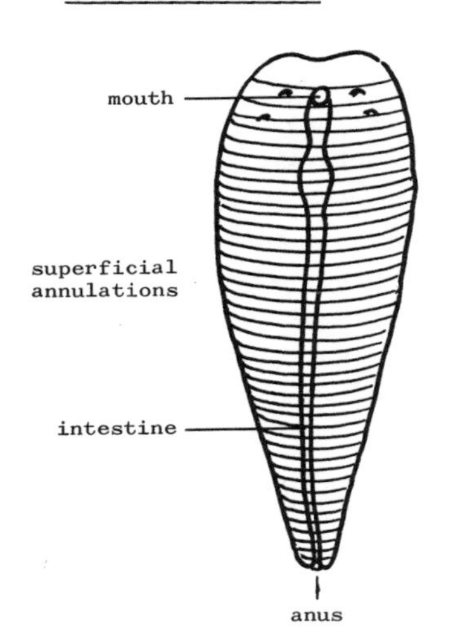

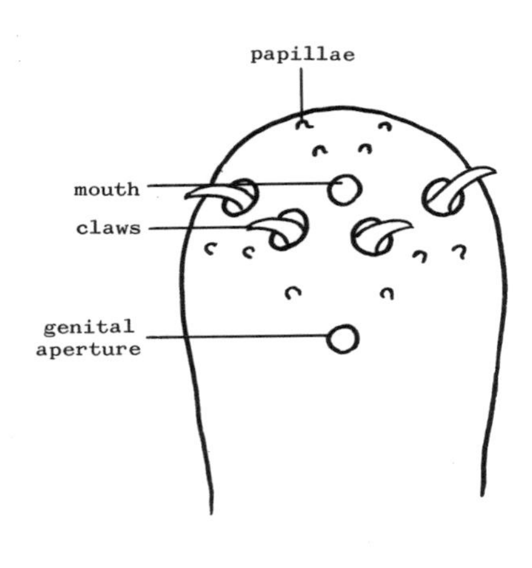

Linguatula

12 Molluscs

Animals tend to live in 'boxes', at least for some of the time, because these provide them with protection against predators and ensure some degree of uniformity of the immediate environmental conditions. A 'box' in this sense may be a crevice, or a hole in the ground, or a decaying tree trunk, or a bird's nest, or the shell of a tortoise. An invertebrate that habitually makes its own 'box' or shell, as an integral part of its structure, is the mollusc. The shell is a characteristic molluscan feature. It may be a single calcareous structure as in the monoplacophorans, gastropods and scaphopods, or a series of plates as in the chitons, or consist of two hinged pieces as in the bivalves, or form a spiral of separate chambers as in the more primitive of the cephalopods. Other characteristic features are the presence of a head, a foot and a visceral hump covered by the mantle which secretes the shell. The molluscs have become variously adapted to a great number of different modes of life which has caused modification of all parts of the body, not least the shell which in many forms has become greatly reduced or lost.

The origin of the molluscs and their relations with other invertebrate phyla is something of a puzzle. They are not segmented and their body cavity is a haemocoel which functionally replaces the coelom. In 1952, however, *Neopilina* was brought up in a dredge from the deep sea in the Pacific off Central America. This mollusc, relatives of which were previously known only as fossils, has a conical shell rather like a limpet and a repetition of parts, including gills, muscles, nerves, excretory organs and gonads, which suggests that it is metamerically segmented. Controversy exists, however, about this, some workers maintaining that the repetition of parts is metameric while others hold that it is a mere replication and not true metamerism and there is no embryological evidence to help. We cannot say, therefore with any certainty, that the molluscs share ancestry with the annelids and arthropods, or with any other group, although most molluscs have a trochophore larva similar to that of the polychaete worms.

In the primitive mollusc the body was evidently entirely covered dorsally by the mantle. This formed a skirt around the animal enclosing a continuous mantle cavity. In the mantle cavity were the gills, an organ of chemical sense (the osphradium) and the excretory and genital apertures. This condition still remains in the chitons and the bivalve molluscs. But, in the prosobranch gastropods during development, the visceral hump is rotated through 180 degrees so that the posterior mantle cavity faces forward and the left side of the body becomes the right and vice versa. Thus the various connections, nervous and others, linking the visceral hump with the head and foot, become twisted into a narrow neck. This process is known as torsion and confers two advantages. It leads to better ventilation of the mantle cavity and gives increased mobility to the head for withdrawal into the shell for protection. The torted gastropod can thus emerge and withdraw into the shell at need. However, many gastropods, such as Patella, have lost this facility and others, the opisthobranchs, have reduced or lost their shell and have undergone varying degrees of untwisting (detorsion). The pulmonate gastropods, which include the slugs and snails; have ventured on land and have converted the mantle cavity into a lung.

The culmination of molluscan evolution is in the cephalopods. They are active predators with a highly complex brain and sense organs endowing them with powers of learning and decision taking of the highest order among invertebrates.

Phylum Mollusca

Eucoelomata in which:-

- 1. The body shows little evidence of segmentation.
- 2. A distinct head is usually present and, characteristically, the body also has a ventral muscular foot and a dorsal visceral mass.

3. The gut is liable to torsion and coiling and the anus may be directed forward.
4. The nervous system typically comprises a circum-oesophageal ring frequently concentrated into cerebral and pleural ganglia. Pedal and visceral ganglia are variously joined to this ring.
5. Organs of special sense are present and may be very elaborate.

- 6. The epidermis does not secrete a cuticle, but the dorsal surface is often extended beyond the body to form a mantle which typically secretes a protective calcareous shell.

7. The appendages, when present, are never jointed.
8. The muscular system is mainly concentrated in the foot region.
9. The coelom is typically restricted to the pericardium and the cavities of the excretory and reproductive organs. In addition, an extensive haemocoel may or may not occur.
10. The excretory organ is the kidney.
11. There is a well-defined blood vascular system which is partly open, i.e. there is a heart, arteries and veins communicating with the haemocoel.
12. The products of the gonads are passed to the exterior through coelomoducts.
13. The sexes may or may not be separate.
14. In most forms the egg develops into a trochophore larva which passes through a veliger stage to the adult.

M O L L U S C A

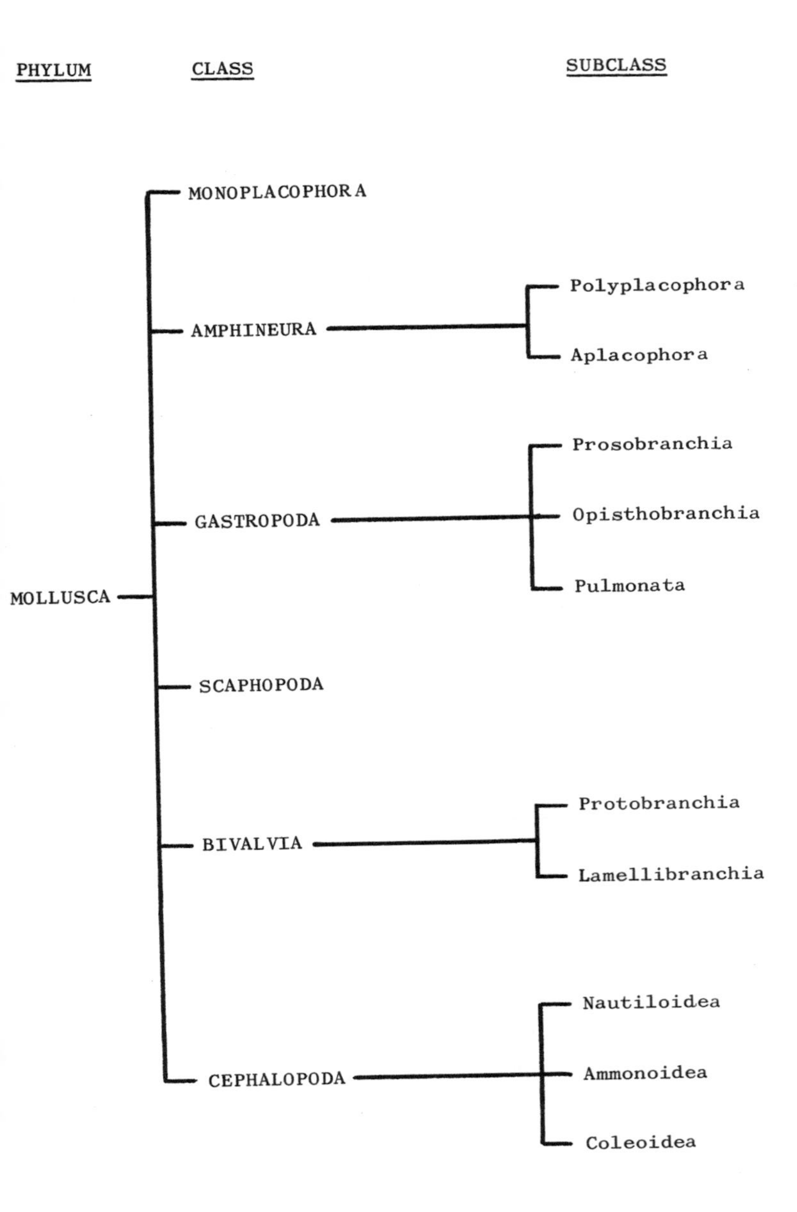

PHYLUM
CLASS
SUBCLASS
MONOPLACOPHORA
AMPHINEURA
Polyplacophora
Aplacophora
GASTROPODA
Prosobranchia
Opisthobranchia
Pulmonata
MOLLUSCA
SCAPHOPODA
BIVALVIA
Protobranchia
Lamellibranchia
CEPHALOPODA
Nautiloidea
Ammonoidea
Coleoidea

M O L L U S C A

Class Monoplacophora

Mollusca in which:-

● 1. The body is circular in shape, bilaterally symmetrical, with an apparent metameric arrangement of organs.

2. The mantle lies just within the edge of the shell.

● 3. The shell is superficially similar to that of a limpet, but with definite growth lines. The apex of the shell is pitched forwards.

4. The head is covered by the mantle.

5. The buccal cavity contains a radula.

● 6. Ctenidia are present as a more or less complete row on each side of the body, and lie in a groove between the mantle and the foot.

7. The nervous system consists of a cerebral commissure surrounding the mouth, from which arise a pair of pedal, and a pair of lateral cords which have many cross-connectives between them.

Example:- Neopilina. (see page 213)

Class Amphineura

Mollusca in which:-

● 1. The body is elongated and bilaterally symmetrical externally, and nearly so internally.

2. The mantle extends over the whole of the dorsal surface.

● 3. The mantle secretes calcareous spicules in a cuticular matrix and these may be fused to form definite shell plates.

4. The head is devoid of eyes or tentacles and is covered by the mantle.

5. The buccal cavity is generally provided with a radula but there is no mandible.

6. Ctenidia, which are probably not homologous with those of the other classes, may or may not be present.

7. The nervous system is without definite ganglia and consists of paired longitudinal pedal and palliovisceral cords. A circum-oesophageal commissure connects these cords anteriorly and each pair is united posteriorly by a commissure dorsal to the rectum.

M O L L U S C A

Subclass Polyplacophora - Chitons

Amphineura in which:-

- 1. The foot is flat and occupies the whole ventral surface of the body.
- 2. The mantle secretes eight calcareous plates and numerous spicules.
- 3. Ctenidia are present as a more or less complete row on each side of the body and lie in a groove between the mantle and foot.

4. The gut is coiled.

Example:- Chiton. (see page 213)

Subclass Aplacophora

Amphineura in which:-

1. The foot is reduced, either to a median ridge, or to a ventral groove, or is absent.
2. The shell is absent but there are numerous calcified spicules on the whole surface of the mantle which is greatly enlarged and completely invests the worm-shaped body.

- 3. Ctenidia are usually present as a more or less extensive circlet on the inner walls of the 'cloacal chamber' (mantle cavity).

4. The gut is straight.

Examples:- Neomenia, Chaetoderma.

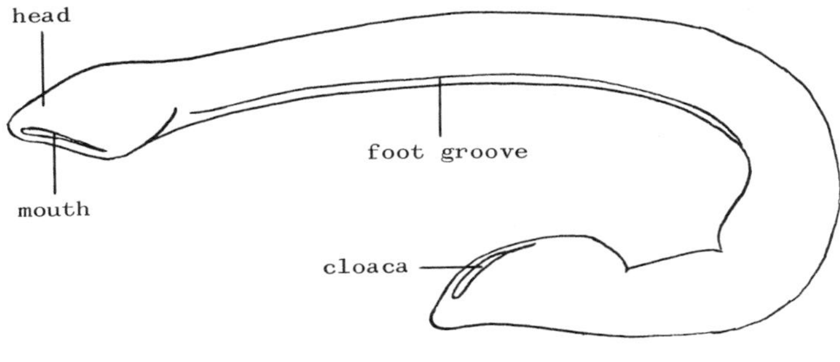

Neomenia

M O L L U S C A

Class Gastropoda

Mollusca in which:-

- 1. The body shows varying degrees of asymmetry due to torsion and coiling of the viscera, but many forms have become secondarily symmetrical. A broad flat foot is characteristic.
- 2. The mantle normally covers the visceral mass and projects around it leaving only the head and foot exposed on the ventra side.
- 3. The shell when present is usually in one piece (univalve).
- 4. The head is well developed and bears tentacles and eyes.
- 5. There is a well-developed radula and usually one or two mandibles are situated at the anterior end of the buccal cavity. They are horny pads against which the radula works.

6. Ctenidia may or may not be present.
7. The nervous system consists typically of paired cerebral, pleural and visceral ganglia and generally a pair of pedal ganglia and a visceral loop.

(see pages 213, 214)

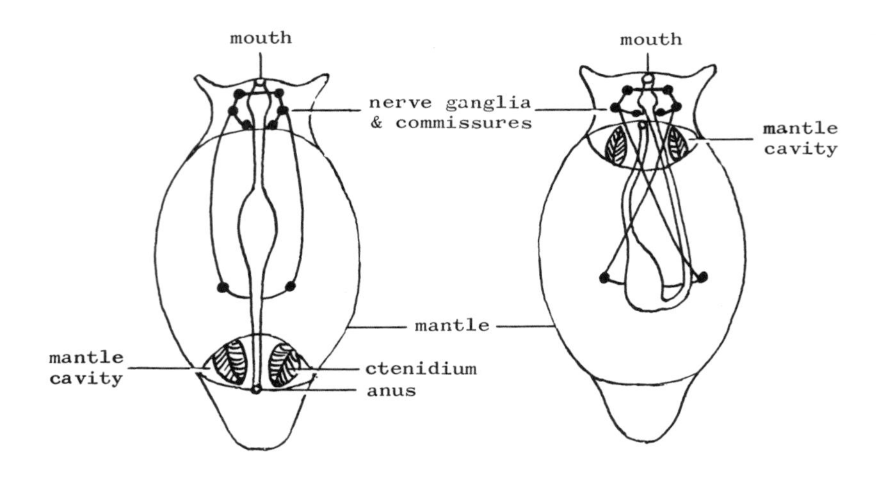

torsion in gastropods

M O L L U S C A

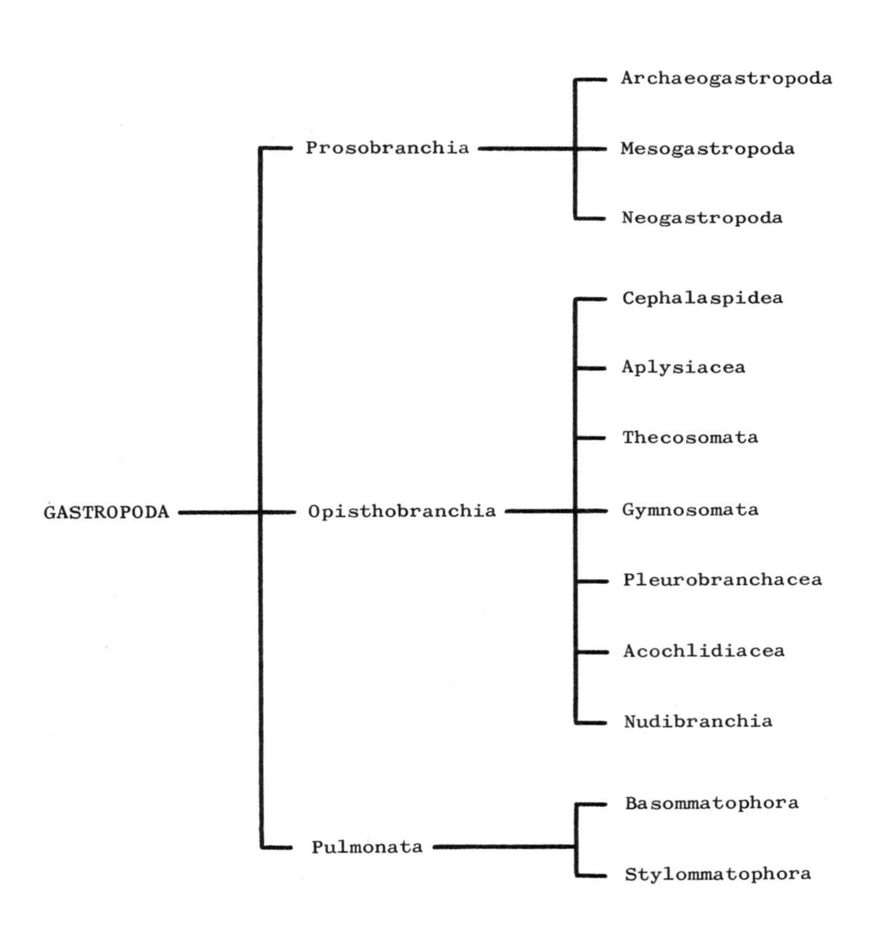
CLASS
SUBCLASS
ORDER
GASTROPODA
Prosobranchia
Opisthobranchia
Pulmonata
Archaeogastropoda
Mesogastropoda
Neogastropoda
Cephalaspidea
Aplysiacea
Thecosomata
Gymnosomata
Pleurobranchacea
Acochlidiacea
Nudibranchia
Basommatophora
Stylommatophora

M O L L U S C A

Subclass Prosobranchia

Gastropoda in which:-

● 1. Torsion is exhibited to the maximum degree by the viscera mass, the anus being directed forward. The visceral commissure is twisted into a figure of eight (streptoneur

● 2. A shell and an operculum are usually present.

● 3. The mantle cavity opens anteriorly with a wide aperture.

4. There are one or two ctenidia in almost all forms.

5. The sexes are separate in most forms.

6. Larvae of the trochophore and veliger types are present.

Order Archaeogastropoda - Limpets etc.

Prosobranchia in which:-

● 1. The radula has the teeth arranged in transverse rows Each row has numerous (more than seven) teeth.

2. There is no siphon.

3. The ctenidia, where present, have two rows of lamell (aspidobranch ctenidia). In Patella the ctenidia a replaced by pseudo ctenidia.

4. The heart usually has two auricles.

5. There are typically two kidneys.

6. The nervous system shows little concentration toward the head end.

● 7. The shell is often cone-shaped without an operculum, but it may be spirally coiled with an operculum present.

Examples:- Fissurella, Haliotis, Patella, Acmaea.

(see page 214)

Haliotis

M O L L U S C A

Order Mesogastropoda - Winkles etc.

Prosobranchia in which:-

● 1. The radula almost always has seven teeth to the row.
2. There may or may not be a siphon.
3. There is a single ctenidium with one row of lamellae (pectinibranch ctenidium).
4. The heart has one auricle.
5. There is only one kidney.
6. The nervous system shows some concentration toward the head.

● 7. The shell is spirally coiled typically with an operculum. The shell may be secondarily reduced.

Examples:- Littorina, Cypraea, Crepidula, Trivia.

(see page 214)

Order Neogastropoda - Whelks etc.

Prosobranchia in which:-

● 1. The radula is narrow with not more than three teeth to the row.
2. A siphon leading to the mantle cavity is present.
3. There is a single ctenidium with one row of lamellae (pectinibranch ctenidium).
4. The heart has one auricle.
5. There is only one kidney.
6. The nervous system is highly concentrated.

● 7. The shell is spirally coiled with an operculum.

Examples:- Buccinum, Murex, Turris, Conus.

(see page 214)

Conus

Subclass Opisthobranchia

Gastropoda in which:-

- 1. The members show varying degrees of detorsion in the adul and the visceral commissure shows corresponding degrees c untwisting.
- 2. The shell is usually reduced or absent. There is no operculum.
- 3. The mantle cavity, when present, is widely open and tends to be placed posteriorly.
- 4. There is one ctenidium or none. In the latter case the whole body surface may be respiratory or accessory organs of respiration may be present.
- 5. The members are hermaphrodite.
- 6. The larva is a veliger.

Order Cephalaspidea

Opisthobranchia in which:-

- 1. Shell and mantle cavity moderately well developed.
- 2. Lateral parapodia are prominent.

Examples:- Actaeon, Bulla, Philine.

Order Aplysiacea - Sea hares

Opisthobranchia in which:-

- 1. Shell is usually reduced and internal; mantle cavit small, on the right side.
- 2. Parapodia are prominent.

Example:- Aplysia. (see page 214)

Order Thecosomata - Shelled pteropods

Opisthobranchia in which:-

- 1. Shell is spirally coiled or a non-spiral 'pseudo-conch'; mantle cavity is well developed.
- 2. Parapodial fins are present.

Examples:- Peracle, Limacina.

M O L L U S C A

Order Gymnosomata - Shell-less pteropods

Opisthobranchia in which:-

- 1. The body is naked and there is no mantle cavity.
- 2. Small, ventral parapodial fins are present.

Example:- Clione.

Order Pleurobranchacea

Opisthobranchia in which:-

- 1. Shell is either external or reduced and internal; there is no mantle cavity, but a naked ctenidium is protected by the mantle on the right side.
- 2. The body is flattened. Parapodia are absent.

Example:- Pleurobranchus.

Order Acochlidiacea

Opisthobranchia in which:-

- 1. The visceral sac is naked, projecting behind the foot and covered with spicules.
- 2. Parapodia are absent.

Example:- Acochlidium.

Order Nudibranchia - Sea lemons and Sea slugs

Opisthobranchia in which:-

- 1. The mantle and shell are almost always absent in the adult.
- 2. Parapodia are absent.

Examples:- Doris, Onchidoris, Eolis.

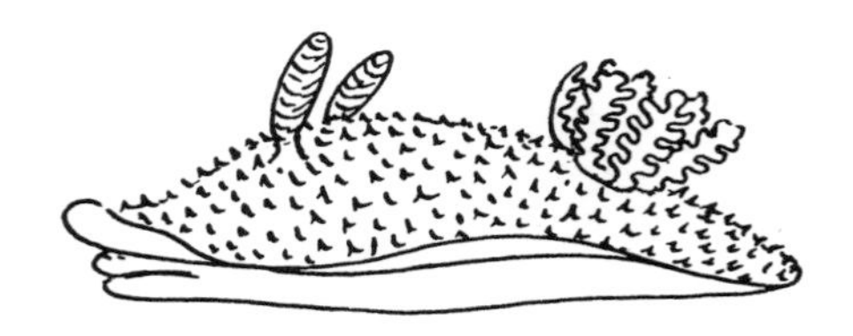

Acanthodoris

M O L L U S C A

Subclass Pulmonata - Snails and Slugs

Gastropoda in which:-

- 1. Torsion is exhibited by most members, but the visceral connectives are so shortened, and the ganglia so concentrated into the oesophageal mass, that the nervous system has become symmetrical.
- 2. A shell is present but may be reduced or absent. There is never an operculum.
- 3. The mantle cavity opens by a small anterior aperture. The mantle wall is highly vascular and acts as a lung.

4. There is no ctenidium.
5. The members are hermaphrodite.
6. The development is usually direct.

Order Basommatophora - Pond snails

Pulmonata in which:-

- 1. The eyes are placed at the base of the single pair of tentacles.
- 2. The tentacles cannot be invaginated.

Examples:- Limnaea, Planorbis, Physopsis.

Order Stylommatophora

Pulmonata in which:-

- 1. The eyes are placed at the tips of the posterior of the two pairs of tentacles.
- 2. The tentacles can be invaginated within the head.

Examples:- Helix, Archachatina, Limax, Testacella.

(see page 214)

Arion

PHYLUM MOLLUSCA

CLASS MONOPLACOPHORA

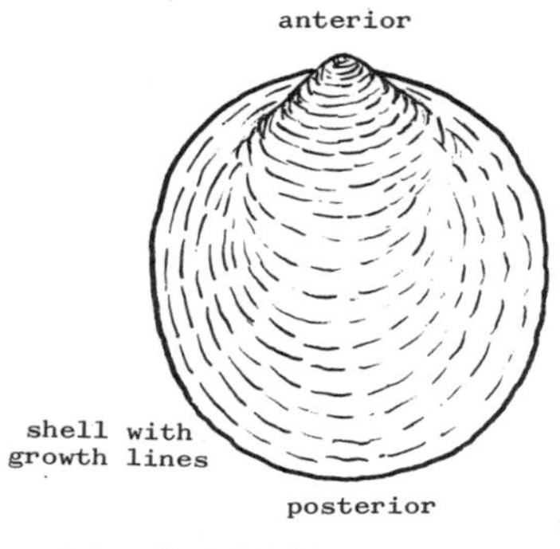

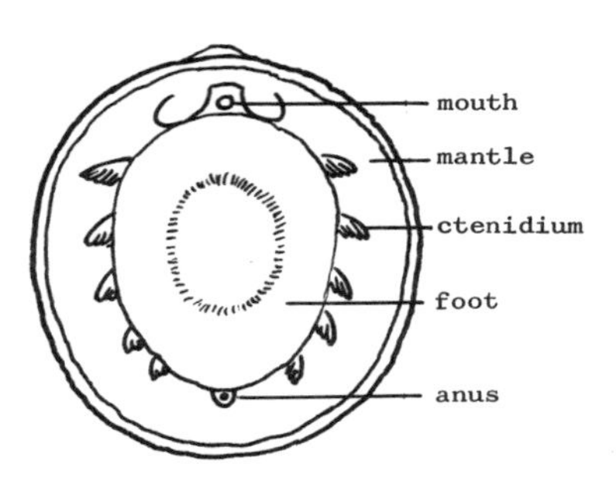

Neopilina

CLASS AMPHINEURA

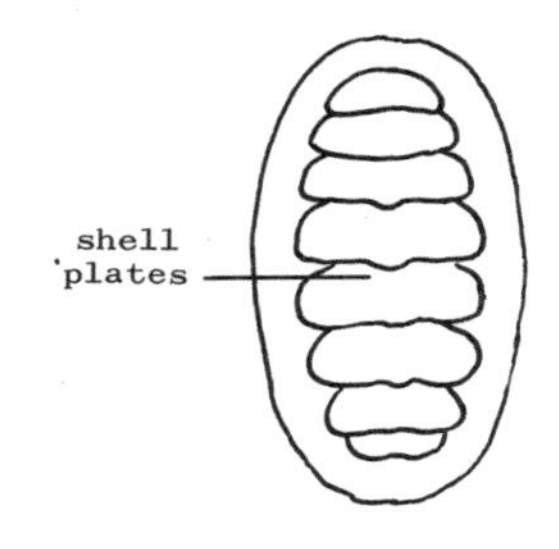

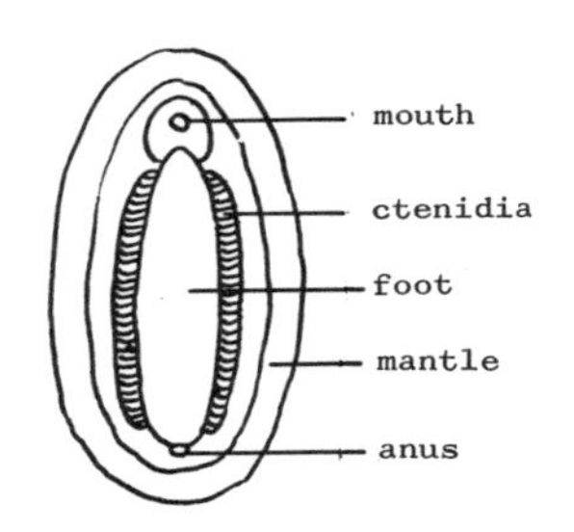

Chiton

CLASS GASTROPODA

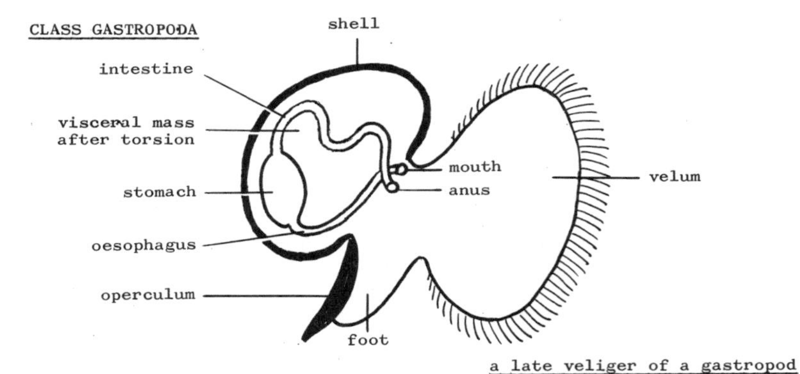

a late veliger of a gastropod

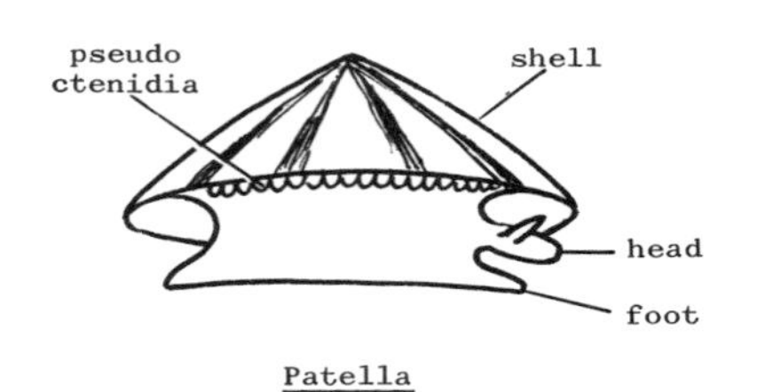

Patella

mesogastropod
radula teeth

archaeogastropod
radula teeth

neogastropod
radula teeth

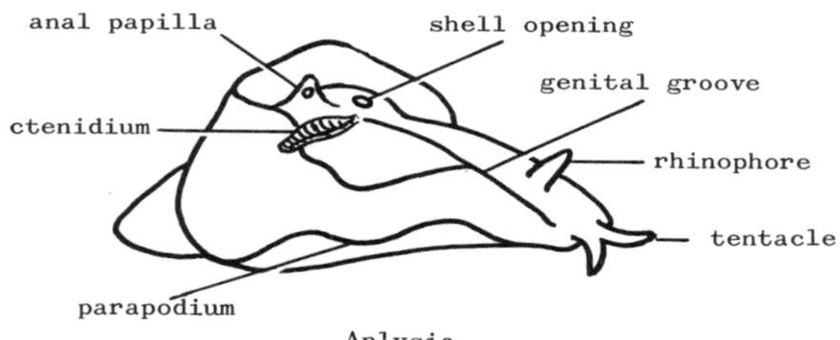

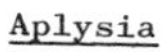

Aplysia

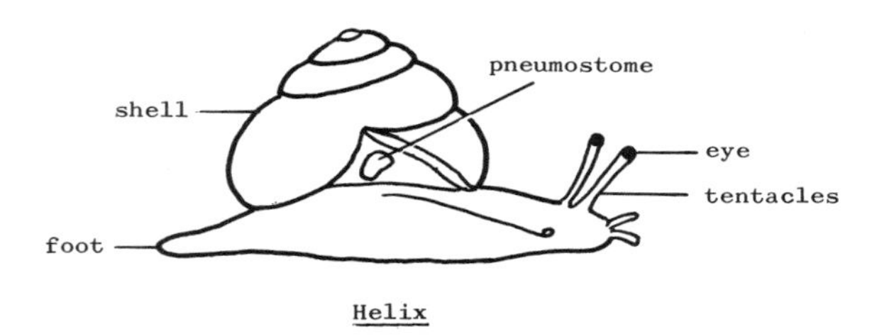

Helix

M O L L U S C A

Class Scaphopoda - Elephant's Tusk Shells

Mollusca in which:-

- 1. The body is elongated, nearly cylindrical and externally bilaterally symmetrical.
- 2. The mantle completely encircles the body like a tube; its right and left edges being united ventrally.
- 3. The shell is an external slightly curved tube, open at both ends and wider anteriorly.
- 4. The head is rudimentary and without eyes. The mouth is situated on a proboscis, and, behind it, prehensile sensory filaments are present on a pair of small lobes.
- 5. There is a short but well-developed radula.

6. Ctenidia are absent.
7. The nervous system consists of separate paired cerebral and pleural ganglia, pedal and visceral ganglia and a symmetrical visceral loop.
8. The circulatory system is very simple and there is no distinct heart.

Example:- Dentalium. (see page 216)

Class Bivalvia

Mollusca in which:-

- 1. The body is usually bilaterally symmetrical and laterally compressed. The foot is characteristically tongue-shaped.
- 2. The mantle consists of enlarged right and left lobes which almost always enclose the rest of the body.
- 3. The shell is bivalved and typically joined dorsally by an elastic ligament. A hinge of varying complexity is also usually present.
- 4. The head is rudimentary and devoid of eyes and tentacles. The lips of the mouth are extended to form a pair of ciliated labial palps on each side.
- 5. There is no radula and mandibles are absent.

6. There are two ctenidia which may be large and complicated in form and are used in filter feeding (lamellibranchs).
7. The nervous system consists of fused cerebral and pleural ganglia connected with the pedal and visceral ganglia by elongated commissures.

(see page 216)

PHYLUM MOLLUSCA

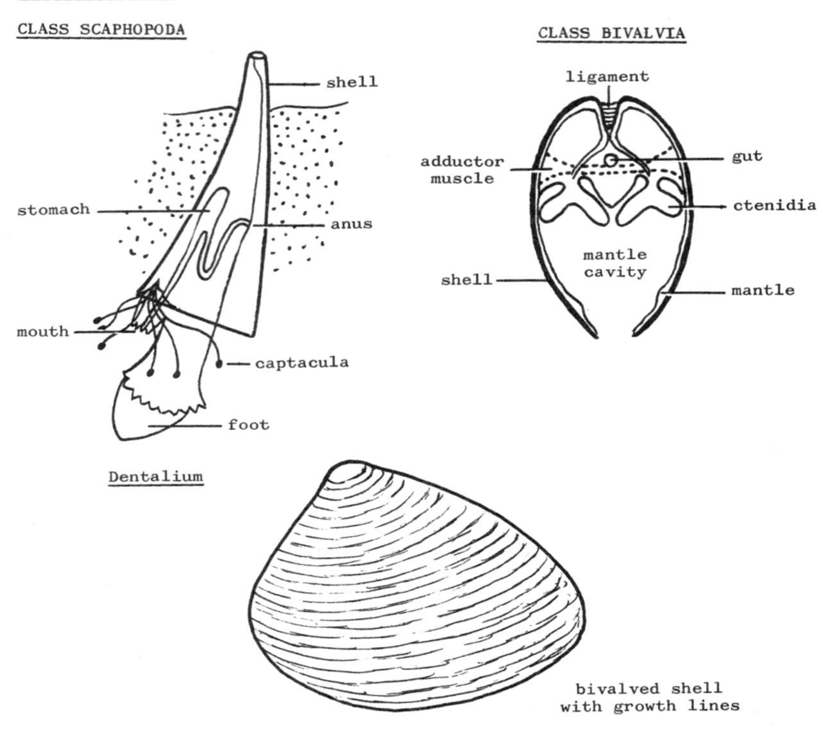

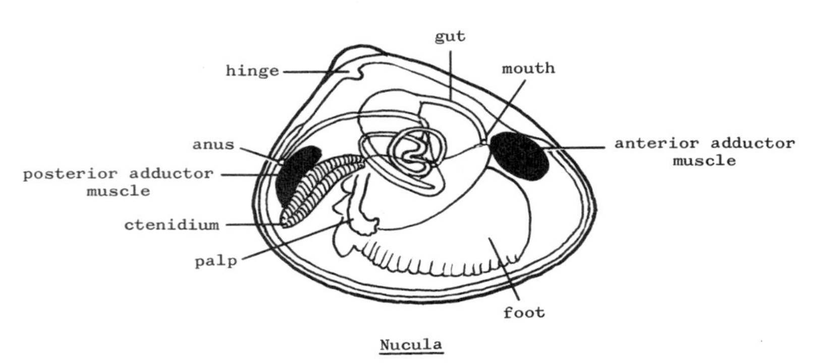

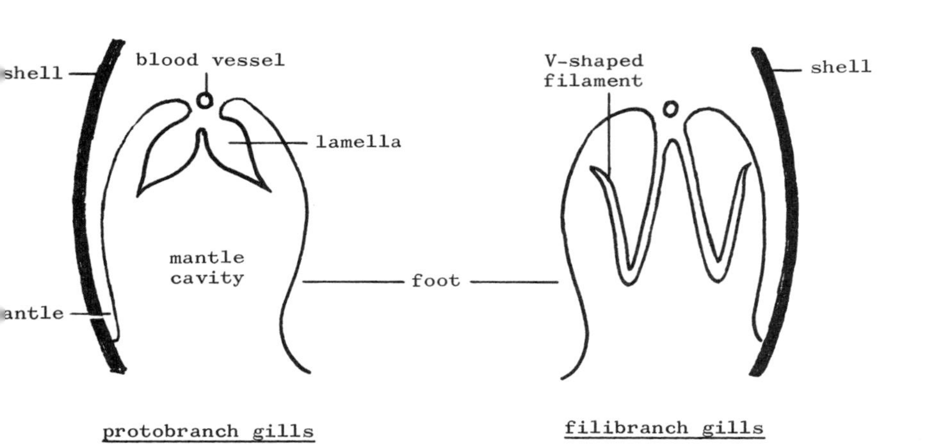

protobranch gills

filibranch gills

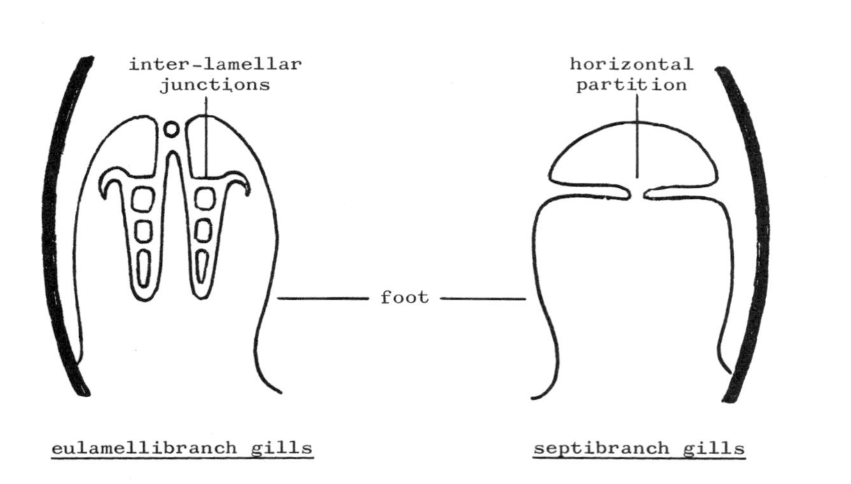

eulamellibranch gills

septibranch gills

patterns of ctenidia in Bivalvia

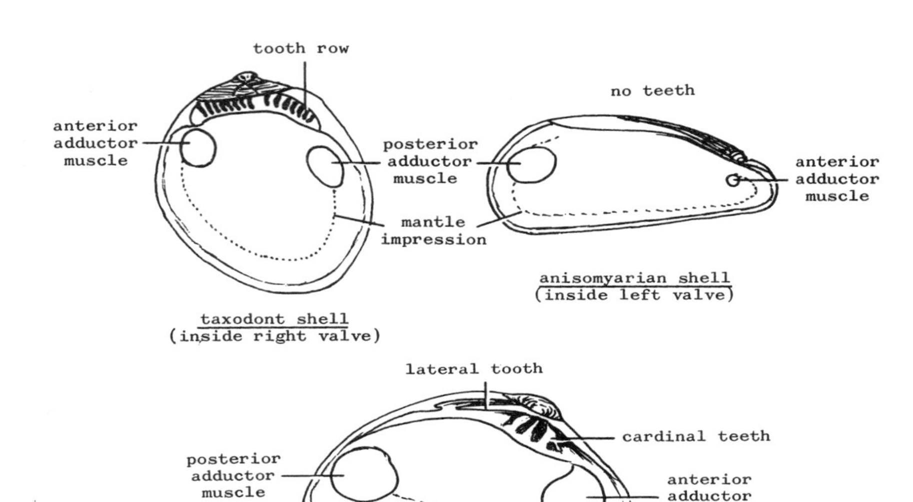

taxodont shell
(inside right valve)

anisomyarian shell
(inside left valve)

heterodont shell
(inside left valve)

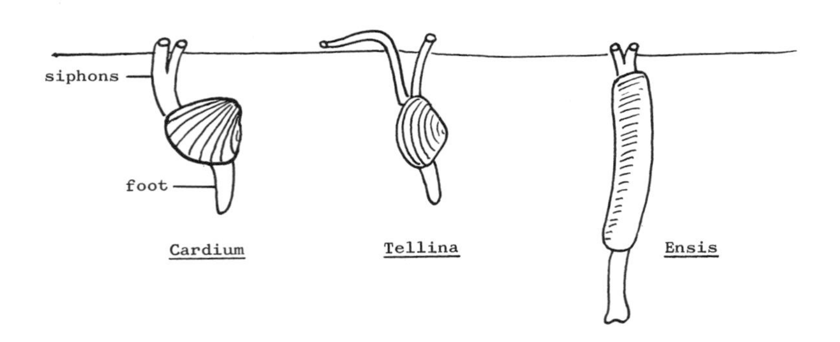

Cardium Tellina Ensis

M O L L U S C A

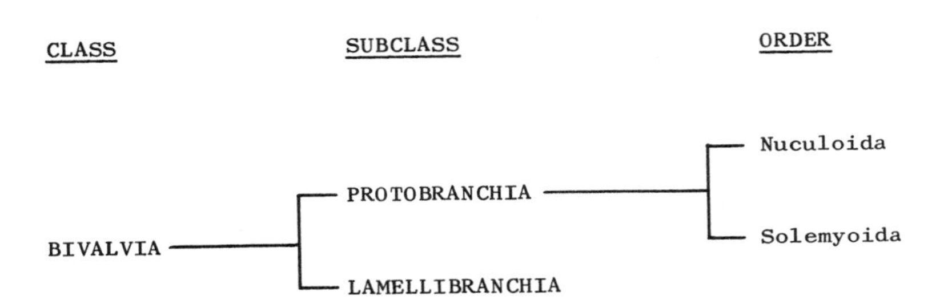

<u>Subclass Protobranchia</u>

Bivalvia in which:-

- 1. The foot has a divided sole fringed with papillae.
  2. The ctenidia are plume-like. Each ctenidium consists of two rows of short compressed lamellae arising from a central axis, but otherwise unconnected with one another.
- 3. Both anterior and posterior adductor muscles are always present.

(see page 216)

<u>Order Nuculoida</u>

Protobranchia in which:-

- 1. The hinge teeth are taxodont.
- 2. The adductor muscles are usually of equal size.
- 3. The valves are of equal sizes and their inside surfaces are nacreous.

Example:- <u>Nucula</u>.

(see page 216)

<u>Order Solemyoida</u>

Protobranchia in which:-

- 1. Hinge teeth are absent.
- 2. The adductor muscles are unequal (heteromyarian).
- 3. Valves of equal size and not nacreous.

Example:- <u>Solemya</u>.

MOLLUSCA

Subclass Lamellibranchia

Bivalvia in which:-

1. The foot has an undivided sole.
2. The ctenidia are typically W-shaped in section being composed of two rows of numerous separate V-shaped filaments arising from a central axis. The filaments may be held apart only by patches of interlocking cilia or by vascular interfilamentar junctions. The ctenidia are reduced to horizontal muscular partitions in *Poromya*, that is they are septibranch.
3. Anterior and posterior adductor muscles may be present, equally or unequally developed, or the anterior adductor may be lacking.

(see pages 217, 218)

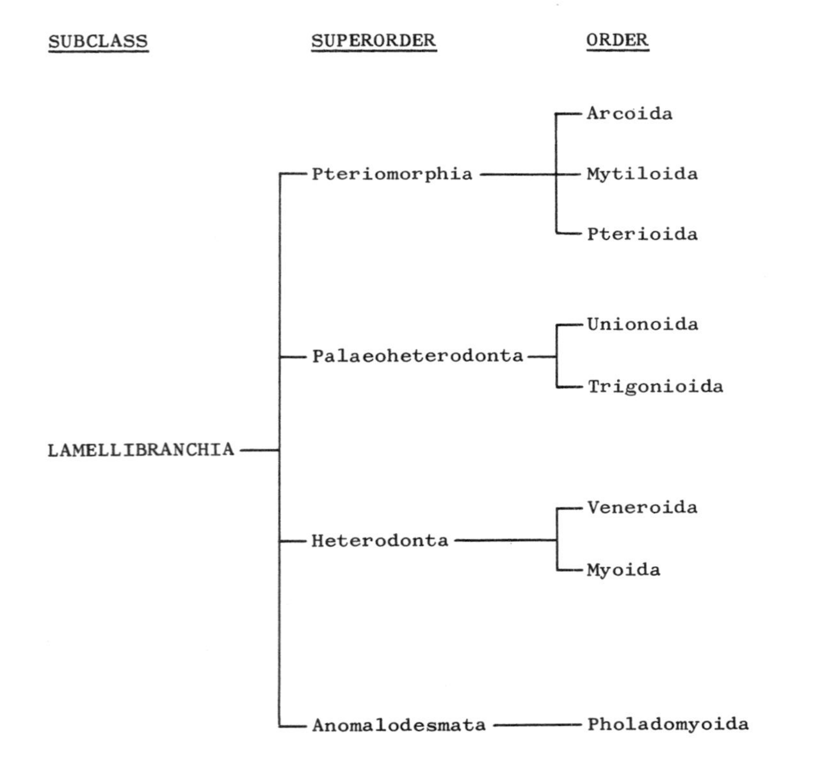

M O L L U S C A

Superorder Pteriomorphia

Lamellibranchia in which:-

- ● 1. The hinge teeth are either absent, or there are numerous teeth and sockets.
- 2. Adductor muscles are variable in size and number.
- ● 3. The mantle margins are not fused and do not form siphons.
- 4. The valves are variable, some equal in size, others unequal. Some nacreous, others not.
- 5. The gills are filibranch or eulamellibranch.

(see page 217)

Order Arcoida - Ark-shells etc.

Pteriomorphia in which:-

- ● 1. The hinge teeth are numerous, alternating with sockets (taxodont).
- ● 2. The valves are equal in size.
- 3. The ligament is duplivincular.
- ● 4. The adductor muscles are of equal sizes (isomyarian).
- 5. Adults are usually attached by byssus threads.

Example:- Arca, Glycymeris. (see page 218)

Order Mytiloida - Mussels

Pteriomorphia in which:-

- ● 1. The hinge has no teeth but may bear crenulations.
- ● 2. The valves are equal in size.
- 3. The ligament may be internal, or external.
- ● 4. The adductor muscles are unequal (heteromyarian), posterior muscle large, anterior small (anisomyarian).
- 5. Adults are often anchored by byssus threads.

Examples:- Mytilus, Pinna. (see page 218)

M O L L U S C A

Order Pterioida - Scallops and oysters

Pteriomorphia in which:-

- ● 1. There are no hinge teeth.
- ● 2. The valves are unequal.
- 3. The ligament is internal, often in a triangular pit.
- ● 4. There is only one adductor muscle (monomyarian).
- 5. The adults are usually sessile, either cemented by one valve, or anchored by a byssus.

Examples:- Pteria, Pecten, Ostrea.

Superorder Palaeoheterodonta

Lamellibranchia in which:-

- ● 1. Either posterolateral teeth originate at shell beaks and below ligament or lateral and pseudolateral teeth absent.
- ● 2. The adductor muscles are unequal (heteromyarian).
- ● 3. The mantle margins are free and do not form siphons.
- ● 4. The valves are equal in size and their inside surfaces are nacreous.
- 5. The gills are either eulamellibranch or filibranch.

(see page 217)

Order Unionoida - Swan mussels

Palaeoheterodonta in which:-

- ● 1. Lateral or pseudolateral teeth are present.
- 2. The gills are eulamellibranch.
- 3. All species are freshwater.

Examples:- Unio, Anodonta. (see pages 217, 218)

Order Trigonioida

Palaeoheterodonta in which:-

- ● 1. Both lateral and pseudolateral teeth are absent.
- 2. The gills are filibranch.
- 3. All species are marine.

Example:- Neotrigonia. (see pages 217, 218)

M O L L U S C A

Superorder Heterodonta

Lamellibranchia in which:-

- 1. Both cardinal and lateral teeth are present.
- 2. The adductor muscles are of equal size or almost so (isomyarian).
- 3. The mantle margins are fused and usually form siphons.
- 4. The valves are of equal size and their internal surfaces are not nacreous.

5. The gills are eulamellibranch.

(see pages 217, 218)

Order Veneroida - Cockles

Heterondonta in which:-

- 1. Well differentiated hinge teeth in which the laterals rarely reach the beaks in adults.

2. Many are active burrowers and include many of the common shallow water species.

Examples:- Venus, Astarte, Cardium, Tridacna, Tellina.

(see page 218)

Order Myoida - Burrowing bivalves

Heterondonta in which:-

- 1. The hinge is weak and valves may be separated, some have a chondrophore, others an apophysis.

2. Most species are deep burrowers, others tunnel into rock or timber.

Examples:- Mya, Pholas, Teredo, Ensis.

(see page 218)

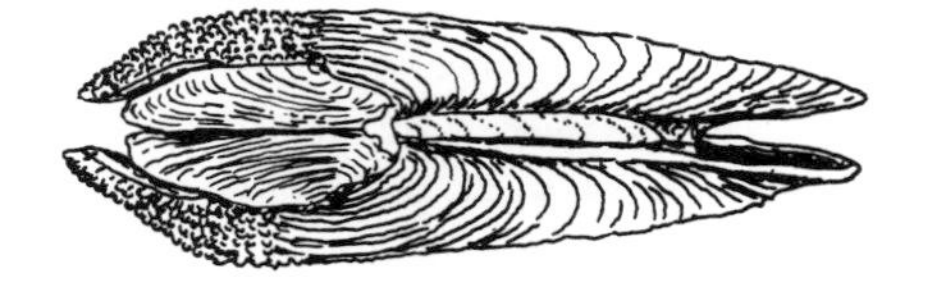

Pholas

Superorder Anomalodesmata, Order Pholadomyoida

Lamellibranchia in which:-

- ● 1. The hinge plate and teeth are poorly developed, or absent.
- ● 2. The adductor muscles are unequal, or even absent.
- ● 3. The mantle margins are fused to form siphons, sometimes very long.
- ● 4. The valves are mostly equal but there are some unusual forms where the valves have fused in the adult to form a tube. The internal surfaces are nacreous.
- 5. The gills are eulamellibranch or septibranch.
- 6. The ligament is either internal in a pit (resilium) or attached to a chondrophore (resilifer).

Examples:- Pandora, Clavagella, Poromya.

(see pages 217, 218)

Class Cephalopoda

Mollusca in which:-

- ● 1. The body is bilaterally symmetrical. The anterior part of the foot is fused with the head; the posterior part forms an exit funnel from the mantle cavity.
- 2. The mantle is highly muscular and is posterior (ventral) in position.
- 3. The shell, when present, is internal or external and may or may not be chambered. In most recent members it is internal and reduced or absent.
- ● 4. The head is well developed and surrounded by circum-oral tentacles probably derived from the edges of the anterior part of the foot. The eyes are prominent and may be of complex structure.
- ● 5. A radula is present and also a pair of horny mandibles resembling a parrot's beak.
- ● 6. There are one or two pairs of ctenidia in the mantle cavity.
- 7. The nervous system is well developed and the chief ganglia are localised around the oesophagus to form a highly organised brain.
- 8. The members produce large yolky eggs which undergo direct development.

Subclass Nautiloidea

Cephalopoda in which:-

- ● 1. The shell is external and many chambered, coiled or straight.
- 2. The siphuncle of the shell is central.
- 3. The suture line between chambers of the shell is simple.
- 4. The recent members comprise three species of a single genus found only in the Indo-Pacific region.
- ● 5. The head has numerous retractile tentacles which lack suckers.
- 6. The siphonal funnel is formed of two separate folds.
- 7. There are two pairs of ctenidia, kidneys and auricles.
- 8. The eyes are open vesicles without cornea or lens.
- 9. The ink gland is absent.
- 10. Chromatophores are absent.

Example:- Nautilus. (see page 229)

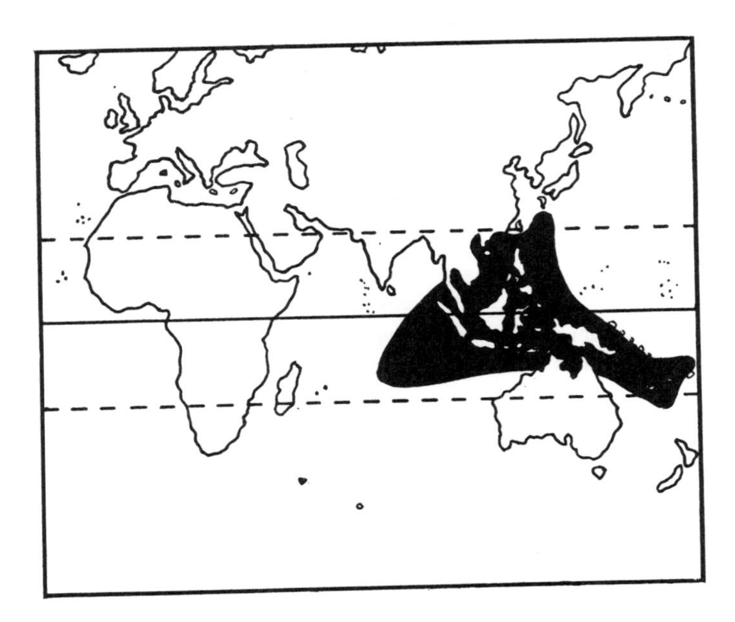

distribution of Nautilus

M O L L U S C A

Subclass Ammonoidea - Ammonites

Cephalopoda in which:-

● 1. The shell is external, septate, usually spirally coiled.

2. The siphuncle of the shell is marginal.

● 3. The suture line between chambers of the shell is frilled.

● 4. The members are known only from the shell and commonly occur as Mesozoic fossils.
Soft parts are not known.

Example:- Ceratites.

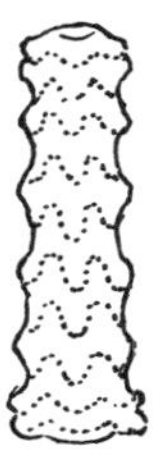

Ceratites

Subclass Coleoidea

Cephalopoda in which:-

● 1. The shell is typically internal and may be reduced but when external is not chambered.

2. The siphuncle is variously developed or may be lacking.

3. Suture lines are lacking.

4. Members include all living Cephalopoda, except Nautilus, plus the extinct belemnites.

● 5. The head bears 8 non-retractable tentacles and may also bear two additional retractable tentacles. All tentacles bear suckers.

6. The siphonal funnel is a complete tube.

7. There is one pair of ctenidia, kidneys and auricles.

8. The eyes are complex structures with a crystalline lens.

9. The ink gland is typically present.

10. Chromatophores are present.

M O L L U S C A

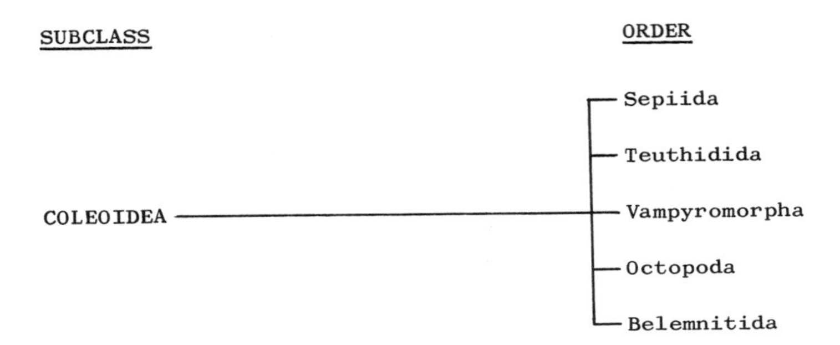

Order Sepiida - Cuttlefishes

Coleoidea in which:-

- 1. There are ten arms, two of which are longer than the rest. The arms are not joined by a swimming web.
- 2. The arms bear suckers on stalks with horny rings.
- 3. Lateral fins are well developed.
- 4. An internal, chambered, calcareous shell is well developed and is either flat (*Sepia*) or coiled (*Spirula*). It is used in the maintenance of neutral buoyancy.

5. They are shallow to mid-water forms.

Examples:- *Sepia*, *Spirula*.

Order Teuthidida - Squids

Coleoidea in which:-

- 1. There are ten arms, two of which are longer than the rest. The arms are not joined by a swimming web.
- 2. The arms bear suckers on stalks with horny rings.
- 3. Lateral fins are well developed.
- 4. An internal, non-chambered, horny shell is present.

5. They are shallow water (*Loligo*) or deep sea pelagic animals (*Architeuthis*).

Examples:- *Loligo*, *Architeuthis*. (see page 229)

M O L L U S C A

Order Vampyromorpha

Coleoidea in which:-

- ● 1. There are eight main arms and two small, cirrus-like tentacles. A swimming web or umbrella is developed between the arms.
- ● 2. The arms bear very small suckers with small appendages (cirri).
- ● 3. Lateral fins are present.
- 4. There is no shell.
- 5. They are abyssal animals.

Example:- _Vampyroteuthis_.

Order Octopoda - Octopuses and Paper nautilus

Coleoidea in which:-

- ● 1. There are eight arms, which are not joined by a swimming web.
- ● 2. The suckers are not borne on stalks and do not have horny rings.
- ● 3. There are typically no lateral fins.
- ● 4. The shell is reduced or absent. In the paper nautilus (_Argonauta_), the female produces a false shell by secretion from the arms which is used as a brood pouch.
- 5. They are typically shallow water forms (_Octopus_) but a few live in the deep sea (_Cirroteuthis_).

Examples:- _Octopus_, _Argonauta_, _Cirroteuthis_.

Order Belemnitida - Belemnites

Coleoidea in which:-

- ● 1. They are a group of extinct cephalopods with large internal skeletons. There is usually a small, chambered buoyancy section, the phragmacone, at the anterior end. They are common fossils in Mesozoic rocks.

Example:- _Belemnites_.

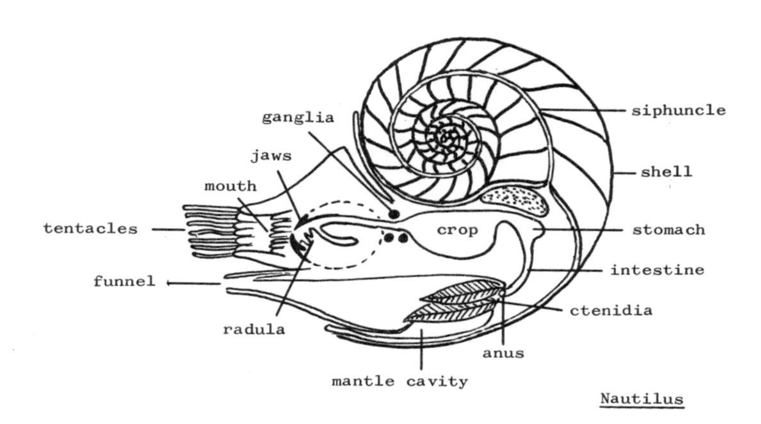

Nautilus

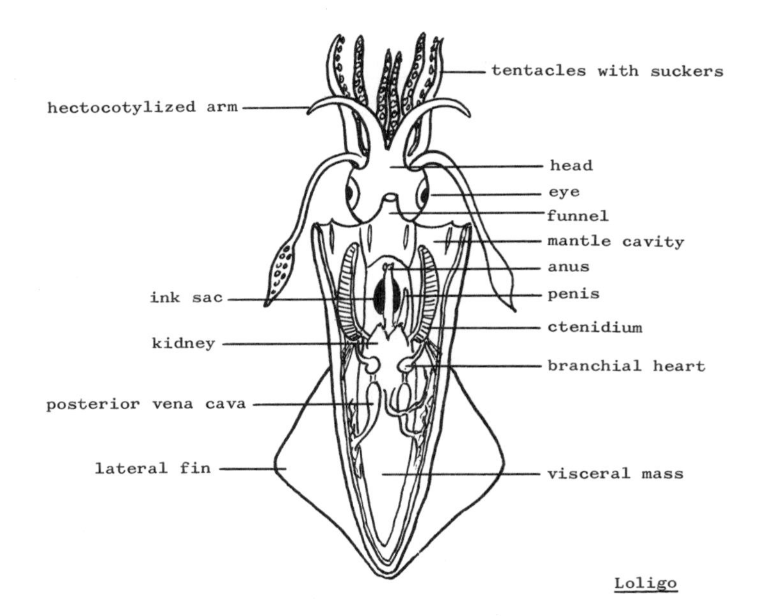

Loligo

13 Minor Eucoelomate Phyla

The eight phyla treated in this chapter are all relatively small groups, at least in terms of their living representatives, and tend to be unfamiliar to the student of zoology, although many are not at all uncommon. They fall into three groups according to their nearness or otherwise to the annelid-arthropod line of evolution. The first group comprises the Echiurida, Sipunculida, Priapulida and Pogonophora which are evidently close to the annelids. In fact the echiurids and sipunculids are sometimes included with the annelids as aberrant members and the pogonophores, until recently thought to have chordate affinities, have now been shown to be much closer to the annelids. The position of the priapulids, however, is not so clear, but they probably have proto-annelid connections.

The second group, more remote from the annelids, covers the Brachiopoda, Bryozoa and Phoronidea, all of which are characterized by the presence of a lophophore, a circular, crescentic or spirally coiled crown of ciliated tentacles surrounding the mouth. The body is divided into three sections by means of partitions, the anterior being the epistome which overhangs the mouth, the second surrounding the anterior part of the gut, while the third is the remainder of the body. In common with a number of sessile organisms the gut is U-shaped.

The living brachiopods are but a remnant of a once widespread and extensive group. They have a bivalved shell superficially like that of the bivalved molluscs, but the hinge of the shell is horizontal and posterior unlike the mollusc shell which has a dorsal hinge aligned with the main axis of the body. Internally the brachiopod is totally different from the mollusc. Brachiopods are found as fossils from the Cambrian period onward and reached a peak of enormous abundance in the Silurian, though common enough thereafter.

The Bryozoa, unlike the brachiopods, are all colonial. They encrust rocks and weed mainly in the sea, though one class, the Phylactolaemata, are fresh-water. Each animal or zooid lives in a small box or zooecium with a lid or operculum. The zooid extends its lophophore when feeding. Many of the bryozoans are polymorphic and in some there are zooids very much resembling a bird's head with a snapping beak. The Phoronidea, on the other hand, are small worm-like animals crowned by a lophophore. They live in bunches in leathery tubes, but are not colonial. If an animal has a through gut and lives in a box or a tube with a single opening it is clear that the gut must be U-shaped and the anus brought forward near the mouth.

The third group is the Chaetognatha or arrow-worms, many of which are abundant in marine plankton where they prey on other small animals. They are the only animals outside the chordates to have an extension of the body beyond the anus, that is a post-anal tail. This is not to suggest that they are related to the chordates, and they are certainly distinct from the annelid stock, in fact the position of the chaetognaths is not understood.

Some of the planktonic species of chaetognaths are used by marine biologists as 'indicator' species because they are characteristically found in particular areas of the sea. For example, *Sagitta setosa* and *S. elegans* occur commonly in the waters around the British Isles, but not usually together. *S. elegans* tends to be an open water northern species extending southward as far as the English Channel and is characteristic of mixed western and Channel waters. *S. setosa*, on the other hand, is a coastal form and indicates coastal and Channel waters.

MINOR EUCOELOMATE PHYLA

A convenient grouping of Eucoelomata in which:-

- ● 1. The body is not metamerically segmented at least in the adult, but may be annulated.
- ● 2. There is no distinct head, although a prostomium or proboscis may be present. The body is often worm-like.
- 3. The gut is straight, coiled or U-shaped.
- 4. The nervous system is simple: a cerebral ganglion may be present or absent; a circum-oesophageal ring connects with a single ventral nerve cord which may or may not be ganglionated.
- 5. Organs of special sense are usually lacking.
- 6. The epidermis may be covered with a thin cuticle or it may secrete a shell or tube around the body.
- ● 7. Appendages are generally lacking, although tentacles or spines are sometimes present anteriorly.
- 8. The body usually contains circular and longitudinal muscles, but these may be lacking in certain Bryozoa. Circular muscles are lacking in the Chaetognatha.
- 9. A coelom is present and is often subdivided into distinct regions.
- 10. Excretory organs may be present or absent. When present they are of the nephridial type.
- 11. Blood vascular system is often reduced or lacking. When present it is of the closed type.
- 12. The products of the gonads are passed to the exterior through nephridia or via the coelom through gonoducts.
- 13. The sexes may or may not be separate.
- 14. Larval forms of various kinds occur, some of which resemble trochophores.

M I N O R E U C O E L O M A T E P H Y L A

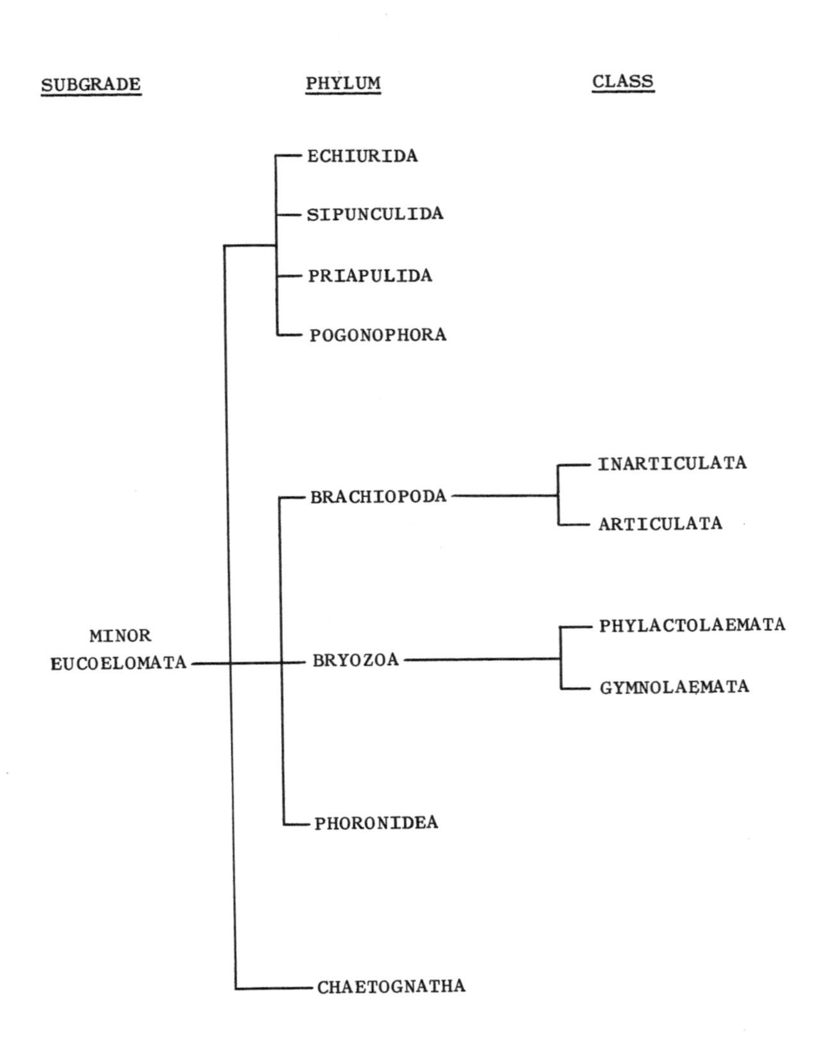

Phylum Echiurida

Eucoelomata in which:-

- ● 1. There is a single pre-oral segment, the prostomium or proboscis, which is entire or bifurcated, and sometimes of great length.
- ● 2. There are no appendages of any kind, but most forms bear a few chaetae.
- 3. The body wall contains an outer circular and an inner longitudinal muscle layer.
- 4. There is a spacious perivisceral coelom.
- 5. The chief excretory organs are a pair of anal vesicles opening into the rectum and, in addition, there may be one or more pairs of nephridia further forward.
- 6. There is a closed blood vascular system.
- 7. The nephridia function as gonoducts.
- ● 8. The sexes are separate. There may be extreme sexual dimorphism with the male, a small ciliated organism, parasitic in the nephridium of the female.
- 9. The larva is a trochophore.
- ●10. Segmentation is almost entirely lost in the adult but is evident during development.
- 11. The adult nerve cord is non-ganglionated and there are no organs of special sense.

Examples:- Bonellia, Echiurus. (see page 237)

Phylum Sipunculida

Eucoelomata in which:-

- ● 1. The mouth is borne at the end of a retractible proboscis.
- ● 2. Appendages are lacking, but chitinous papillae occur at the anterior end.
- 3. The body wall contains an outer circular, a middle oblique and an inner longitudinal muscle layer.
- 4. There is a spacious perivisceral coelom.
- 5. The excretory system consists of a pair of nephridia which are large and sac-like.
- 6. There is a closed blood vascular system, which is very much reduced. In some forms it may be lacking.
- 7. There are no definite gonads, but gametes are produced seasonally from germinative cells on connective tissue. The nephridia function as gonoducts.
- 8. The sexes are separate.
- 9. The larva is a trochophore.
- ●10. The body is worm-like, but not metamerically segmented.
- 11. The nerve cord is non-ganglionated, and there are no organs of special sense.

Examples:- Sipunculus, Phascolosoma. (see page 237)

Phylum Priapulida

Eucoelomata in which:-

● 1. There is no pre-oral segment, the mouth being terminal.

● 2. There are no appendages of any kind, but a bunch of papillae, which is thought to be respiratory, is found at the posterior end.

3. The body wall contains an outer circular and an inner longitudinal muscle layer.

4. There is a perivisceral coelom which extends into the posterior papillae.

5. There are no special excretory organs: excretion seems to be effected by the genital ducts and their branches.

6. There is no blood vascular system.

7. The products of the gonads are passed to the exterior by ducts of doubtful origin opening close to the anus.

8. The sexes are separate.

9. The larva resembles the adult but is encased in a chitinous envelope.

●10. The body is unsegmented but is marked with many superficial annulations.

11. The nerve cord is non-ganglionated and there are no organs of special sense.

Example:- only <u>Priapulus</u>. (see page 237)

PHYLUM ECHIURIDA

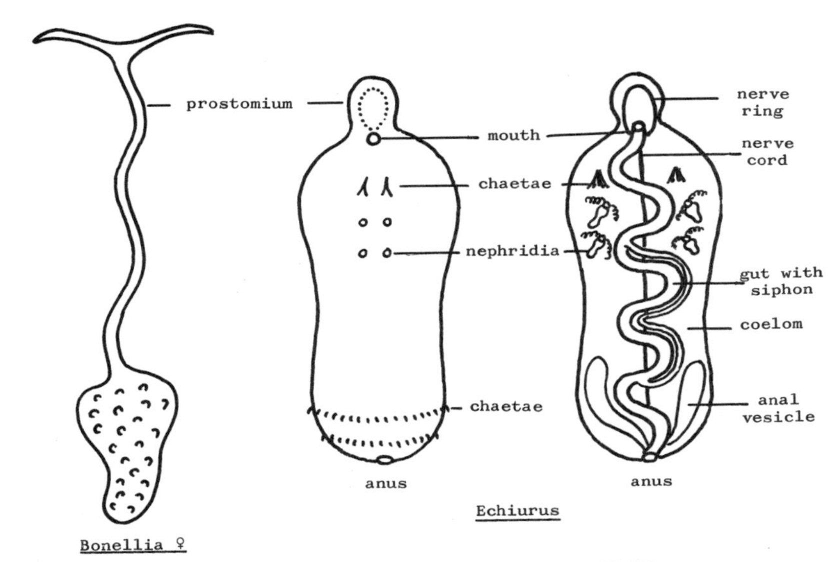

Bonellia ♀

Echiurus

PHYLUM SIPUNCULIDA

PHYLUM PRIAPULIDA

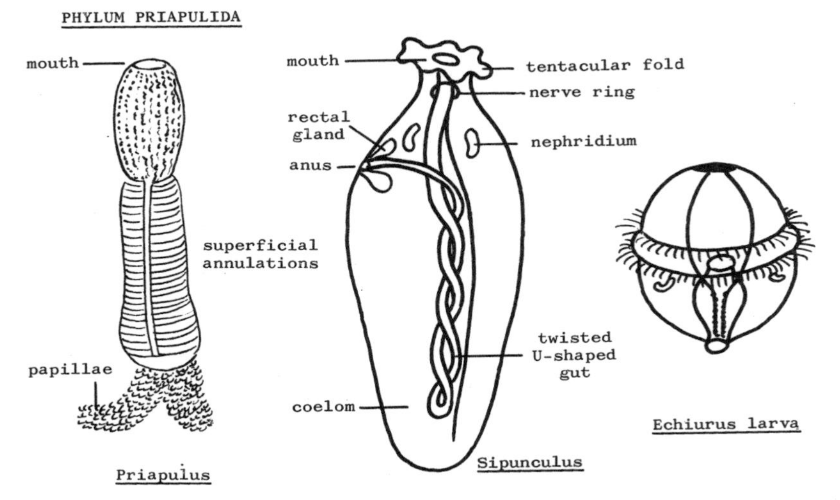

Priapulus

Sipunculus

Echiurus larva

Phylum Pogonophora

Eucoelomata in which:-

● 1. The body is divided into three regions, namely (1) a short anterior protosome bearing one to many tentacles, (2) a mesosome, and (3) a posterior metasome, or trunk, of considerable length.

2. The mesodermal blocks of the three body regions are separate.

3. There is no alimentary canal.

4. The nervous system is well developed, with the main ganglion located in a cephalic lobe on the protosome.

5. The coelom is tripartite, corresponding to the body divisions.

6. Excretion is carried out by coelomoducts and nephrocytes.

7. The circulatory system is closed. The ventral vessel has contractile walls. Haemoglobin is present in the blood.

8. The epidermis contains an extensive nerve plexus. The body wall musculature allows peristaltic locomotory movements. There are no lateral fins.

9. The sexes are separate.

●10. The members are solitary, worm-like, marine animals living in tubes which they secrete around themselves.

11. The larva has three body regions, each with a ciliated band.

Examples:- Oligobranchia, Siboglinum. (see page 239)

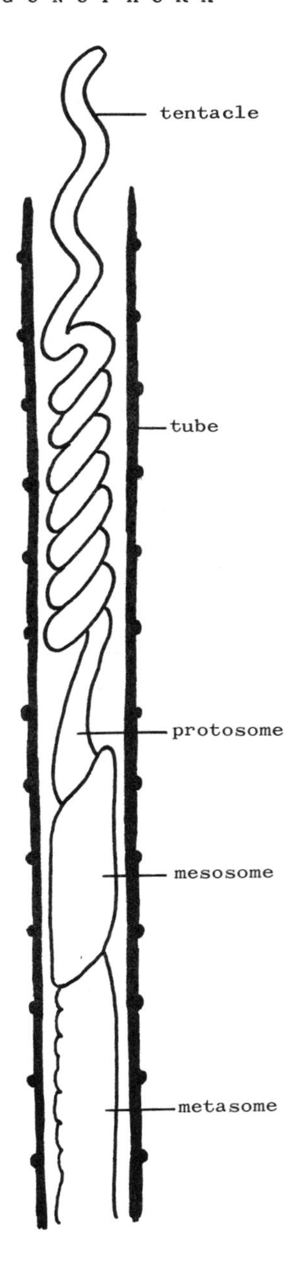

<u>Siboglinum</u>

Phylum Brachiopoda

Eucoelomata in which:-

- ● 1. The members are marine sedentary forms that never form colonies.
- ● 2. The lophophore may be simple but is often much coiled at the ends. It bears numerous tentacles. The mouth is overhung by an epistome.
- ● 3. The body is enclosed in a bivalve shell the valves of which are dorsal and ventral. The shell is secreted by folds from the body, the mantle lobes, the enclosed space being the mantle cavity.
- 4. The blood vascular system is poorly developed and consists of a dorsal longitudinal vessel with a dorsal 'heart' from which vessels radiate to end blindly.
- 5. The nervous system comprises a ganglionated circum-oesophageal ring from which peripheral nerves arise.
- 6. There are one or two pairs of excretory ducts opening widely into the coelom by nephrostomes.
- 7. The sexes may or may not be separate.
- 8. The gonads are arranged in two pairs and discharge through the excretory ducts.
- 9. There is a larva related in structure to the trochophore.

(see page 241)

B R A C H I O P O D A

Class Inarticulata

Brachiopoda in which:-

- 1. The valves of the shell are not hinged.
- 2. The shell is chitinoid with a varying degree of calcification.
- 3. There is no internal skeleton.
- 4. There is an anus.

Examples:- Lingula, Crania. (see page 242)

Class Articulata - Lamp shells

Brachiopoda in which:-

- 1. The valves of the shell are hinged together.
- 2. The shell is calcareous and more or less robust.
- 3. An internal calcareous skeleton supports the lophophore.
- 4. There is no anus.

Examples:- Terebratula, Waldheimia. (see page 242)

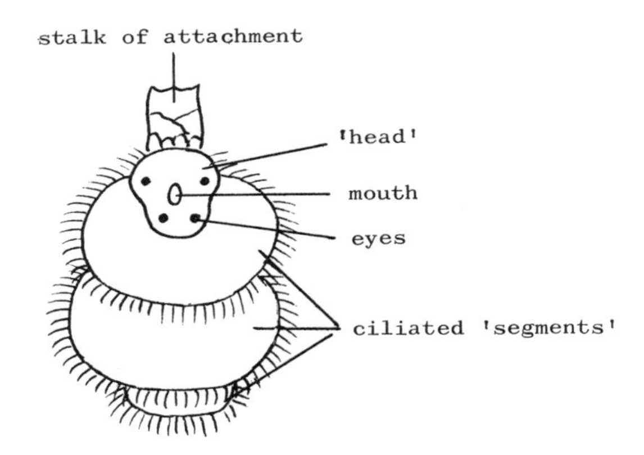

Brachiopod larva of Thecidium

PHYLUM BRACHIOPODA

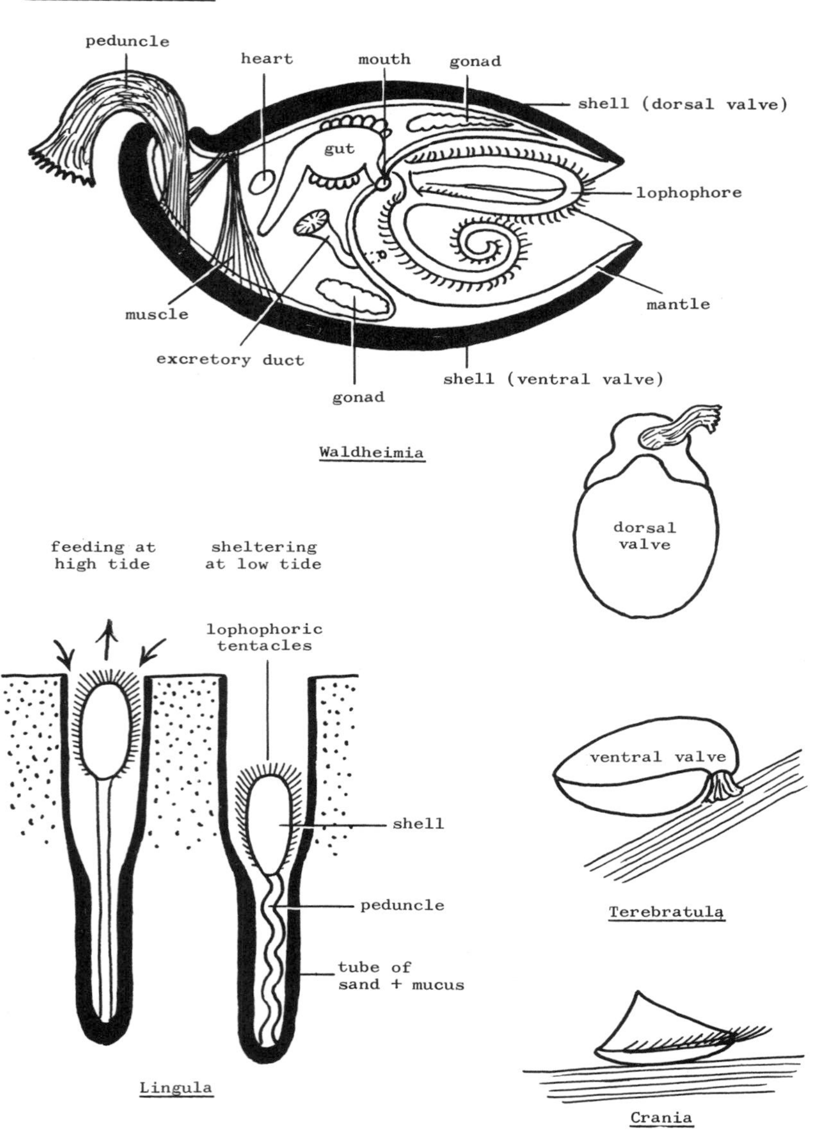

Phylum Bryozoa (Polyzoa Ectoprocta)

Eucoelomata in which:-

- ● 1. The members are freshwater or marine sedentary forms, living in colonies which may show polymorphism.
- ● 2. The lophophore is either circular or horse-shoe shaped and the mouth may or may not be overhung by an epistome (pre-oral lobes or prostomium).
- ● 3. The zooids of the colony (polypides) are enclosed, partially or completely, by a zooecium which may be gelatinous, horny or calcified.
- 4. There is no blood vascular system.
- 5. The nervous system is represented only by a ganglion between the mouth and the anus.
- 6. There are no special excretory organs.
- 7. The members are generally hermaphrodite.
- 8. The gonads shed their products into the coelom where fertilisation is believed to occur. Reproduction by budding also occurs leading to the colonial organisation.
- 9. The larva is a modified trochophore, known as the Cyphonautes larva.

(see page 244)

Class Phylactolaemata

Bryozoa in which:-

- ● 1. The lophophore is horse-shoe shaped.
- ● 2. There is an epistome.
- 3. The members are restricted to fresh-water.

Examples:- Cristatella, Plumatella.

Class Gymnolaemata - Sea mats

Bryozoa in which:-

- ● 1. The lophophore is circular.
- ● 2. There is no epistome.
- 3. The members are almost all marine.

Examples:- Paludicella, Bugula, Flustra.

(see page 244)

PHYLUM BRYOZOA

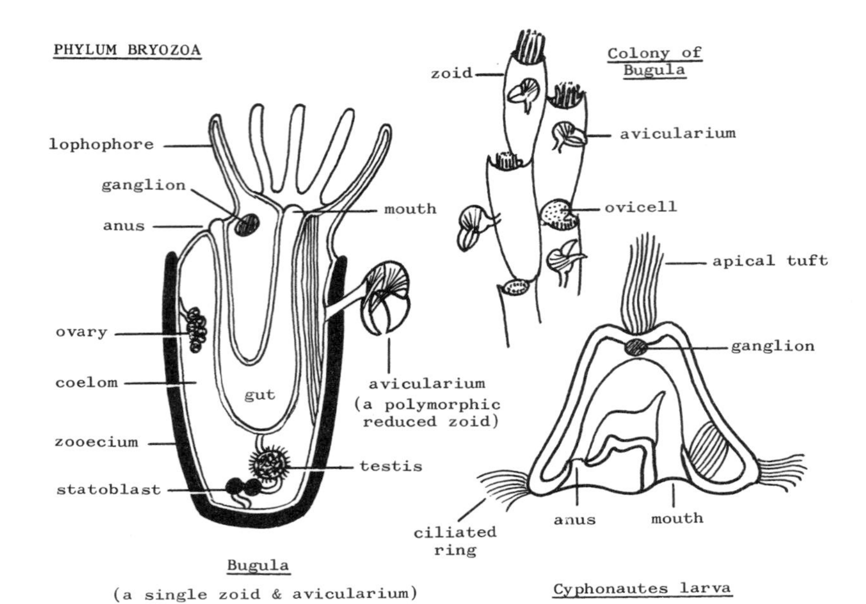

Bugula

(a single zoid & avicularium)

Cyphonautes larva

PHYLUM PHORONIDEA

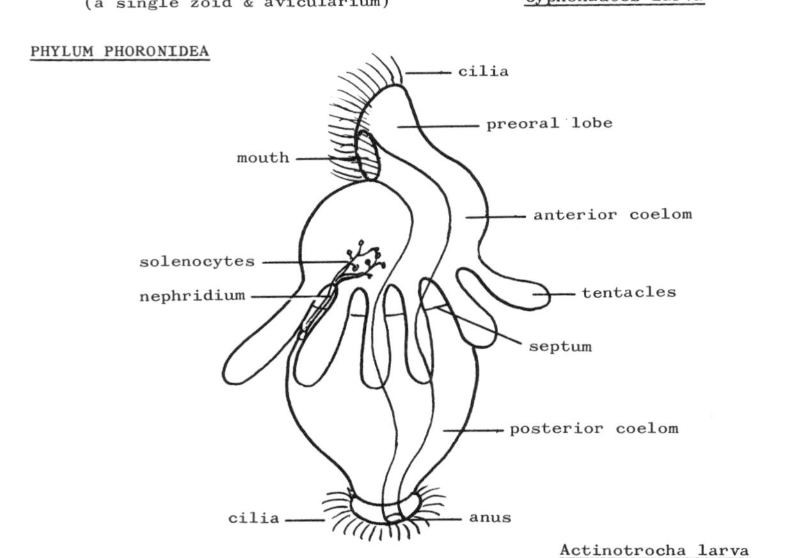

Actinotrocha larva

Phylum Phoronidea

Eucoelomata in which:-

- ● 1. The members are worm-like marine tubicolous animals, that are often found closely aggregated, though colonies are not formed.
- ● 2. The lophophore is coiled to a variable extent in the different species.
- ● 3. The body is found in a membranous tube of leathery consistency.

4. There is a well-developed blood vascular system whose vessels have contractile walls. The blood contains haemoglobin.
5. The nervous system comprises a circum-oral ring with a ganglion between the mouth and anus and nerve cords supplying the tentacles: the nerve cells lie immediately beneath the epidermis.
6. The excretory organs comprise a pair of nephridial tubes opening externally near the anus and internally by two apertures into the posterior coelom.
7. The members are hermaphrodite.
8. The gonads shed their products into the coelom.
9. The larva is a modified trochophore known as the actinotrocha larva.
10. The coelom is divided into a small anterior coelom extending into the tentacles and a spacious posterior perivisceral coelom.

Example:- <u>Phoronis</u>. (see pages 244, 246)

PHYLUM PHORONIDEA

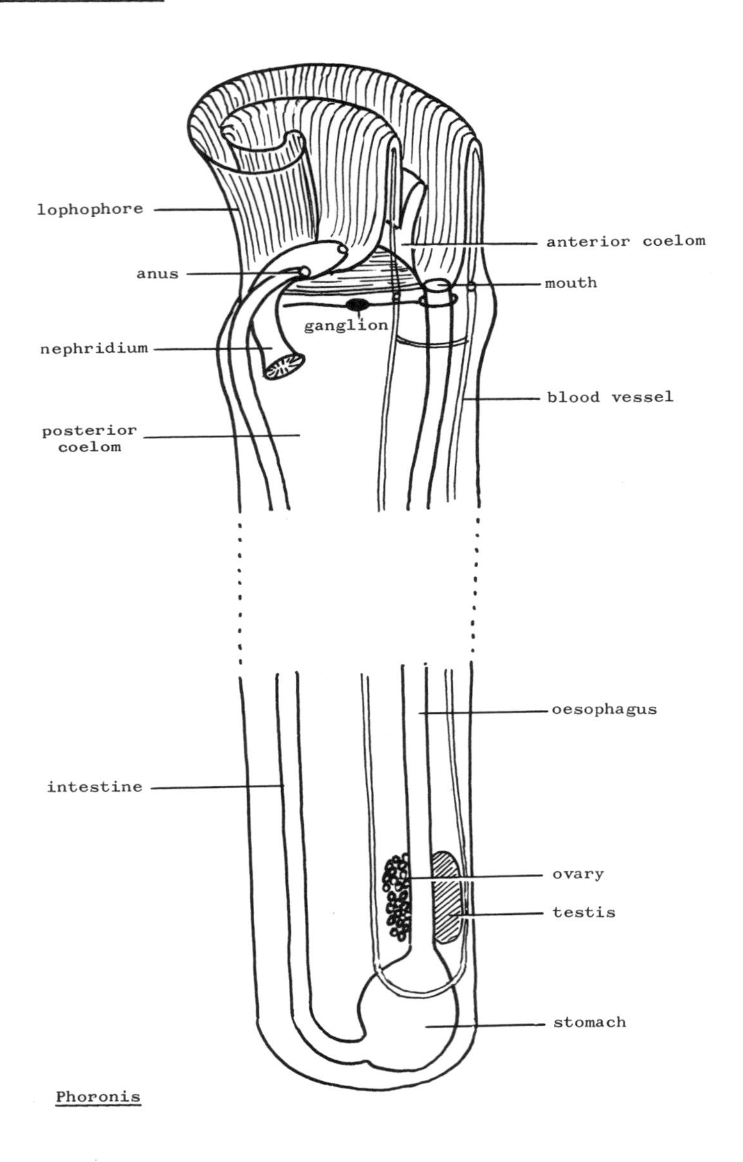

Phoronis

Phylum Chaetognatha

Eucoelomata in which:-

- ● 1. The bilaterally symmetrical body is divided into three regions: head, trunk and post-anal tail. Typically the head bears several pairs of chitinous spines, which function as jaws, on either side of the subterminal mouth.
- 2. The mesoderm of the head, trunk and tail are separate. This is sometimes regarded as evidence of segmentation.
- 3. The gut is straight and opens posteriorly through a subterminal anus. There are no lateral openings or pouches to the foregut (gill slits or pouches).
- 4. The nervous system is well developed and consists of a cerebral ganglion and a ventral ganglion situated in the trunk. These ganglia are joined by circum-pharyngeal commissures and nerves radiate from the ganglia to all parts of the body.
- 5. The coelom is spacious and, in agreement with the mesodermal blocks, is divided by vertical septa into paired perivisceral sacs in the head, trunk and tail respectively.
- 6. There are no special excretory organs.
- 7. There is no blood vascular system.
- ● 8. The body wall comprises an epidermis, covered with a cuticle, and four longitudinal bands of muscles (dorso-lateral and ventro-lateral) rather like those of Nematoda. There are lateral fins in the trunk and tail regions.
- 9. The members are hermaphrodite having paired ovaries situated in the trunk coelom and paired testes in the tail coelom. Cross fertilisation occurs.
- ●10. The members are marine and pelagic and are never colonial.
- 11. There is a free swimming larva which does not resemble a trochophore.

Example:- <u>Sagitta</u>. arrow worms (see page 248)

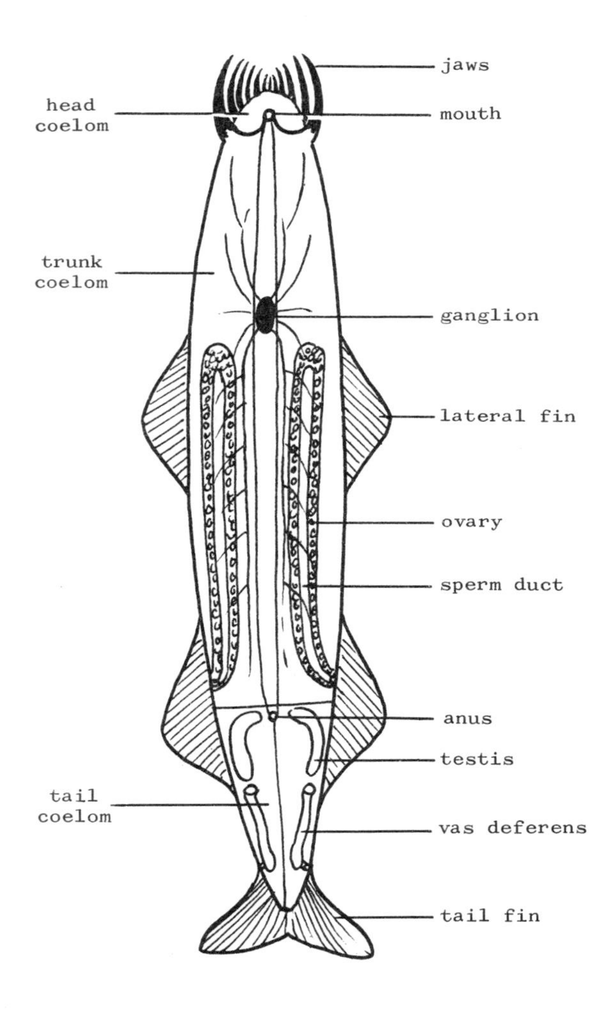
jaws
head coelom
mouth
trunk coelom
ganglion
lateral fin
ovary
sperm duct
anus
testis
tail coelom
vas deferens
tail fin

Sagitta

14 Echinoderms

In the majority of animals, the fertilised egg repeatedly divides and forms a hollow ball of cells, the blastula, which, by invagination, gives rise to a two-layered gastrula with its internal cavity or archenteron in communication with the exterior through the blastopore. The blastopore represents, in a sense, the site of invagination of the blastula which has become constricted by movement and growth of cells to form a narrow opening. In the annelids, arthropods and molluscs and their allies, the mouth forms at the site of the blastopore, that is they are protostomes. The echinoderms and chordates, on the other hand, are deuterostomes, the blastopore forming the anus and the mouth subsequently developing at the opposite end of the embryo. This appears to be one of a number of links between echinoderms and chordates and a distinction from the evolutionary line represented by the annelids and arthropods.

The echinoderms have a number of peculiarities in which they differ from all other invertebrates. All living and most fossil echinoderms have a structure based on five-sided symmetry, although some have increased this number by duplication, and others, notably the sea cucumbers, have regained a functional bilateral symmetry. Radial symmetry is associated as a rule with a sessile habit, and the earliest echinoderms were sessile being attached by a stalk to the sea-bed as the deep-sea crinoid sea lilies are today. But all other living forms have lost permanent attachment and have adopted a more or less active existence as suspension feeders, herbivores and predators, modifying their symmetry structurally or through behaviour in accordance with these varied modes of life.

Another characteristic of echinoderms is the internal skeleton of calcium carbonate present sometimes as separate spicules as in the sea cucumbers, or forming articulating vertebra-like ossicles as in the arms of brittle stars, or as a complete test of interlocked plates in the sea urchins. Echinoderms are exclusively marine, and the sea provides the calcium carbonate for skeleton formation. The sea water, little modified except for an increased concentration of potassium, also fills the capacious coelomic spaces of echinoderms. These are peculiar in that, unlike other animals, the coelom is in direct connection with the external medium. An important part of the coelom forms the water vascular system which is unique in echinoderms. This system operates hydraulically a large number of tube feet which are used for various purposes in different echinoderms. The tube feet may end in suckers and serve for locomotion, or to obtain attachment to a bivalve mollusc shell in the case of predatory starfish. On the other hand they may be more or less pointed, without suckers, and used for passing food toward the mouth in the suspension feeders such as the brittle stars. In some echinoderms, for example the heart urchin, *Echinocardium*, there may be different kinds of tube feet serving different functions. In most echinoderms the tube feet are sites for oxygen uptake and also have a sensory function.

The name echinoderm means spiny skinned. Most, except the sea cucumbers, have movable calcareous spines which may be very large as in the slate-pencil sea urchin, *Heterocentrotus*, or extremely long as in *Diadema*. In starfishes and sea urchins the spines are often interspersed with pedicellariae, movable projections with snapping jaws of different kinds. The pedicellariae serve to remove small animals such as settling larvae from the surface of the animal and thus keep the body free from epizoic growths.

E C H I N O D E R M A T A

Most echinoderms have a 'pluteus' larva which is planktonic, bilaterally symmetrical and ciliated with modifications of form characteristic of the various classes of the phylum. Radial symmetry is imposed at metamorphosis. These pluteoid larvae are clearly different from the trochophore larva of polychaetes and molluscs, so that the origin of the echinoderms, like that of so many of the invertebrates, is obscure. It would seem necessary, therefore, to go back to a post-nemertine pre-annelid level of organisation for an echinoderm ancestor and to envisage an evolutionary line distinct from the complex that has given rise to the annelids, arthropods and molluscs.

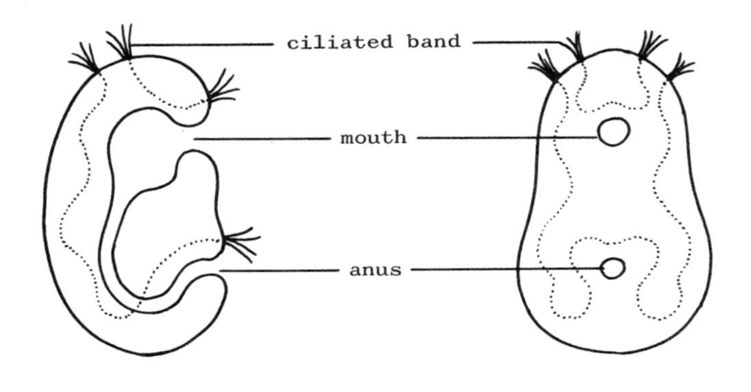

lateral view

ventral view

bilaterally symmetrical 'pluteoid' larva

Phylum Echinodermata

Eucoelomata in which:-

1. There is evidence of metameric segmentation in the early larva though this is completely obscured in the adult. The body of the adult is secondarily radially symmetrical (usually pentaradiate) being developed from a bilaterally symmetrical larva.
2. The adult body is of two main types, radiate or globular, with oral, aboral, radial and interadial regions. Radiate forms have a central disc and arms. There is no head.
3. The gut is very variable in form and may have no anus. There are no lateral openings or pouches to the foregut (gill slits or pouches).
4. The nervous system is well developed but diffuse, much remaining epidermal.
5. Organs of special sense are typically present but poorly developed.
6. The body wall comprises a ciliated epidermis overlying a dermis containing calcareous ossicles which are often produced into spines (giving the phylum its name).
7. The appendages are highly characteristic tube feet (podia) and sometimes pedicellariae.
8. Body wall musculature is usually weakly developed.
9. There is a spacious coelom which forms the body cavity and which arises in three distinct regions. The middle left coelom gives rise to the complex water vascular system.
10. There are no special excretory organs.
11. The blood vascular system is doubtfully represented by strands of lacunar tissue (the so-called 'haemal system'). Many of the functions normally associated with a blood system are performed by the coelomic system, which communicates with the exterior by the madreporite.

12. The products of the gonads are passed to the exterior through gonoducts.
13. The sexes are separate.
14. There are free swimming larvae of various forms, each associated with a particular class. All are essentially 'pluteoid' in type with the main ciliary band peri-oral.

(see page 251)

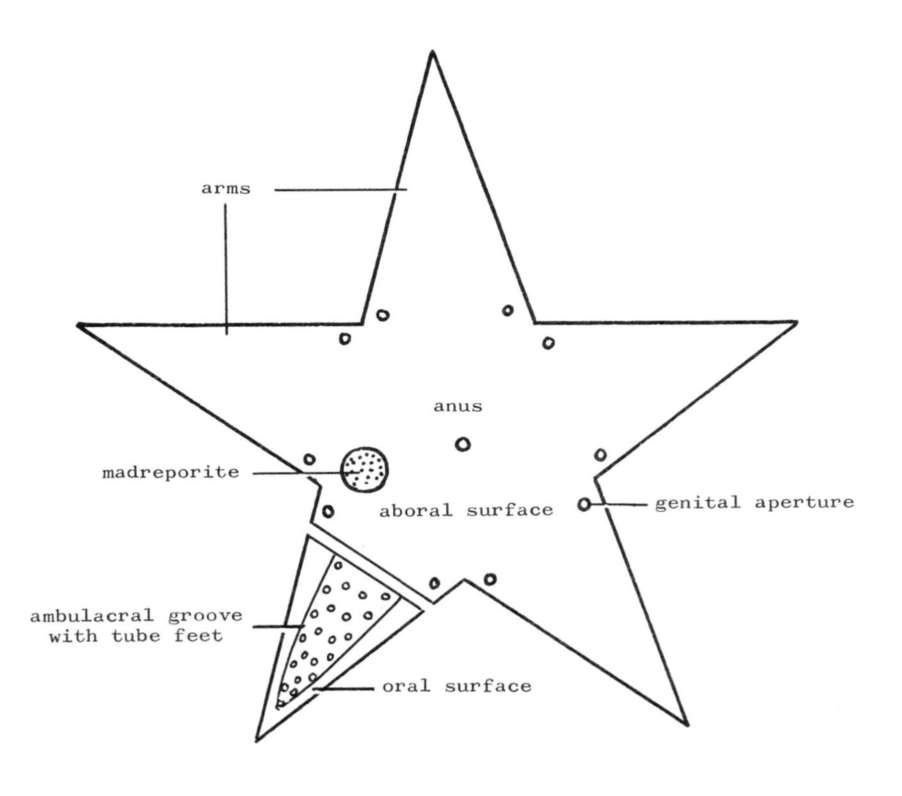

generalised pentaradiate echinoderm

E C H I N O D E R M A T A

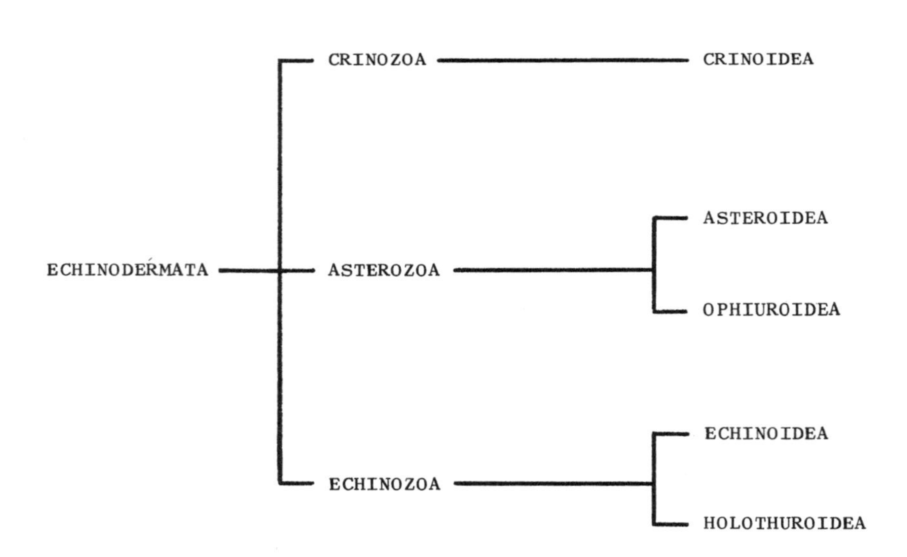

E C H I N O D E R M A T A

Subphylum Crinozoa

Echinodermata in which:-

- 1. The adult, or in some cases the larva only, is stalked or sessile.
- 2. The ambulacral grooves are narrow and ciliated, functioning as food-grooves in carrying food to the mouth: the tube feet, when present, are tentacular and strongly ciliated.
- 3. The anus is usually on the oral surface.
- 4. The mouth is directed upwards.

Class Crinoidea - Sea lilies and Feather stars

Crinozoa in which:-

- 1. The body is more or less hemispherical.
- 2. The arms are five in number and branched. The gonads and coelom extend into the arms.
- 3. There is no madreporite.
- 4. The ambulacral grooves are open.
- 5. Tube feet without suckers are present.

6. There is a skeleton of large ossicles.
7. There are no pedicellariae or spines.

- 8. The anus is on the oral surface.

9. The larva is a pentacrinoid (in Antedon).
10. The members are known from the Lower Cambrian to Recent.

Examples:- Antedon, Pentacrinus. (see page 257)

Subphylum Asterozoa

Echinodermata in which:-

- 1. Members are radially symmetrical, free living, with star-shaped body and no stem.
- 2. The ambulacral grooves bear a double series of tube feet which typically possess terminal suckers.
- 3. The anus is usually on the aboral surface.
- 4. The mouth is directed downwards.

E C H I N O D E R M A T A

Class Asteroidea - Starfishes

Asterozoa in which:-

● 1. The body is star-shaped and usually pentagonal with a central disc.

● 2. Arms are present which are not usually distinctly marked off from the central disc and contain prolongations of the coelom, gonads and gut.

● 3. The madreporite is aboral.

● 4. The ambulacral grooves are open.

● 5. Tube feet, usually terminating in suckers, are present.

6. The skeleton consists partly of a mesh-work of ossicles and partly of a series of closely set, discrete, plates.

● 7. Pedicellariae are usually present and may be of more than one kind.

● 8. The anus is aboral.

9. The larva is typically a bipinnaria developing into a brachiolaria before metamorphosis.

Example:- Asterias. (see page 258)

Class Ophiuroidea - Brittle stars

Asterozoa in which:-

● 1. The body is pentagonal with a central disc.

● 2. Arms are present which are distinctly marked off from the central disc but do not contain prolongations of either t perivisceral coelom or the gut. The arms may be branched

● 3. The madreporite is oral.

● 4. The ambulacral grooves are usually covered.

● 5. Tube feet are present but they lack suckers.

● 6. The skeleton consists of calcareous plates in the disc an typically of articulating ossicles in the arms.

7. There are no pedicellariae.

8. There is no anus.

9. The larva is an ophiopluteus.

Examples:- Ophiothrix, Gorgonocephalus. (see page 257)

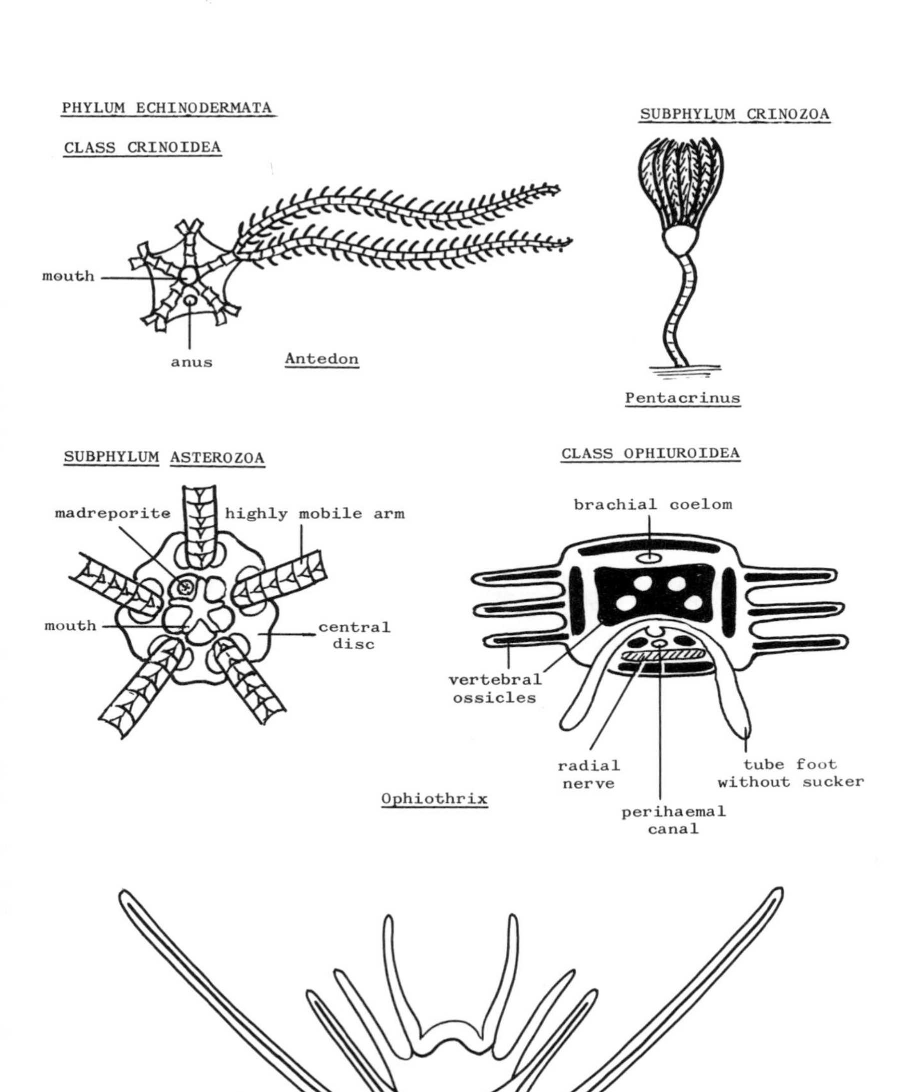
PHYLUM ECHINODERMATA
SUBPHYLUM CRINOZOA
CLASS CRINOIDEA
mouth
anus
Antedon
Pentacrinus
SUBPHYLUM ASTEROZOA
CLASS OPHIUROIDEA
madreporite
highly mobile arm
mouth
central disc
brachial coelom
vertebral ossicles
radial nerve
tube foot without sucker
perihaemal canal
Ophiothrix
internal skeletal rod with forked end
ophiopluteus

CLASS ASTEROIDEA

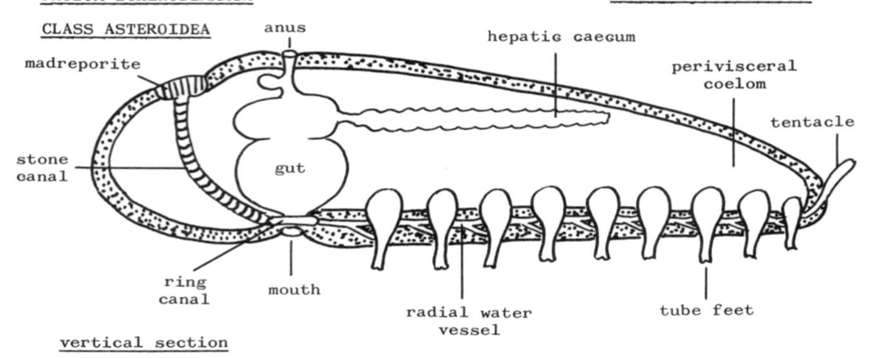

vertical section

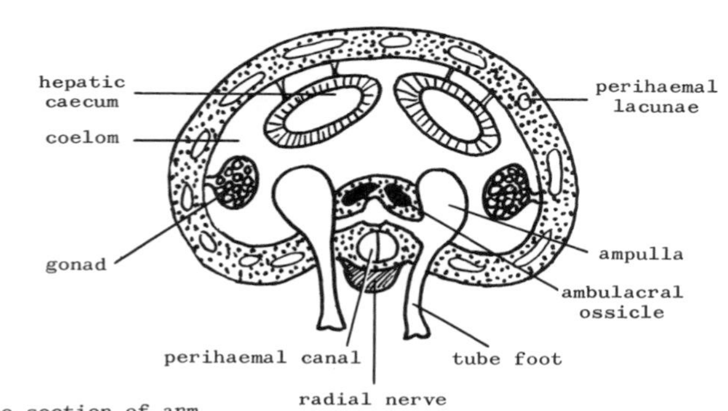

transverse section of arm

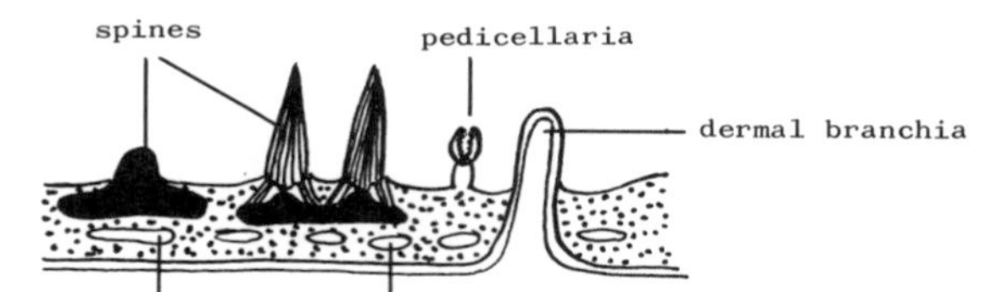

section of body wall

Asterias

E C H I N O D E R M A T A

Subphylum Echinozoa

Echinodermata in which:-

- 1. Members are globular in shape; arms are never developed.
- 2. Ambulacral grooves are covered and the tube feet have suckers.
- 3. The position of the anus is variable.
- 4. The mouth is directed downwards or forwards.

Class Echinoidea - Sea Urchins and Sand Dollars

Echinozoa in which:-

- 1. The body is spheroidal, heart-shaped, or discoidal.
- 2. Oral-aboral axis is vertical. Mouth on lower surface.
- 3. The madreporite is aboral.
- 4. The ambulacral grooves are covered and are meridional in position.
- 5. The tube feet end in suckers and form five double meridional rows.
- 6. The calcareous plates of the skeleton regularly interlock to form a complete shell.
- 7. The pedicellariae are numerous and varied and are interspersed with long, movably articulated spines.
- 8. The anus is primitively aboral but may migrate to the oral surface.
- 9. The larva is an echinopluteus.

Examples:- Echinus, Spatangus. (see page 260)

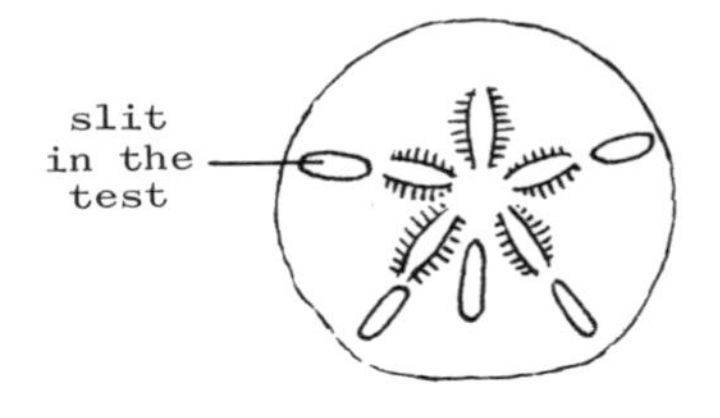

Mellita

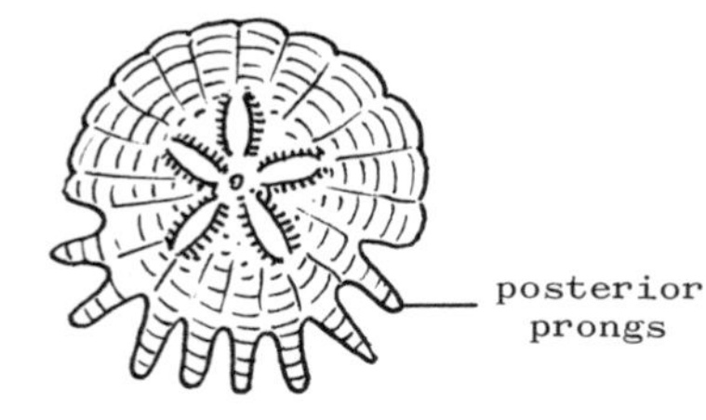

Rotula

(spines removed)

PHYLUM ECHINODERMATA

SUBPHYLUM ECHINOZOA

CLASS ECHINOIDEA

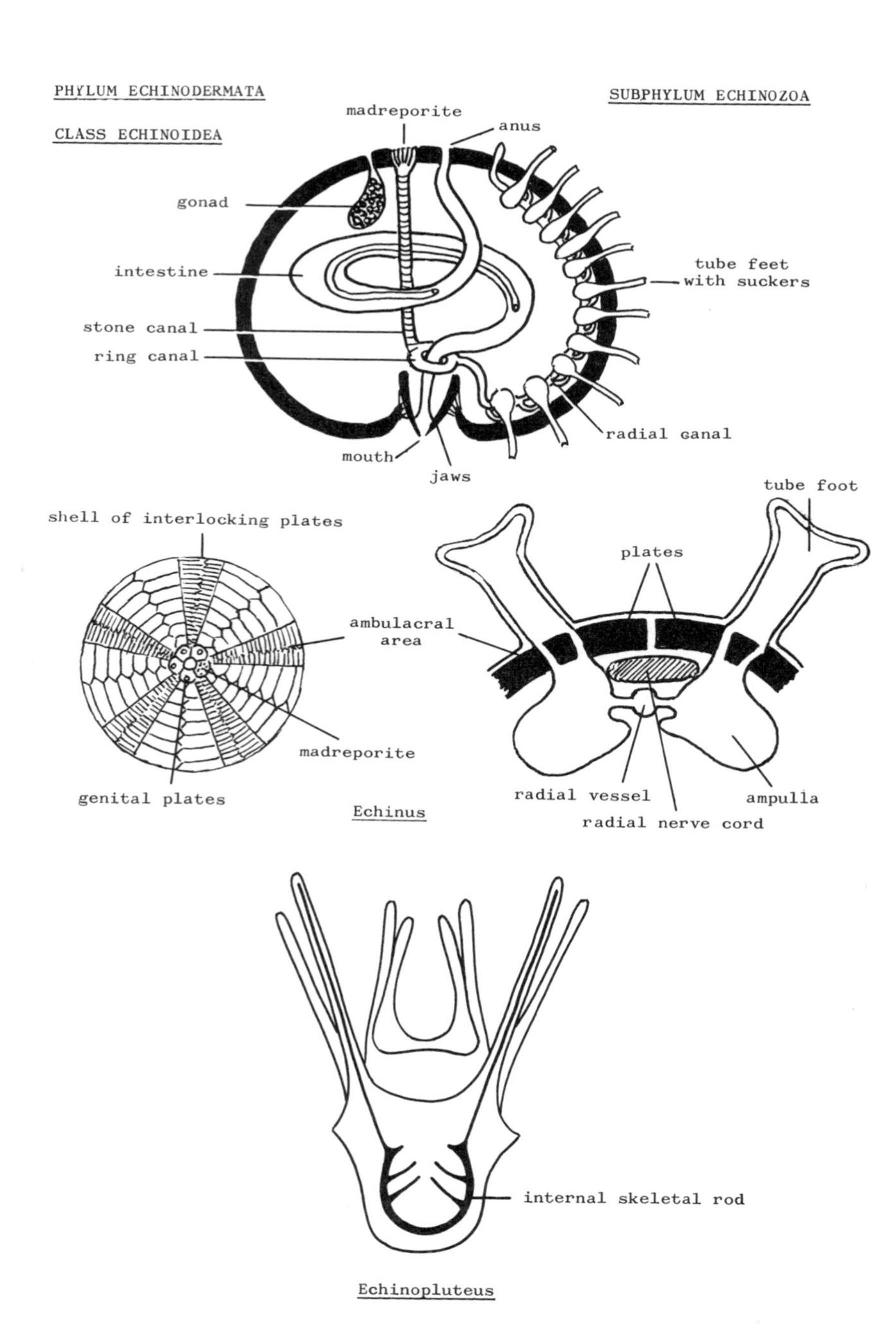

Echinus

Echinopluteus

E C H I N O D E R M A T A

Class Holothuroidea - Sea Cucumbers

Echinozoa in which:-

- 1. The body is elongated along the oral-aboral axis.
- 2. Oral-aboral axis is horizontal. Mouth anterior in position.
  3. The madreporite is internal except in some Elasipoda.
- 4. The ambulacral grooves are covered and run longitudinally.
- 5. The tube feet, when present, usually possess suckers and are either arranged in rows or are irregularly scattered; those surrounding the mouth are modified to form tentacles.
- 6. The body wall, which is dermo-muscular, contains very small separate ossicles.
  7. There are no pedicellariae or spines.
- 8. The anus is aboral with paired 'respiratory trees' usually present and opening into the cloaca.
  9. The larva is characteristically an auricularia which develops into a doliolaria before metamorphosis.

Examples:- Holothuria, Cucumaria. (see page 262)

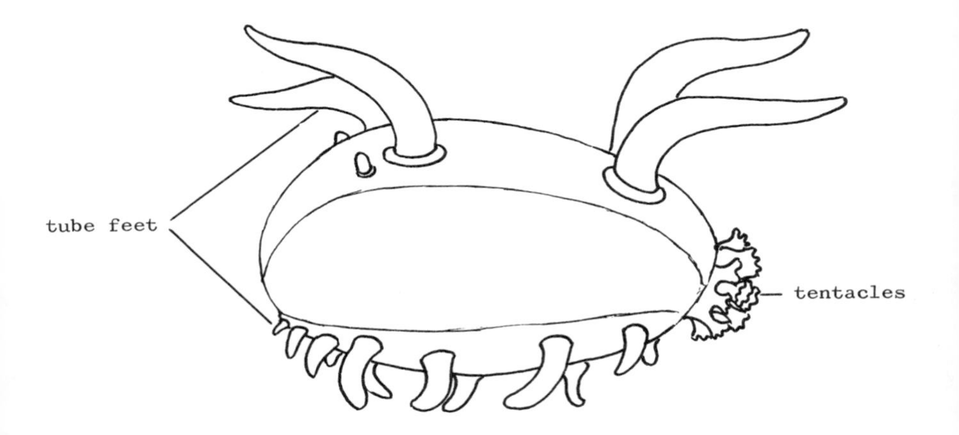

Scotoplanes
(a deep-sea holothurian)

CLASS HOLOTHUROIDEA

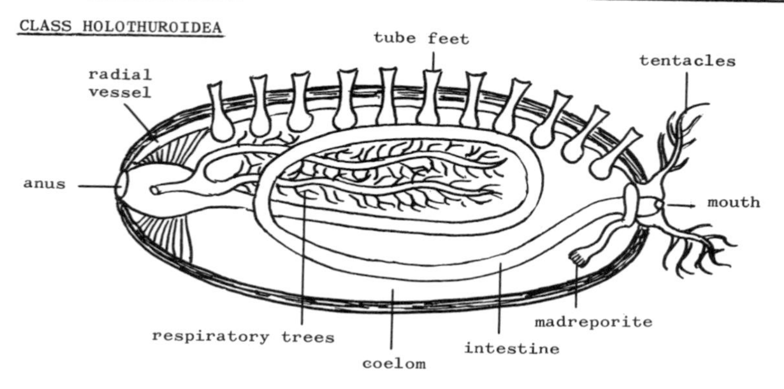

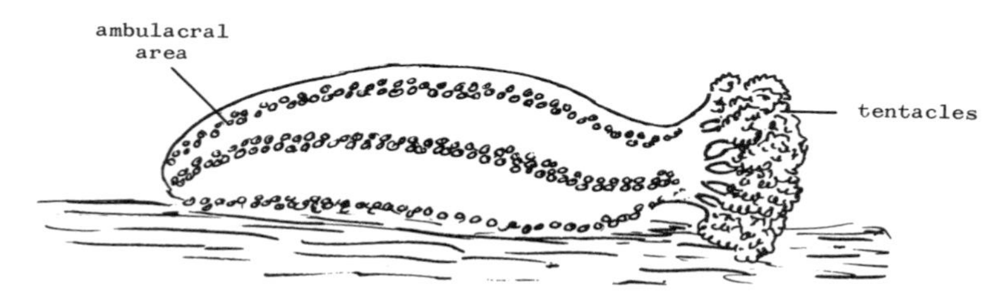

Cucumaria

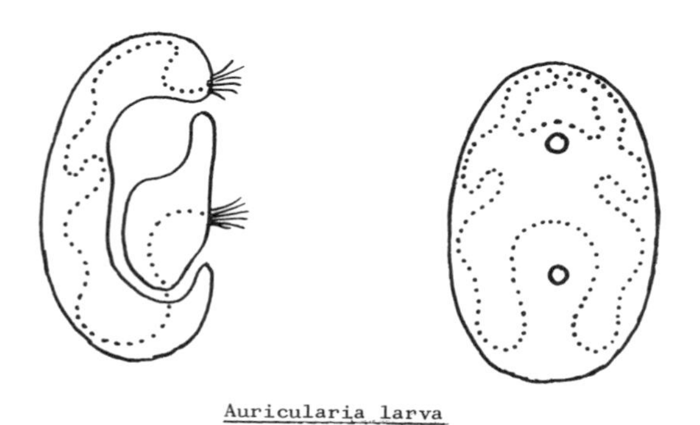

Auricularia larva

15 Hemichordates and Chordates

The names vertébrés and invertébrés were introduced by Lamarck in 1797 as a major division of the animal kingdom. But this division, although universally accepted by zoologists, is not easily represented in a formal classification of the phyla. The Chordata are so named because they have an internal axial skeleton, the notochord, which in higher forms is replaced by the vertebral column, but is always present, at least in the embryo. The phylum Chordata, therefore, contains both invertebrate and vertebrate animals, but it is only the former which are treated in this guide, the different classes of vertebrates being reserved for subsequent volumes.

The chordates have other basic characters beside the notochord. The principal nerve cord is dorsal and hollow, in contradistinction to the invertebrate phyla where the nerve cord is ventral and solid. The pharynx of the chordate gut has lateral openings, permitting a respiratory current of water entering the mouth to pass to the exterior. These pharyngeal clefts are modified to form other structures in the adults of higher chordates living on land, but are present in the embryo. A post-anal tail is also present, at least in the embryo or larva.

Until comparatively recently the Hemichordata, including the acorn worms, *Balanoglossus*, and the Pterobranchia, were classified as a subphylum of the Chordata. They have undoubted affinities with the chordates as shown by the presence of pharyngeal clefts, but they lack a true notochord and a post-anal tail and have various primitive invertebrate features. The division of the coelom into three distinct regions is reminiscent of the larval echinoderms and the lophophorate phyla Brachiopoda, Bryozoa and Phoronidea, a link which is strengthened by a lophophore-like crown of tentacles and a U-shaped gut in the Pterobranchia. Moreover, *Balanoglossus* has a ciliated larva, the tornaria, very similar to the echinoderm pluteus larva. These 'half-chordates', as the name suggests, are of the greatest interest as intermediate forms whose evolutionary position is best represented by a separate phylum.

Among the true chordates, two groups remain which are invertebrate, the Urochordata and the Cephalochordata. The Urochordata are the sea squirts and salps and their allies. As adults they are not obviously chordates except for the presence of pharyngeal clefts, sometimes few and sometimes many. They are either sessile (Ascidiacea) or pelagic (Larvacea and Thaliacea) and may be solitary or colonial. In either case, sessile or pelagic life, particularly as a colony, has involved loss of structures normally associated with free-swimming chordates, so that the notochord and tail have disappeared and the nerve cord is reduced often to a single ganglion. But most Urochordates have a free-swimming larva in which all the basic chordate characters are evident.

The Cephalochordata include *Branchiostoma* and a few closely allied forms commonly known collectively as amphioxus or the lancelet. Amphioxus is a text-book example of a basic chordate. Notochord, hollow dorsal nerve cord, pharyngeal clefts and tail are demonstrated to perfection, but there are no vertebrae and so it is not a vertebrate. Moreover, amphioxus has a number of very primitive characteristics such as a flame cell nephridial excretory system and muscle cells with cytoplasmic extensions that connect with the nervous system. These features are commonly found in primitive phyla such as the Platyhelminthes, Nemertea and Nematoda. They suggest a very early origin for the chordates, probably different from that of the annelids and arthropods. They are coelomate but, in common with the echinoderms, the mode of development of the coelom is enterocoelic (see Chapter 6). They are also segmented, but here again the metamerism is different from that of the annelids since only the dorsal part of the mesoderm is divided while the ventral part remains unsegmented and is known as the lateral plate. It is perhaps surprising that the vertebrates may well have arisen from a nemertine-like ancestor and share that ancestor with such unlikely animals as sea squirts, acorn worms, starfishes and *Phoronis*.

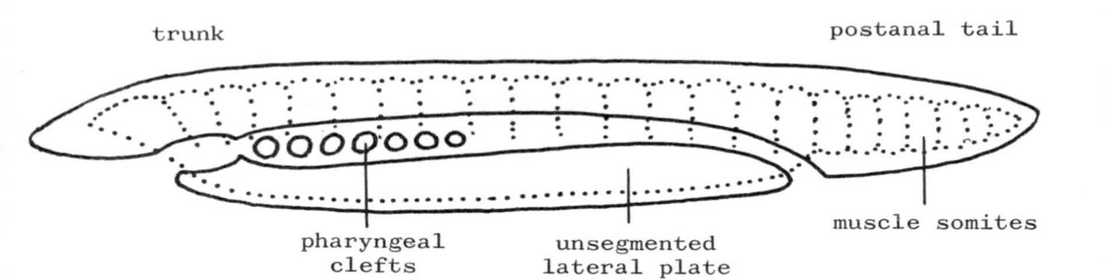

a generalised chordate showing segmentation, pharyngeal clefts and tail

Phylum Hemichordata

Eucoelomata in which:-

- ● 1. The body is divided into three regions, the proboscis, the collar and the trunk, which correspond to the three primary divisions of the coelom. There is no tail.
- 2. There is no true notochord, but an anterior gut diverticulum (stomochord) projects into the proboscis.
- ● 3. There is no atrium, the pharyngeal clefts, where present, opening directly to the exterior.
- 4. The greater part of the nervous system is a subepidermal plexus thickened in places to form tracts and commissures.
- 5. The 'heart' is dorsal to the stomochord and the blood flows <u>forward</u> in the <u>dorsal</u> vessel.
- 6. The body wall is composed of a ciliated glandular epidermis covering muscles resembling those of annelid worms.
- 7. The sexes are usually separate.

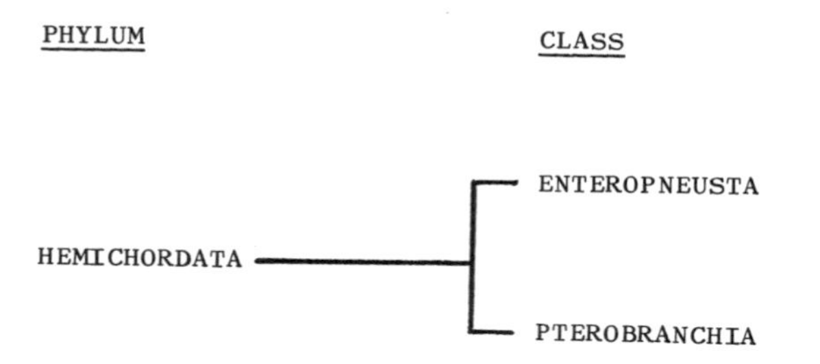

H E M I C H O R D A T A

Class Enteropneusta - Acorn Worms

Hemichordata in which:-

- ● 1. The proboscis is large.
- ● 2. The collar does not bear 'arms' or tentacles.
- ● 3. The alimentary canal is straight.
- ● 4. There are numerous pharyngeal clefts.
- ● 5. The members are marine, free-living and worm-like. They are found burrowing in the sea bed.
- 6. The sexes are separate and the larval form may be a tornaria with close resemblances to the auricularia larva of Holothuroidea.

Examples:- Balanoglossus, Ptychodera. (see page 268)

Class Pterobranchia

Hemichordata in which:-

- ● 1. The proboscis is small.
- ● 2. The collar bears arms from which arise numerous pinnate tentacles.
- ● 3. The anus is near the mouth, the alimentary canal being U-shaped.
- ● 4. There is a single pair of pharyngeal clefts (Cephalodiscus) or a pair of ciliated grooves (Rhabdopleura).
- ● 5. The members are marine, sessile and colonial, secreting a common gelatinous test.
- 6. The sexes are usually separate. The larval development is imperfectly known. The adults also reproduce asexually.

Examples:- Cephalodiscus, Rhabdopleura. (see page 268)

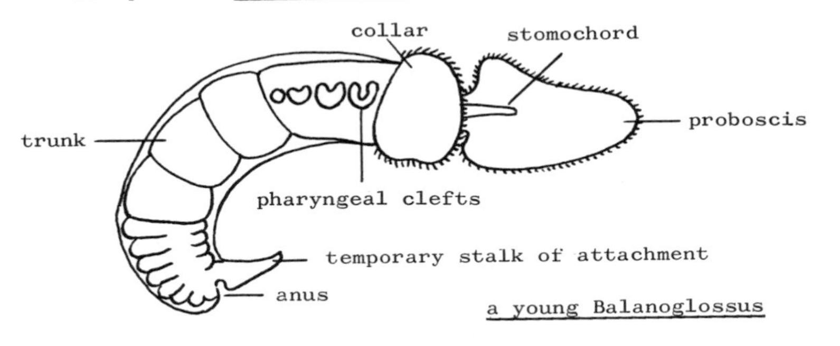

a young Balanoglossus

PHYLUM HEMICHORDATA

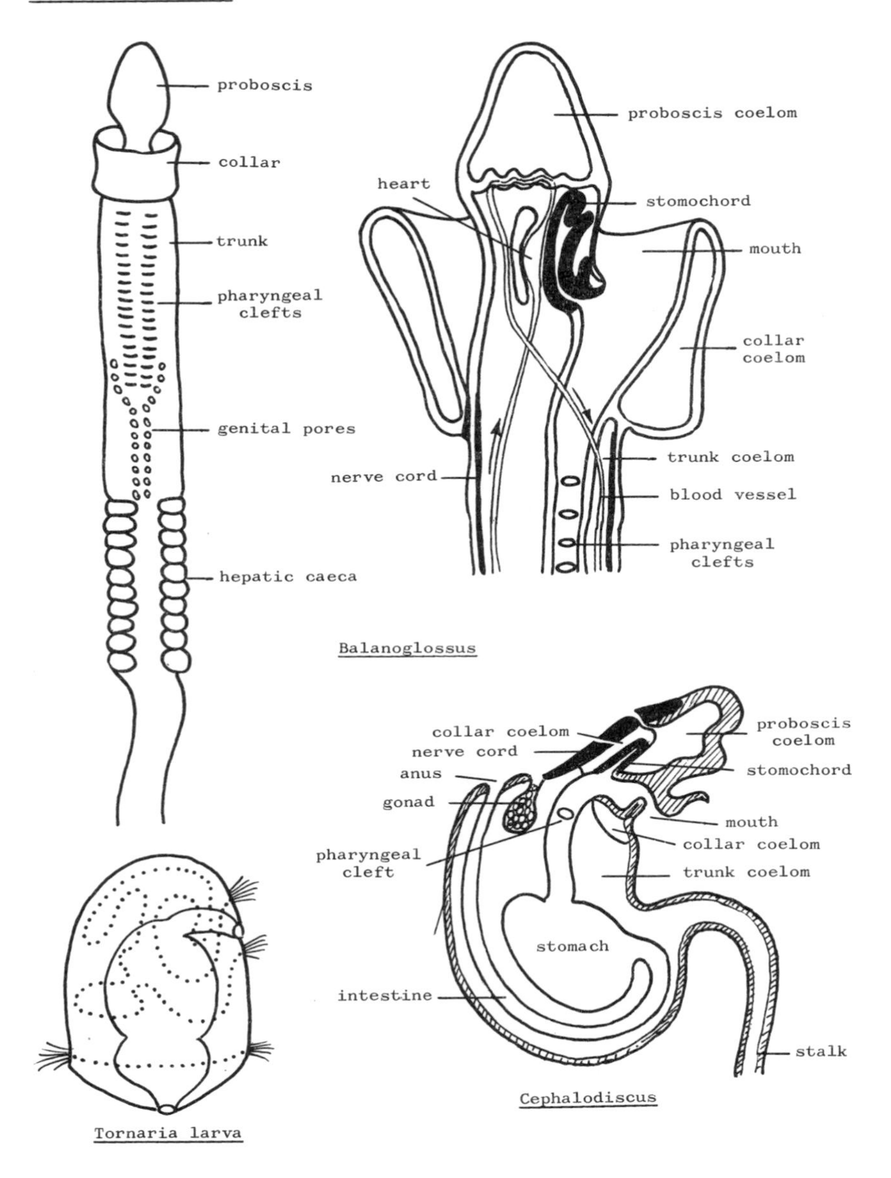

Balanoglossus

Tornaria larva

Cephalodiscus

Phylum Chordata

Eucoelomata in which:-

- ● 1. The body is bilaterally symmetrical and, in higher forms, is divided into head, trunk and post-anal tail regions. The body is metamerically segmented, but the segmentation is of a different nature from that of the other metameric eucoelomates.
- ● 2. There is a notochord, a skeletal rod lying ventral to the central nervous system. In higher forms the notochord is replaced during development to a greater or lesser degree by the vertebral column.
- ● 3. The pharynx possesses lateral openings or pouches (pharyngeal or visceral clefts) which may be transitory, appearing only during development. An endostyle or its homologue (the thyroid) is also present.
- ● 4. The central nervous system is dorsal and tubular.
- 5. There is a well-developed blood vascular system typically possessing a heart, ventral to the gut, through which the blood flows forwards.
- 6. Typically the epidermis of the body wall is stratified. A dermis of mesodermal origin lies between the epidermis and the elaborate (primitively segmental) musculature.
- 7. Typically the sexes are separate.

(see pages 265, 270)

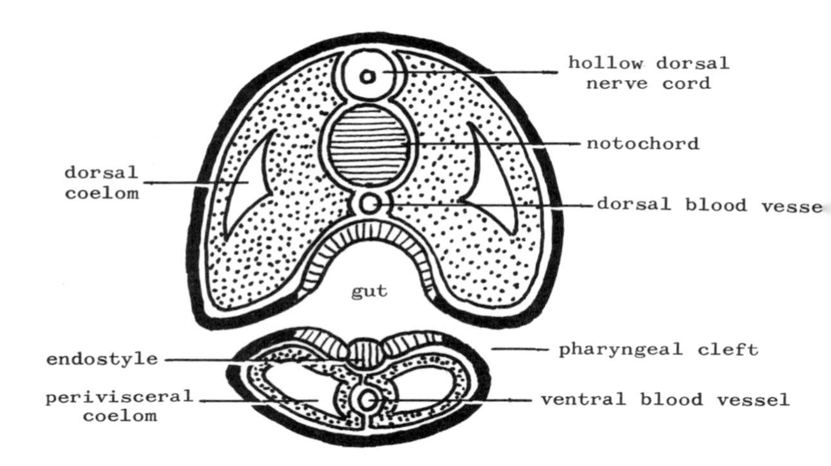

T.S. pharyngeal region of lower chordate

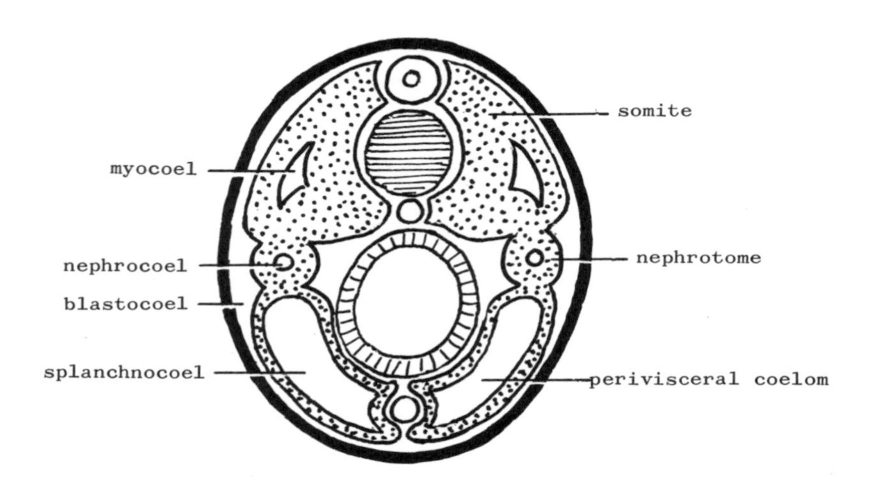

T.S. postpharyngeal region of a vertebrate embryo

C H O R D A T A

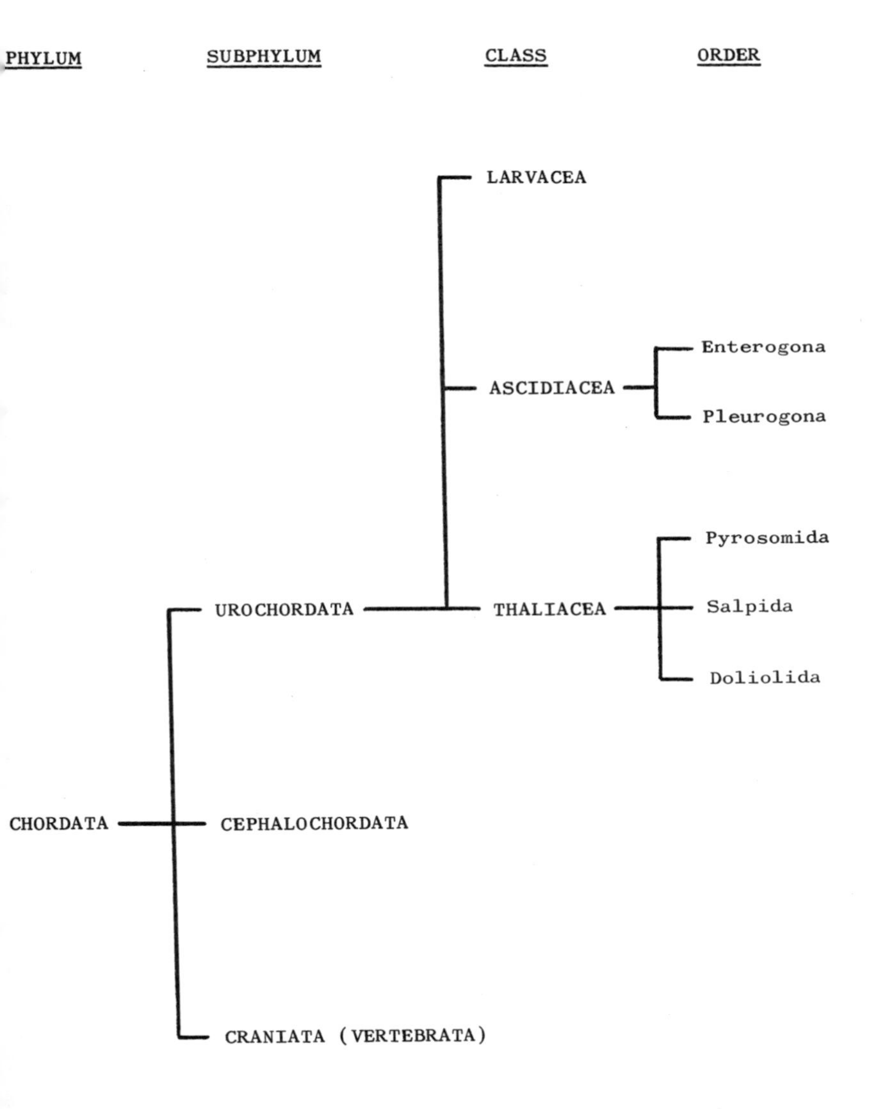
PHYLUM
SUBPHYLUM
CLASS
ORDER
LARVACEA
Enterogona
ASCIDIACEA
Pleurogona
Pyrosomida
UROCHORDATA
THALIACEA
Salpida
Doliolida
CHORDATA
CEPHALOCHORDATA
CRANIATA (VERTEBRATA)

C H O R D A T A

Subphylum Urochordata

Chordata in which:-

1. The body is not regionally divided and the coelom is absent.
2. There is a notochord in the tail of the larva, but is lost in the adult (except Larvacea)
3. There is a post-anal tail in the larva.
4. There is an atrium into which the pharyngeal clefts open in the adult.
5. The central nervous system is separated from the epidermis and in the adult, is reduced to a single, solid, elongated ganglio although in the larva the central nervous system is more prominent and hollow.
6. There is typically a well-developed blood system with a ventra heart through which the direction of flow of the blood is reversed from time to time.
7. The body of the adult is enclosed in a test usually composed o tunicin, a substance related to cellulose.
8. Most of the members are hermaphrodite.

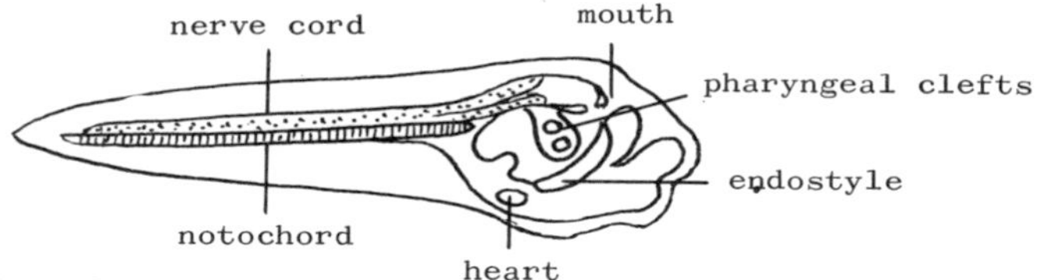

an ascidian larva

Class Larvacea

Urochordata in which:-

1. The adult retains the form of the larva and possesses a tail.
2. The test is temporary and barrel-shaped. It is gelatinous and is not composed of tunicin.
3. There are two simple pharyngeal clefts.
4. There is no atrium.
5. Budding does not occur.
6. The nervous system is relatively well developed.
7. The members are solitary, free swimming and pelagic.

Examples:- Oikopleura, Appendicularia. (see page 274)

C H O R D A T A

Class Ascidiacea - Sea squirts

Urochordata in which:-

1. The adult has lost the larval tail and is variable in form.
2. ● The test is permanent and thick.
3. ● There are several pharyngeal clefts usually subdivided by longitudinal and transverse bars.
4. ● There is an atrium opening dorsally.
5. Budding usually occurs.
6. The nervous system is reduced to a single ganglion.
7. ● The adult is always sedentary and often colonial.

Order Enterogona

Ascidiacea in which:-

1. ● The gonad is unpaired and lies close to the intestine.
2. The body may or may not be divided into 'thorax' and 'abdomen'.
3. The atrial cavity develops from paired lateral rudiments that later fuse mid-dorsally.

Examples:- *Ciona*, *Phallusia*. (see page 274)

Order Pleurogona

Ascidiacea in which:-

1. ● The gonads are normally paired and always lie in the lateral mantle wall.
2. The body is never divided into 'thorax' and 'abdomen'
3. The atrial cavity is developed from an originally single median dorsal invagination of the ectoderm.

Examples:- *Styela*, *Botryllus*.

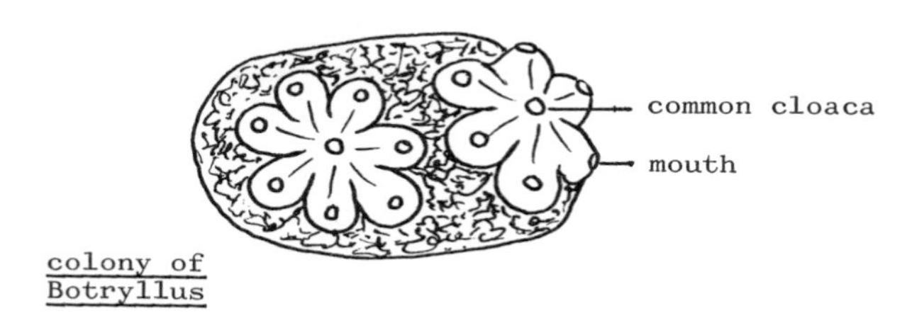

colony of Botryllus

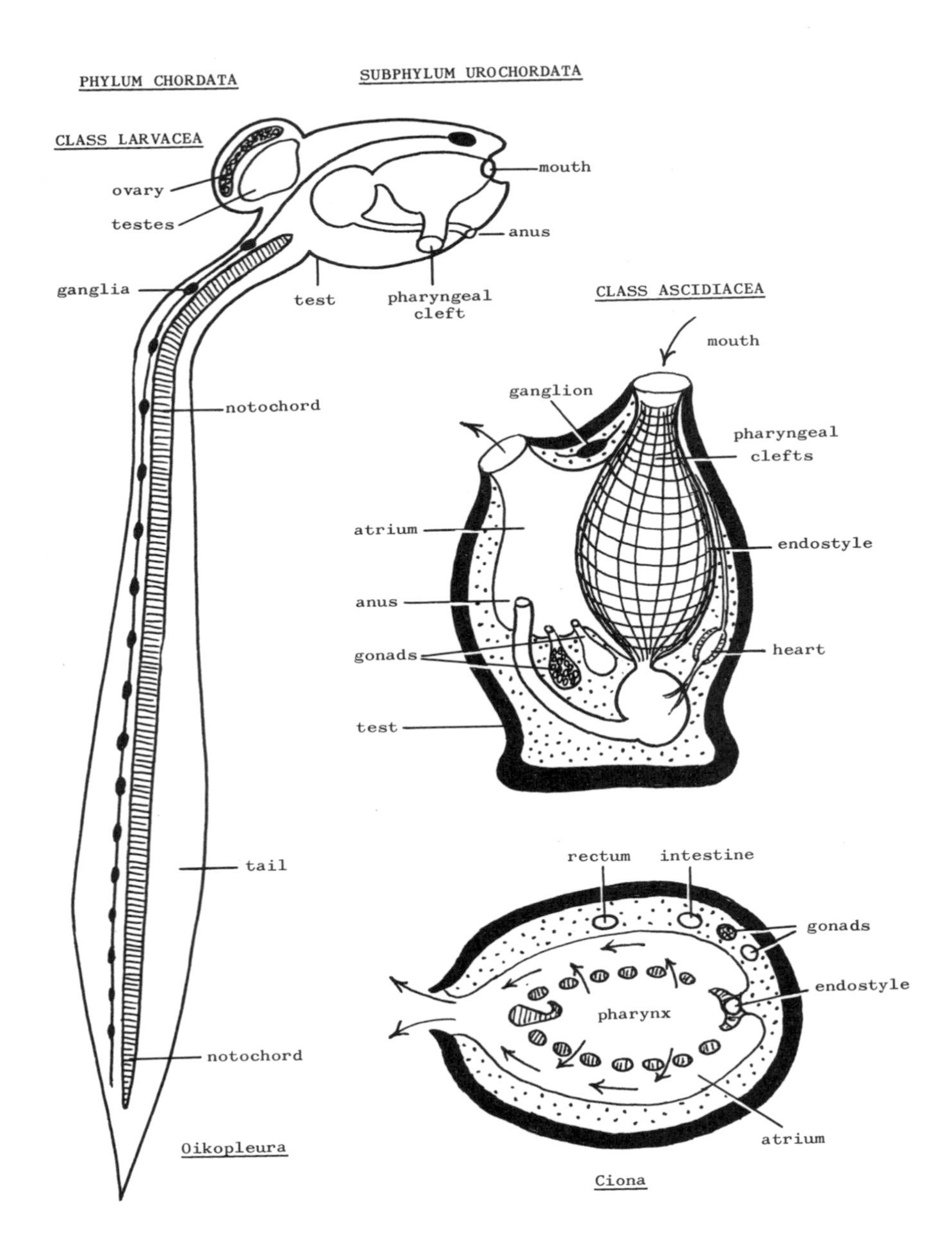
PHYLUM CHORDATA
SUBPHYLUM UROCHORDATA
CLASS LARVACEA
ovary
testes
mouth
anus
ganglia
test
pharyngeal cleft
notochord
tail
notochord
Oikopleura
CLASS ASCIDIACEA
mouth
ganglion
pharyngeal clefts
atrium
endostyle
anus
gonads
heart
test
rectum
intestine
gonads
endostyle
pharynx
atrium
Ciona

C H O R D A T A

Class Thaliacea - Salps

Urochordata in which:-

1. The adult lacks a tail.
2. The test is permanent.
- ● 3. There are either two large or numerous small pharyngeal clefts which are not subdivided by longitudinal bars.
- ● 4. There is an atrium opening posteriorly.
- ● 5. There is a complex stolon from which budding occurs.
6. The nervous system is degenerate.
- ● 7. The members are pelagic and colonial.

Order Pyrosomida

Thaliacea in which:-

1. There is no tailed larva.
2. The oozoid is degenerate and is retained within the parent.
- ● 3. There is a single epicardial tube in the stolon.
4. The blastozoids first form a short chain and then, by budding, a hollow cylindrical colony.
- ● 5. There are numerous pharyngeal clefts.
- ● 6. The oral and atrial apertures are terminal, the oral being directed toward the exterior and the atrial opening toward the interior of the colony.
- ● 7. The body of the individual zoid is spindle-shaped and there are no circular muscle bands around it.

Example:- Pyrosoma. (see page 277)

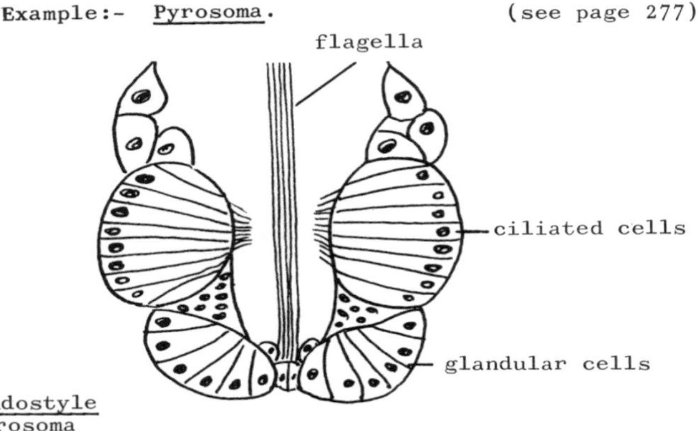

T.S. endostyle of Pyrosoma

Order Salpida (Hemimyaria)

Thaliacea in which:-

1. There is no tailed larva.
2. The oozoid is well developed and liberated from the parent.
3. ● There is a single epicardial tube in the stolon.
4. The blastozoids do not bud but adhere as a chain and break free in groups.
5. ● The primary pharyngeal clefts enlarge and occupy the entire lateral wall of the pharynx.
6. ● The oral and atrial apertures are subterminal.
7. ● The body is fusiform and bears muscle bands which do not form complete rings.

Example:- Salpa. (see page 277)

Order Doliolida (Cyclomyaria)

Thaliacea in which:-

1. There is a tailed larva.
2. The oozoid is well developed and liberated from the parent.
3. ● There is more than one separate epicardial tube in t stolon.
4. The blastozoids are set free singly from the stolon buds which subsequently become attached to the cadophore, a dorsal process of the parent, where the are carried for a time.
5. ● The pharyngeal clefts are short, few in number in th oozoid, but numerous in the blastozoid.
6. ● The oral and atrial apertures are terminal.
7. ● The body is barrel-shaped and bears muscle bands whi form complete rings.

Example:- Doliolum.

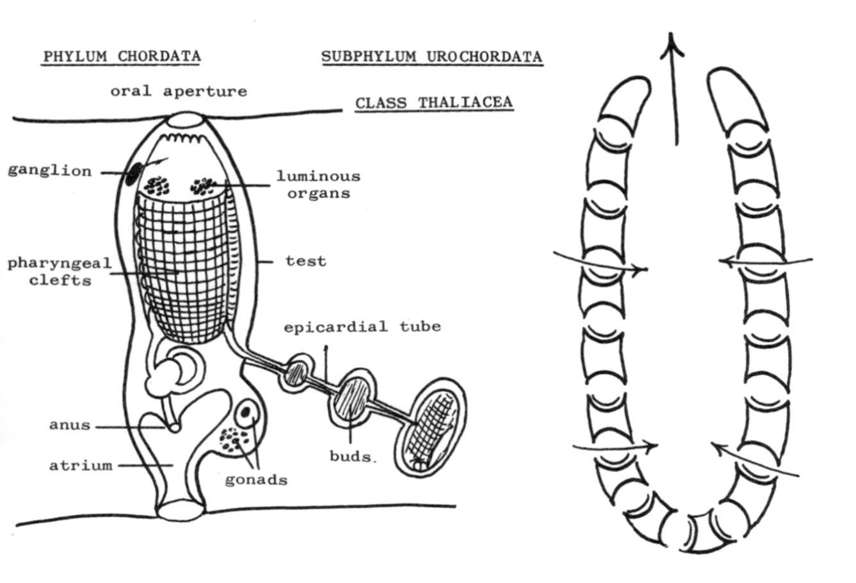

Pyrosoma

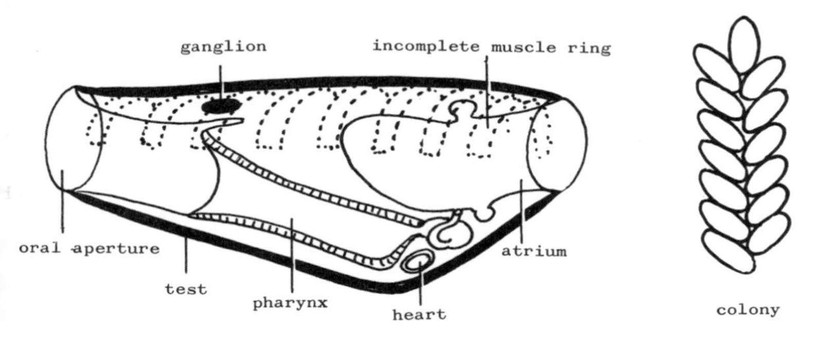

Salpa

C H O R D A T A

__Subphylum Cephalochordata (Acrania)__ - Lancelets

Chordata in which:-

● 1. The body is divided into two regions, a trunk and a post-anal tail. The coelom is well developed.

● 2. There is a well-developed notochord extending the entire length of the body both in the larva and in the adult.

● 3. There is a post-anal tail both in the larva and in the adult.

● 4. An extensive atrium into which the numerous pharyngeal clefts open is developed in the adult.

● 5. There is a well-developed hollow dorsal nerve cord lying above the notochord.

6. There is a well-developed blood system in which the blood flow forward along the contractile ventral vessel, but no heart is present.

7. There is no test.

8. The sexes are separate.

9. The epidermis consists of a single layer of cells and is not ciliated except in the embryo and young larva. There is a dermis and a musculature of segmental pattern similar to that of higher chordates.

10. The excretory system consists of segmentally arranged nephridi with solenocytes limited to the pharyngeal region.

●11. The members are marine. The larva is planktonic and bears a strong resemblance to the adult which is an active animal found burrowing in sand.

Examples:- __Branchiostoma__, __Asymmetron__. (see page 279)

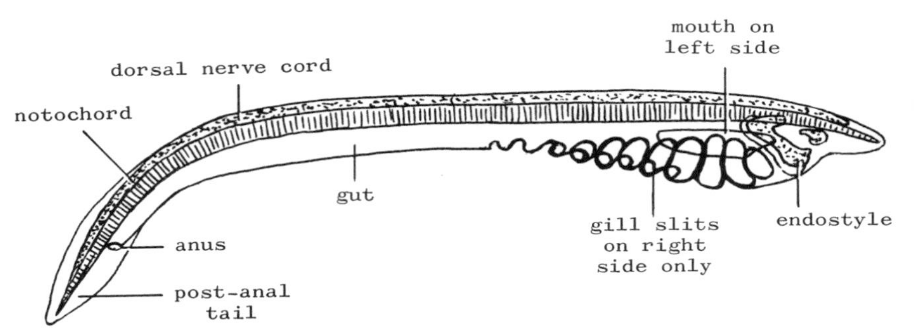

__larva of Branchiostoma__

PHYLUM CHORDATA SUBPHYLUM CEPHALOCHORDATA

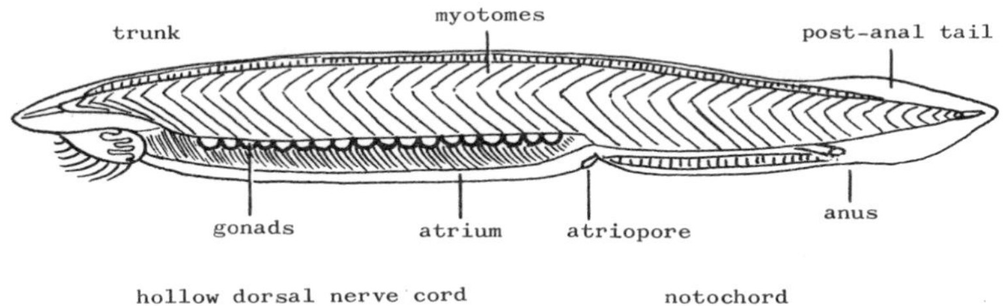

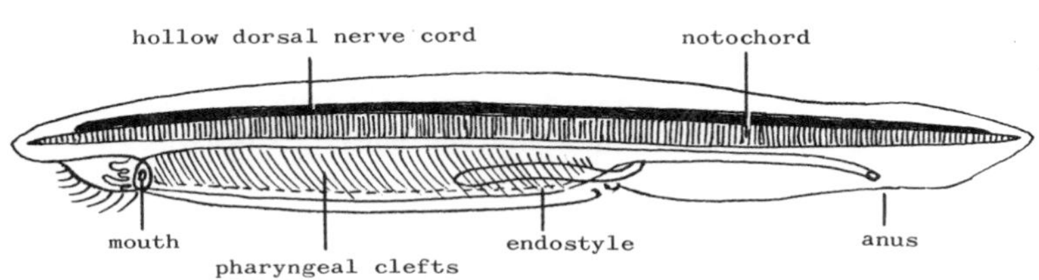

entire animal and with myotomes removed.

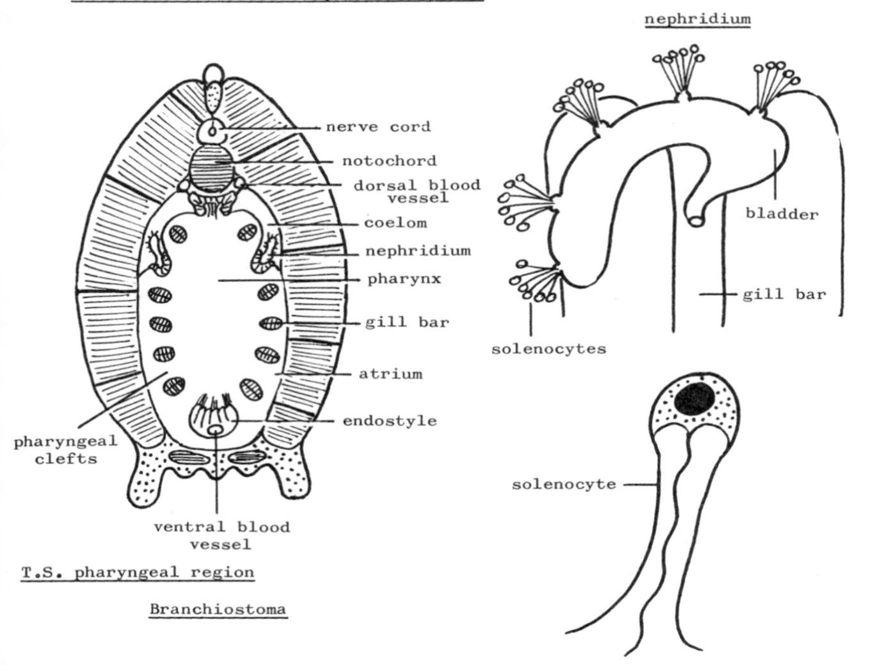

nephridium

T.S. pharyngeal region

Branchiostoma

C H O R D A T A

Subphylum Craniata (Vertebrata)

Chordata in which:-

- 1. The body is divided into three regions, a head with an internal skeletal cranium, a trunk and a post-anal tail. The head bears the mouth and the organs of special sense (olfactory organs, paired eyes, a median dorsal pineal eye and semicircular canals for balance).
- 2. The notochord terminates at the cranium and is supported, and in advanced forms replaced by, cartilaginous and/or bony elements which constitute the vertebral column.
- 3. The post-anal tail is basically for propulsion in the undulatory swimming of lower forms (fishes).
- 4. There is no atrium. The pharyngeal clefts are never more than 14 pairs and usually 4 to 6 pairs. In higher forms they are restricted to the embryo and become highly modified in the adu

5. A complex brain associated with the organs of special sense is formed at the anterior end of the dorsal nerve cord and is encased by the cranium.
6. There is a well-developed ventral heart consisting of a sequence of contractile chambers through which the blood flows forward.
7. There is no test but most craniates have some exoskeletal covering, developed in the skin, and differing in the various classes.
8. The sexes are separate.
9. The skin is stratified and consists of an ectodermal epidermis and a mesodermal dermis closely associated with it.
10. The excretory system is the kidney. It is variously develope from the nephrotome extending backward in the trunk on either side of the vertebral column and divided into pro-, meso- and metanephric regions with their associated ducts leading to the exterior.

16 Glossary

Aboral

Located away from, or on the opposite side of the body to the mouth.

Acontium

A thread-like extension of the mesentery in Anthozoa. It lies in the gastric cavity and can be protruded through the mouth. It bears numerous nematocysts and is used in the capture of prey.

Adoral

Located on the same body surface as the mouth.

Agamete

Reproductive body found in the Mesozoa. It divides by a form of cleavage to produce a daughter individual within the body of the parent.

Ambulacral groove

A linear depression associated with a distinct series of skeletal plates (ambulacrum) on the body surface of echinoderms.

Amphiblastula

Flagellated larva found in the Porifera. At metamorphosis the flagellated cells move to the interior and become choanocytes.

Anastomosis

A linkage, or joining together of a number of branches.

Anthocodium

The exposed, distal part of the feeding polyp in the colonial Alcyonaria (Coelenterata).

Apophysis

A narrow finger-like projection on the inside of the valves of some myoidan molluscs to which are attached the foot muscles.

GLOSSARY

<u>Apterous</u>

Lacking wings.

<u>Arista</u>

A short, bristle-like appendage found on the antennae of certain insects.

<u>Auricularia larva</u>

Larval form found in asteroid and holothurian echinoderms. It is characterised by the presence of a ciliated band whic runs around the outlines of the body.

<u>Avicularium</u>

A zoid resembling a bird's head found in some polymorphic colonial Bryozoa. Its function is largely unknown, but it may be protective.

<u>Bipinnaria larva</u>

Larval form found in asteroid echinoderms. It is derived from the auricularia but differs from this in the stronger, more complicated development of the ciliated bands.

<u>Biramous</u>

Having two branches.

<u>Blastocoel</u>

Fluid-filled cavity, also known as the segmentation cavity, which appears at an early stage in embryonic development as the internal space within the blastula. It may persist in post-embryonic stages as a space between the ectoderm and th endoderm, and as the blood vascular space in Chordates.

<u>Blastozoid</u>

Member of a colony of animals produced by asexual budding. Found in certain Urochordata.

<u>Blepharoplast</u>

Granular body found at the base of the flagellum in Mastigophora.

<u>Bothrium</u>

A sucking groove found on the scolex of certain Cestoda.

<u>Botryoidal tissue</u>

Connective tissue and parenchyma which invade the coelom of the Hirudinea.

GLOSSARY

Brachiolaria larva

Larval form found in asteroid echinoderms. It succeeds the Bipinnaria, during development, and bears three pre-oral adhesive processes.

Brachypterous

Term used to describe insects in which both pairs of wings are reduced in size.

Branchiae

Thin-walled, branched extensions of the body wall which function as external gills, for example, in various Polychaeta.

Campodeiform

Term used to describe a type of larval insect in which there are three pairs of relatively long legs, a well-developed head capsule and biting mouthparts similar to those of the adult. Such larvae are usually active predators.

Captacula

Prehensile tentacles arising from the base of the proboscis in the molluscan Scaphopoda.

Caudal furca

A forked extension of the telson, or tail-piece, composed of two rami, or branches, found in certain Crustacea.

Cerci

A pair of appendages, typically cylindrical or cone-shaped, arising from the most posterior abdominal segment in many insects. They are probably sensory in function.

Chelicera

Pre-oral appendage modified as a jaw and used mainly for food capture in arachnids and their relatives.

Cheliped

Thoracic limb, occurring in certain Crustacea, which is greatly enlarged and terminates in a large claw.

Chelophore

Limb-like appendage located on each side of the proboscis in the Pycnogonida. It bears a jaw, or chelicera at its tip and functions as a mouthpart.

Choanocyte

Flagellated collar cell found as a lining of the internal cavities of the Porifera.

G L O S S A R Y

Chondrophore

The pit found in certain bivalves on the inside of the shell to which the internal ligament is attached.

Chromatophore

A pigment cell found in the body wall of animals.

Cirri

Slender, tentacle-like appendages found on various parts of the body in, for example, the Polychaeta.

Coarctate

A type of pupa occurring in Diptera (Cyclorrhapha) in which the cuticle of the last larval instar persists as a protective case (puparium) around the pupa.

Coelomoduct

A duct of mesodermal origin which runs from the coelom and opens on the external surface of the body.

Coenenchyma

Matrix, or connecting substance in coelenterates, sometimes fleshy but often calcified, linking the polyps of colonial forms.

Coenosarc

Inner living material found in the stems of colonial Coelenterata, linking the individuals.

Colloblast

Adhesive cell found on the tentacles of Ctenophora. These cells are used in food capture.

Cormidium

An assemblage of various forms of polyp in the Siphonophora (Coelenterata), which is usually repeated along the length of a stem, or stolon.

Coxal gland

Complex, glandular structure, excretory in function, which opens at the base of the legs in certain arthropods.

Coxal vesicle

An eversible sac associated with the abdominal style or the coxa in certain uniramous arthropods.

Coxopodite

The basal segment of the biramous abdominal limb of various Crustacea.

Ctene

Ciliated band used for locomotion in the Ctenophora.

G L O S S A R Y

Ctenidium

Respiratory surface, or gill, of aquatic Mollusca.

Cucullus

A hinged plate attached to the carapace and covering the mouthparts in the Ricinulei (Arachnida).

Cypris larva

Larval form occurring in Cirripedia (Crustacea) which is characterised by the presence of a bivalved carapace in which the body is enclosed.

Dactylozoid

Protective or defensive polyp found in certain colonial Coelenterata.

Diploblastic

Having two layers of cells in the body wall.

Doliolaria

Larval form which develops from the auricularia in holothurian Echinodermata, and in which the ciliated band is arranged in rings around the body.

Duplivincular

A ligament in bivalve molluscs which is not of a uniform texture but is formed from alternate bands of hard and soft tissue.

Echinopluteus larva

Larval form occurring in sea urchins (Echinodermata) which is broadly triangular in shape due to the development of 'arms' which bear ciliated bands.

Echiurus larva

Larva of the trochophore type found in the Sipunculida.

Endopod (= Endopodite)

The inner ramus, or branch of the biramous limb of Crustacea.

GLOSSARY

Endostyle

A ciliated groove lying in the floor of the pharynx in the Urochordata and Cephalochordata. It secretes mucus which is used to entrap food particles.

Enteron

The body cavity of coelenterates.

Epicardial tube

A peri-visceral space formed from outgrowths of the pharynx in the Urochordata.

Epipodite

An accessory appendage, typically leaf-like in appearance, borne on the basal segment of the limb in various Crustacea.

Epistome (Crustacea)

A ventral plate which lies in front of the mouth in such Crustacea as crabs.

Epistome (Bryozoa and Endoprocta)

A small ridge or lobe located at the base of the lophophore and overhanging the mouth.

Epizoic

Living externally on another organism and attached to its outer surface.

Exarate

A type of pupa found in various insects, in which the appendages are free and capable of movement.

Exopod (= Exopodite)

The outer ramus, or branch, of the biramous limb of Crustacea.

Exuvium

The cast exoskeleton produced by moulting in arthropods.

Gametocyst

Shell-like protective covering which develops around the gametes of certain Protozoa.

Gastrozoid

Feeding polyp found in polymorphic colonial Coelenterata.

G L O S S A R Y

Gill book

A series of plate-like gills borne on certain of the opisthosomatic segments of the chelicerate *Limulus*. The plates are arranged like the leaves of a book and are protected by a lateral extension of the carapace.

Glycogen

A carbohydrate (polysaccharide) food reserve found in animals.

Gnathobase

An expanded process on the basal portion of a limb, found in certain arthropods. It is used for the manipulation of food.

Gonopore

The external aperture of a gonadial duct.

Gonotheca

A cylindrical capsule enclosing the reproductive polyp in certain colonial Coelenterata.

Gonozoid

Reproductive polyp found in certain colonial Coelenterata.

Haemocoel

A body cavity filled with blood which replaces the perivisceral coelom, especially in arthropods and molluscs.

Hamula

Short abdominal appendage on the ventral surface of various apterygote Insecta which is used to hold the springing organ in position.

Hectocotylized arm

A specialized tentacle, found in the cephalopod Mollusca, which is used for sperm transfer.

Heterotrophic

Feeding on an external source of nutrients of plant or animal origin.

Hologamete

A gamete formed from the entire protistan cell body.

Holozoic

Feeding on other organisms, plant or animal.

G L O S S A R Y

Hypostome

A mouthpart, present in certain arachnids, which frequently takes the form of a single median process directed forwards below the mouth. In ticks, the hypostome bears rows of curved teeth and is used for penetrating the skin of the ho

Imago

The adult stage in the development of an insect.

Infundibulum

That part of the gastrovascular cavity, sometimes termed th pharynx, in Ctenophora, from which the radial canals origin

Kinetonucleus

A large granular body found near the blepharoplast in certai flagellate Protozoa.

Lacinia mobilis

A small movable, tooth-like process on the mandible of crustacean Peracarida.

Laurer's canal

A canal, present in digenean Platyhelminthes, which leads fr the junction of the oviduct and vitelline duct to open on th dorsal surface of the body.

Lung book

Respiratory structure found in certain air-breathing arachni It consists of a sac-like invagination of the body, the wall of which are folded into plates which lie like leaves of a book. The cavity connects with the exterior by a spiracle.

G L O S S A R Y

Madreporite

A perforated plate, found in most echinoderms, through which sea water passes to the water vascular system.

Manubrium

A cone-shaped process, an extension of the subumbrella surface, bearing the mouth in various Coelenterata.

Meganephrostomal

Condition pertaining to the nephridia of Oligochaeta in which the nephridial funnel is well developed, with a multicellular horse-shoe shaped upper lip.

Merogamete

Protozoan gamete formed by the division of the parent, and therefore smaller than the parent.

Mesogloea

The layer in the body wall of Coelenterata between the epidermis and the gastrodermis (endodermis).

Mesonephrostomal

Condition pertaining to the nephridia of Oligochaeta in which the upper lip of the nephridial funnel is reduced to a few cells.

Micronephrostomal

Condition of the nephridia of Oligochaeta in which the upper lip of the nephridial funnel is lacking.

Monilliform

Beaded, like a necklace of spherical beads.

Myoepithelial cell

Columnar cell, found in the ectoderm and endoderm of various Coelenterata, epithelial-like in appearance but with basal contractile fibres.

Nacreous

An iridescent pearly inner surface of some bivalve shells.

Nauplius

Earliest larval stage in the Crustacea. It is ovoid in shape, unsegmented, but with three pairs of appendages.

G L O S S A R Y

Nauplius eye

Simple median eye found in the nauplius larva, but also persisting in many adult crustaceans. It consists of pigment cups filled with retinal cells and, sometimes, a lens.

Nectocalyx

Bladder-like swimming bell present in some Siphonophora. Water is drawn in, and pumped out, by rhythmical contractions of the bladder, and this creates a jet propulsive type of locomotion.

Nematocyst

Stinging cell found on the tentacles and mesenteries of coelenterates.

Nephrocyte

Cell present in the blood of certain arachnids which is specialized for storing excretory products.

Nephromixium

A structure formed by the association of a nephridium and a coelomoduct in various Polychaeta, such that the products of the gonads and excretory organs are discharged through the same pore.

Nephrostome

The opening of the nephridium, internally into the coelom, in the Polychaeta.

Neuropodium

Ventral lobe of the parapodium in Polychaeta.

Notopodium

Dorsal lobe of the parapodium in Polychaeta.

Obtect

A type of pupa found in various insects, in which the appendages are glued, by a secretion, to the sides of the body and are incapable of free movement.

Ocellus

A simple eye, usually consisting of a pigment cup containing a retina and surmounted by a lens.

GLOSSARY

Olynthus

A post-embryonic intermediate stage which develops from the amphiblastula larva in sponges. It forms when the larva becomes attached to the substratum, and the exhalent pore becomes apparent. It has a simple system of pore canals.

Oocyst

An encysted zygote produced by the fusion of gametes in certain parasitic Protozoa.

Ootype

Specialized part of the oviduct which secretes the shell around the fertilized egg in digenean Platyhelminthes.

Oozoid

Member of a colony of urochordate animals produced from an ovum (cf. blastozoid).

Operculum

A horny or calcareous disc secreted by, and attached to, the edges of the mantle and the foot of certain Mollusca, which closes off the aperture of the shell during hibernation.

Ophiopluteus larva

Larval form occurring in brittle stars (Echinodermata) which resembles the echinopluteus, but differs in having fewer 'arms'.

Osphradium

Sense organ present in certain Mollusca. Located near the gill, it may be a simple, knob-like prominence or a more elaborate leaf-like structure. May be used for detecting sediment in the water, and may also be chemosensory.

Ossicles

Calcareous plates forming a skeletal system in the body wall of animals such as echinoderms. These plates are closely placed together but do not unite to form a continuous shell.

Ostium

An opening. Usually applied to the perforations in the wall of the heart through which blood passes from the pericardial sinus. Also used to denote the small, inhalent openings, or pores, in the wall of a sponge.

Oviger

A limb, occurring in the Pycnogonida, located immediately behind the pedipalp, which is used for carrying the egg mass.

GLOSSARY

Paramylum

Carbohydrate food reserve found in certain Protozoa.

Parapodium

Lateral projections of the body wall found in various Polychaeta. They are often paddle-shaped and used in locomotion, but may be modified in sedentary forms for various purposes such as to produce feeding currents.

Parenchyma

Name given to the tissue which fills the interior of the body in Platyhelminthes. Also called mesenchyme. It is composed of irregular cells and extensive intercellular spaces. Probably its main function is for the transport of food materials.

Pectine

Comb-like sensory organ found on the ventral surface of the opisthosoma of scorpions.

Pedicel

A constriction, or 'waist', linking the prosoma and opisthosoma in certain arachnids or the thorax and abdomen in insects.

Pedicellariae

Small grasping organs, formed from modified spines, found on the external body surface of various Echinodermata. They are used for cleaning and protecting the skin.

Pedipalp

First post-oral appendage of the Chelicerata. It may have a simple, limb-like form, or be heavily developed with a terminal pincer. It is often used for food capture and as a sensory organ.

Peduncle

A stalk.

Pelagic

Living in the surface waters of the sea.

Pentacrinoid larva

A stalked larva of some free-living crinoid Echinodermata such as Antedon.

Pereiopod

The name given to the limbs used for walking in the Crustacea.

Pericardium

The cavity in which the heart is located.

GLOSSARY

Peri-oral

Surrounding the mouth.

Perisarc

Horny layer covering the stem of various colonial Coelenterata.

Peristome

Membrane surrounding the mouth.

Phasmid

Small, pit-like sensory structure located in the tail region of certain Nematoda.

Pilidium larva

Larval form found in the Nemertea, which shows many resemblances to a trochophore, but within which the young nemertean is produced.

Pinacocyte

A flattened cell forming a covering layer in the body wall of sponges. Such cells have the ability to change their shape. They function as a pavement epithelium.

Planula larva

Free-swimming, ciliated larva found in the Coelenterata.

Plastids

Bodies containing chlorophyll found in the protistan Phytomastigophora.

Pleopod

Abdominal appendages, found in various Crustacea, which are adapted for swimming. They are usually slender and fringed.

Pneumatophore

Bag-like structure, filled with gas and acting as a float in certain Coelenterata.

Pole capsule

A body found within the spore of certain sporozoan Protozoa which contains a long filament. The filament can be discharged to provide an anchoring mechanism which allows the germinating spore to become attached to the host.

Polymorphism

The occurrence of at least two, usually several, radically different body forms within colonial or social organisms.

Pre-oral

Located in front of the mouth.

G L O S S A R Y

Proglottides

Segments of the body of Cestoda.

Protopodite

The common stem to which are attached the endopodite and exopodite of the biramous crustacean limb.

Pterostigma

Terminal pigmented area found on the wings of certain insects

Pygidium

The hindmost part of the body which usually (but not always) carries the anus in certain arthropods.

Racquet organ

Sensory structure found on the fourth pair of legs in solifugids, so named because it consists of a slender stalk and an expanded, flattened head.

Radula

Chitinous ribbon bearing a number of transverse rows of teeth located on the floor of the buccal cavity of most Mollusca.

Resilifer

A flat plate-like extension near the hinge on the inside of the shell in bivalve molluscs to which is attached the internal ligament.

Resilium

An internal ligament in bivalve molluscs reacting against the adductor muscles and causing the shell to open.

Rhabdite

Rod-shaped bodies present in the epidermal cells of free-livi Platyhelminthes. Their function is largely unknown but they may be protective or used in food capture.

Rhopalioid

Marginal sensory body, found in certain Scyphozoa (Coelentera It consists of a small, hollow club lying in a sensory pit an is, essentially, a variant of a tentaculocyst.

Rhynchocoel

Cavity housing the proboscis in the Nemertea. It is completely closed off from the exterior and has muscular wall

G L O S S A R Y

Rostellum

An apical platform, bearing rows of hooks, on the scolex of various Cestoda. Also known as the rostrum.

Rostrum (Crustacea)

Anterior prolongation of the cephalic region of the carapace.

Rostrum (Insecta)

The 'beak' formed by the close apposition of the elongated sucking mouthparts, notably in the Homoptera and Heteroptera.

Saprozoic

Feeding on dissolved substances derived from decaying organisms.

Scleroblast

A type of binucleate cell, found in the Porifera, which is responsible for secreting the spicular skeleton.

Scolex

Anterior end, or 'head', of cestodes.

Scutum

A body plate, part of the exoskeleton of arthropods.

Scyphistoma

Polyp-like stage in the life cycle of scyphozoan Coelenterata. It divides by a series of transverse constrictions to produce a number of saucer-shaped, miniature jellyfish, called ephyra larvae.

Shell beak

The oldest part of the shell in bivalve molluscs at the tip of each valve near the hinge.

Shell gland

Reproductive glands found in the Platyhelminthes which secrete a substance which is responsible for the hardening of the egg shell.

Siphonozoid

Current-producing polyp found in some anthozoan Coelenterata.

G L O S S A R Y

Siphuncle

A slender, tubular prolongation of the visceral hump which traverses the partitions between the chambers in the shell in various cephalopod Mollusca. It carries blood vessels and may secrete gas.

Solenocyte

Cellular organ resembling the flame cells of Platyhelminthe occurring in the nephridium of polychaete Annelida and in t Cephalochordata.

Spinnerets

Appendages usually (but not always) found on the posterior region of the opisthosoma of various arachnids, through whi silk is spun into fine threads.

Spongin

A fibrous scleroprotein which forms a skeleton in some spon

Sporozoite

Spore produced by multiple fission after sexual reproductio in certain Protozoa.

Statoblast

Resistant body found in the Bryozoa. It is formed by intern budding which produces a mass of cells enclosed in a chitin capsule. It is an overwintering stage which germinates in the spring to form new colonies.

Statocyst

Sense organ for detecting gravity. It consists of a vesicl containing sand grains or calcified pellets.

Sternum

Chitinous plate forming the ventral body wall in arthropods.

Stigma

The eye-spot found in certain flagellate Protozoa.

Stolon

A stalk on which colonies of individuals are supported in Coelenterata and Urochordata.

Stomodaeum

The name given to the fore-gut region in many invertebrates.

Stone canal

A duct which connects the madreporite with that part of the water vascular system which surrounds the mouth in Echinoder

GLOSSARY

<u>Style</u>

Short, rod-shaped abdominal appendage of unknown function found in certain arthropods.

<u>Syngamy</u>

Union of two protozoan gametes.

<u>Syzygy</u>

The prolonged, active association in pairs end to end of some Sporozoa.

<u>Telson</u>

A tail-piece found in some arthropods.

<u>Tentaculocyst</u>

Sense organ found mainly in the Scyphozoa (Coelenterata). It consists of a minute, sensory tentacle lying in a sensory pit. The pressure of the tentacle on the sensory wall of the pit stimulates the scyphozoan to re-orientate and maintain its correct attitude in the water.

<u>Tergum</u>

Chitinous plate forming the dorsal body wall in arthropods.

<u>Testate</u>

Possessing a shell, or test.

<u>Torsion</u>

Twisting of the visceral hump or mass, found in most gastropods which results in the mantle cavity occupying an anterior position.

<u>Triploblastic</u>

Having three layers of cells in the body wall.

<u>Trochophore</u>

Ciliated larval form found in various invertebrates. Typically it is oval or pear-shaped with distinct bilateral symmetry, and it swims by means of an equatorial band of cilia.

<u>Trophozoite</u>

The active, feeding stage in the Sporozoa.

<u>Tube feet</u>

Tentacle-like outpushings from the water vascular system which may be used for locomotion in the Echinodermata.

G L O S S A R Y

Uniramous

Consisting of a single elongated process.

Uropod

The most posterior abdominal appendage, found in the Malacostraca, forming, with the telson, a fail fan. It is flattened and turned. It is used when the animal swims rapidly backwards.

Veliger

Larval form occurring in the Mollusca. It is modified from the trochophore by the appearance of adult organs and an enlarged ciliated lobe, the velum.

Velum (Mollusca)

See Veliger.

Velum (Coelenterata)

A narrow fold or ridge which runs around the edge of the umbrella in the medusa of most Hydrozoa. The tentacles are inserted on this ridge.

Vitelline gland

Reproductive gland found in the Platyhelminthes which is responsible for secreting the egg shell.

Viviparous

Giving birth to living young.

Zooecium

Name given to the body wall in the Bryozoa.

Zoid

An individual member of a colony of animals.

G E N E R I C   N A M E S

LIST OF GENERA QUOTED

GENERIC NAMES

GENERIC NAMES

GENERIC NAMES

LIST OF COMMON NAMES QUOTED

C O M M O N   N A M E S

Previously published titles in this series

Guide to Living Mammals (2nd Edition)
Guide to Living Reptiles
Guide to Living Birds
Guide to Living Amphibians
Guide to Living Fishes